THE BANKNOTE YEARBOOK

THE
BANKNOTE YEARBOOK
SEVENTH EDITION

Edited by
John W. Mussell
and
the Editorial Team of BANKNOTE NEWS

Contributing Editors
Barry Boswell
Laurence Pope, LL.B Solicitor
Martin Mac Devitt

ISBN 10: 1-870192-32-X
ISBN 13: 978-1-870192-32-3

Published by
TOKEN PUBLISHING LIMITED
Orchard House, Duchy Road, Heathpark, Honiton, Devon EX14 1YD, UK
Telephone: 01404 46972   Fax: 01404 44788
e-mail: info@tokenpublishing.com   Website: www.tokenpublishing.com

Printed and bound in England by Polestar, Exeter

CONTENTS

5

S OMEHOW it is difficult to believe that this is the seventh edition of Token Publishing's BANKNOTE YEARBOOK—it really does seem like only yesterday that we were mooting the idea of adding to our YEARBOOK stable with a look at the paper money of the British Isles and here we are over a decade later (the move to biennial editions accounts for the apparent time discrepancy) with a book that is bigger, better and more popular than ever. The first edition, published in 2000 was a fairly thin affair, a black and white paperback book of only 232 pages . . . today this full colour, hardback wealth of information has become the pre-eminent banknote catalogue in the country and its publication is always eagerly anticipated. We have been asked on numerous occasions whether we would consider taking the book back to a proper "yearbook", i.e. publish it every year as we do with the COIN YEARBOOK and MEDAL YEARBOOK instead of every other, but at this stage there are no plans to do so. The main reason for this being a two year publication is simple—the prices of banknotes don't change as regularly or as dramatically as those of coins, which often fluctuate in line with the precious metals market. Banknotes are more sedate, less volatile than coins and prices do not change to the same degree—but that isn't to say that the market isn't strong—far from it and once again in this edition you will see a number of significant increases in the values of some notes. The common denominator amongst all those notes that have increased seems to be quality with the highest grade notes continuing to command very high prices. This market strength is reflected both at auction and at the fairs where the choice notes are always eagerly snapped up.

The hobby itself is continuing to grow, with new collectors coming on board and new notes being discovered all the time, for example in the Irish Section new "Ploughman" prefixes are being noted (excuse the pun) and a number of new finds have been recorded in the English section too. There are, sadly, no dedicated bank note fairs in the UK any more apart from the annual World Paper Money Fair in London which this year (2011) moves to a new venue—the Bloomsbury Doyle Hotel (formerly Jury's) on Great Russell Street. This move coincides with the 50th Anniversary of the IBNS and a dinner to mark this milestone will be held at the same venue over the Paper Money Fair weekend at the very end of September. The lack of dedicated fairs hasn't dented the hobby though and a visit to the London Coin Fair, the Bloomsbury Hotel Coin Fair, the York Coin Fair, Birmingham, Eddie Smith's Leeds show, etc., will always see a good number of banknotes on offer. The twice yearly York Coin Fair in particular is always a good place to find an excellent range of notes which is why we chose the July 2010 show to launch our other banknote title "The Standard Catalogue of the Provincial Banknotes of England and Wales" by Roger Outing—the first new work on Provincial Banknotes in decades. So popular did this new work prove that we sold out completely on launch day and as I write this at the beginning of March 2011 there is less than a third of the print run left! Provincial notes have always been popular of course but their scarcity means that developing a decent collection has often been a labour of love over many years; "standard" banknote collecting, acquiring the sort of note featured in this YEARBOOK has always been easier but we are finding more and more that as the hobby becomes more popular the good notes, the high quality notes, the early numbers etc. etc. are becoming harder and harder to find and when they do appear they are commanding very good money indeed. Whilst this is inevitably frustrating to the honest collector and dealer there are some less scrupulous individuals who see it as a business opportunity—take for example the case on a certain on-line auction site where one seller was discovered to be buying low grade notes, doctoring and cleaning them and then selling them on for vastly inflated rates as much higher grade notes. He apparently hadn't spotted that bank notes have numbers and can be easily tracked, he also hadn't accounted for the fact that many collectors, by virtue of their methodical mind-set, do just that—they track each and every note that comes up for sale making it very easy to spot just such a scam. We exposed him in BANKNOTE NEWS and to date he has yet to reappear, we trust our readers will alert us if he does!

Sadly the fleecing of the unsuspecting is something that goes on in any "collectable" hobby with fakes and forgeries appearing in the art world, the medal world, the coin world and even the furniture world. Knowing just who to trust is always a problem and therefore I will once again give the advice that the collector should always buy from a reputable dealer (see the list in the Directory section of this YEARBOOK or the adverts within) and if something seems too good to be true it probably is! On the whole though, there isn't as much to worry about in this hobby as there is in many others—the aforementioned serial numbers mean that checking the provenance of specific notes is relatively easy, and the penalties for forging notes have always been so high that "copies" just aren't found in the same way as they are in say the medal world. So whilst I would always urge caution, particularly when it comes to matters of grading, please don't be overly worried and certainly don't let that worry stop you from enjoying this fascinating hobby! Those of you keen to enjoy it from a different perspective may be interested to know that many of the error notes featured in the YEARBOOK, currently in the collection of Laurence Pope, are to be dispersed to allow other collectors the opportunity to enjoy them. Laurence is, of course one of the people whose advice and guidance has been invaluable in the compiling of this, and previous BANKNOTE YEARBOOKS and my thanks goes out to him and the others who have given so freely of their time. They include Barry Boswell, David Carew, Barnaby Faull, Martin Mac Devitt, Keith McGrath, Mark Ray and Pam West, as well as the many collectors who have sent in amendments and suggestions—all making the BANKNOTE YEARBOOK the leading publication for paper money collectors.

N.B. At the time of writing we learn that Chris Salmon is to become the new Chief Cashier at the Bank of England on April 1, 2011. This will necessitate a new issue of notes bearing his signature. These will, of course, be included in the eighth edition of the BANKNOTE YEARBOOK.

COIN & MEDAL FAIRS LTD

Organisers of the London Coin Fair and Midland Coin Fair

THE LONDON COIN FAIR

HOLIDAY INN
LONDON, BLOOMSBURY
Coram Street, WC1N 1HT

Fair dates:

Dates to be announced, please phone for details

THE MIDLAND COIN FAIR

NATIONAL MOTORCYCLE MUSEUM
BICKENHILL, BIRMINGHAM, B92 0EJ
Opposite the NEC on the M42/A45 junction

Fair dates:
2011: 10th Apr, 8th May, 12 Jun, 10th Jul,
14th Aug, 11th Sept, 9th Oct, 13th Nov, 11th Dec
2012: 8th Jan, 12th Feb, 11th Mar, 8th Apr,
13th May, 10th Jun, 8th Jul, 12th Aug, 9th Sept,
14th Oct, 11 Nov, 9th Dec

*For more information please contact: Lu Veissid
Hobsley House, Frodesley, Shrewsbury SY5 7HD
Tel: 01694 731781*

www.coinfairs.co.uk

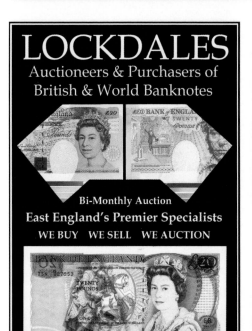

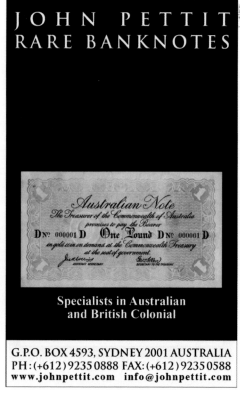

A guide to CONDITION

THE following introduction and Grading Guide is the result of work prepared under the guidance of the Grading Committee of the International Bank Note Society (IBNS) and is reproduced here with their kind permission. This grading guide has become the standard system used throughout the world.

Introduction

Grading is the most controversial component of paper money collecting today. Small differences in grade can mean significant differences in value. The process of grading is so subjective and dependent on external influences such as lighting, that even a very experienced individual may well grade the same note differently on separate occasions.

To facilitate communication between sellers and buyers it is essential that grading terms and their meanings be as standardised and as widely used as possible. This standardisation should reflect common usage as much as practicable. One difficulty with grading is that even the actual grade themselves are not used everywhere by everyone. For example, in Europe the grade "About Uncirculated" (AU) is not in general use, yet in North America it is widespread. The European term "Good VF" may roughly correspond to what individuals in North America call "Extremely fine" (EF).

The grades and definitions as set forth below cannot reconcile all the various systems and grading terminology variants. Rather, the attempt is made here to try and diminish the controversy with some common sense grades and definitions that aim to give more precise meaning to the grading language of paper money.

How to look at a banknote

In order to ascertain the grade of a note, it is essential to examine it out of a holder and under a good light. Move the note around so that the light bounces off at different angles. Try holding the note obliquely, so the note is even with your eye as you look up at the light. Hard to see folds or slight creases will show up under such examination. Some individuals also lightly feel along the surface of the note to detect creasing.

Cleaning, washing, pressing of banknotes

a. Cleaning, washing or pressing paper money is generally harmful and reduces both the grade and the value of the note. At the very least, a washed or pressed note may lose it original sheen and its surface may become lifeless and dull. The defects of a note had, such as folds and creases, may not necessarily be completely eliminated and their tell-tale marks can be detected under a good light. Carelessly washed notes may also have white streaks where the folds or creases where (or still are).

b. Processing of a note which started out as "Extremely Fine" will automatically reduce it at least one full grade.

Unnatural defects

Glue, tape or pencil marks may sometime be successfully removed. While such removal will leave a cleaned surface, it will improve the overall appearance of the note without concealing any of its defects. Under such circumstances, the grade of that note may also be improved.

The words "pinholes", "staple holes", "trimmed". "writing on face", tape marks" etc should always be added to the description of a note. It is realised that certain countries routinely staple their notes together in groups before issue. In such cases, the description can include a comment such as "usual staple holes" or something similar. After all, not

13

everyone knows that certain notes cannot be found otherwise.

The major point of this section is that one cannot lower the overall grade of a note with defects simply because of the defects. The price will reflect the lowered worth of a defective note, but the description must *always* include the specific defects.

The term Uncirculated

The word *Uncirculated* is used in this grading guide only as a qualitative measurement of the appearance of a note. It has nothing at all to do with whether or not an issuer has actually released the note to circulation. Thus, the term "About Uncirculated" is justified and acceptable because so many notes that have never seen hand to hand use have been mishandled so that they are available at best in AU condition.

Either a note is uncirculated in condition or it is not; there can be no degrees of uncirculated. Highlights or defects in colour, centering and the like may be included in a description but the fact that a note is or is not in uncirculated condition should not be a disputable point.

GRADING GUIDE—Definitions of terms

UNCIRCULATED: A perfectly preserved note never mishandled by the issuing authority, a bank teller, the public or a collector. Paper is clean and firm without discoloration. Corners are sharp and square without any evidence of rounding (rounded corners are often a tell tale sign of a cleaned or "doctored" note). *Note: Some note issuers are most often available with slight evidence of very light counting folds which do not "break" the paper. Many collectors and dealers refer to such notes as AU–UNC.*

ABOUT UNCIRCULATED: A virtually perfect note, with some minor handling. May show very slight evidence of bank counting folds at a corner or one light fold through the centre, but not both. An "AU" note cannot be creased, a crease being a hard fold which has usually "broken" the surface of the note. Paper is clean and bright with original sheen. Corners are not rounded. *Note: Europeans will refer to an About Uncirculated or AU note as "EF–Unc" or as just "EF". The Extremely Fine note described below will often be referred to as "GVF" or "Good Very Fine".*

EXTREMELY FINE: A very attractive note with light handling. May have a maximum of three light folds or one strong crease. Paper is clean and firm without discoloration. Corners are sharp and square without evidence of rounding (rounded corners are often a tell tale sign of a cleaned or "doctored" note).

VERY FINE: An attractive note, but with more evidence of handling and wear. May have several folds both vertically and horizontally. Paper must have minimal dirt or possibly colour smudging. Paper itself is still relatively crisp and not floppy. There are no tears in the border area, although the edges do show slight wear. Corners also show wear but not full rounding.

FINE: A note that shows considerable circulation, with many folds, creases and wrinkling. Paper is not excessively dirty but may have some softness. Edges may show much handling with minor tears in the border area. Tears may not extend into the design. There will be no centre hole because of excessive folding. Colours are clear but not very bright. A staple hole or two would not be considered unusual wear in a Fine note. Overall appearance is still on the desirable side.

VERY GOOD: A well used note, abused but still intact. Corners may have much wear and rounding, tiny nicks, tears may extend in to the design, some discoloration may be present, staining may have occurred, and a small hole may sometimes be seen at centre excessive folding. Staple and pinholes are usually present and the note itself is quite limp but NO pieces of the note can be missing. A note in VG condition may still have an overall not unattractive appearance.

GOOD: A well worn and heavily used note. Normal damage from prolonged circulation will include strong multiple folds and creases, stains, pinholes and/or staple holes, dirt, discoloration, edge tears, centre hole, rounded corners and an overall unattractive appearance. No large pieces of the note may be missing. Graffiti is commonly seen on notes in G condition.

FAIR: A totally limp, dirty and very well used note. Larger pieces may be half torn off or missing besides the defects mentioned under the Good category. Tears will be large, obscured portions of the note will be bigger.

POOR: A "rag" with severe damage because of wear, staining, pieces missing, graffiti, larger holes. May have tape holding pieces of the note together. Trimming may have taken place to remove rough edges. A Poor note is desirable only as a "filler" or when such a note is the only one known of that particular issue.

15

Mounting & housing
STORAGE

CERTAIN museum collections and official bank archives are housed in cabinets with sliding frames in which banknotes are mounted on cards between glass panes. While this is a very attractive way of displaying a collection it is also very expensive and takes up a great deal of room. Until relatively recently most notaphilists were content to house their collections in conventional loose-leaf stamp albums, the notes being held in place by transparent mounting corners and the relevant data, such as date of issue, bank and country, could be written up on the page above each note. The disadvantage of this system is that only one side of the banknote could be examined without taking it out of its mounting corners.

An alternative to this, small transparent hinges, like those used by stamp collectors, were used to affix the notes to the album page. By this method the note could easily be turned over so that the back could be examined. This was considered more satisfactory, although many collectors felt uneasy about using stamp hinges which could leave an unsightly mark on the backs of notes and this would detract from their value. This method of mounting is certainly not recommended today.

The solution to these problems, widely disseminated in the 1970s, was the special album with plastic sleeves into which the notes could be inserted. These albums were actually produced initially for housing collections of postcards, but were found to be about the right size for banknotes. Unfortunately it was soon discovered that those sleeves made of polyvinyl chloride (PVC) reacted chemically with notes, either badly discolouring them or even depositing a viscous film on them. Subsequently better types of plastic such as Mylar film or polyethylene were developed, and these seem to have obviated the risk of contamination.

Today there are many different systems available to the note collector. There are cards with clear rigid plastic fronts (often punched with holes to be inserted in ring-binders or which can be stacked in a box or case, with the salient details of the note on narrow cards inserted at the top of the mount and then held upright as if in a filing cabinet), as well as specially-made archival quality clear plastic banknote wallets. These along with a wide range of other systems to preserve your notes are available from Token Publishing Ltd or major accessory suppliers and manufacturers.

Around the
WORLD
Currency denominations of the world

L ISTED here are the names of all the currency units of the world found on banknotesor coins. Many of them have been around for a long time while others are no longer in use. Some of the denominations have been introduced only recently, whilst others are familiar household words, many have been superceded by the euro and other new names. A number of the names are shared by different countries and a few have even been used by different civilisations. We have included all that we know of, past and present.

Abbasi, Abbassi Afghanistan, Georgia, Persia
Afghani Afghanistan
Agora (ot) Israel
Ahmadi Mysore, Yemen
Amani Afghanistan
Anna Burma, India, Pakistan, Kenya, Muscat & Oman
Argentino Argentina
Ariary Malagasy Republic
Ashrafi Afghanistan, Awadh, Bahawalpur, Egypt, Hyderabad
At Laos
Atia Portuguese India
Att Cambodia, Laos, Siam (Thailand)
Aurar (plural **Eyrir**) Iceland
Austral Argentina
Avo Macau, Timor
Baht Thailand
Baiocco (plural **Baiocchi**) Papal States
Baisa Oman
Baiza Kuwait
Baizah Muscat & Oman
Balboa Panama
Ban (plural **Bani** or **Banu**) Roumania
Banica Croatia
Belga Belgium
Besa (plural Bese) Ethiopia, Somalia
Bipkwele Equatorial Guinea
Bir (r) Ethiopia
Bogach Yemen
Bolivar Venezuela
Boliviano Bolivia
Butut Gambia
Cache French Indian Settlements
Candareen China
Carbovanetz Ukraine
Cash China, Hong Kong, India, Mysore, Travancore, Turkestan, Vietnam
Cauri Guinea
Cent Australia, Bahamas, Barbados, Belize, Bermuda, Botswana, British East Caribbean Territories, British Honduras, British North Borneo, British Virgin Islands, Brunei, Canada, Cayman Island, Ceylon, China, Cochin China, Cocos (Keeling) Islands, Cook Islands, Curacao, Cyprus, Danish West Indies, East Africa, Ethiopia, Fiji, French Indochina, Gilbert and Ellice Islands, Guyana, Hawaii, Hong Kong, Indonesia, Jamaica, Kenya, Kiao Chau (Kiatschau), Kiribati, Laos, Liberia, Malaya, Malaysia, Malta, Mauritius, Netherlands, Netherlands Antilles, Netherlands Indies, New Zealand, Nova Scotia, Panama, Prince Edward Island, Sarawak, Seychelles, Sierra Leone, Singapore, Solomon Islands, South Africa, Sri Lanka, Straits Settlements, Suriname, Swaziland, Tanzania, Trinidad and Tobago, Tuvalu, Uganda, United States of America, Virgin Islands, Zanzibar, Zimbabwe
Centas (plural **Centa, Centu**) Lithuania
Centavo Angola, Argentina, Bolivia, Brazil, Cape Verde Islands, Chile, Colombia, Costa Rica, Cuba, Dominican Republic, Ecuador, El Salvador, Guatemala, Guinea-Bissau, Honduras, Mexico, Mozambique, Nicaragua, Paraguay, Peru, Philippines, Portugal, Portuguese Guinea, Portuguese India, Puerto Rico, St Thomas and Prince Islands, Timor, Venezuela
Centecimo Bolivia
Centesimo Bolivia, Chile, Dominican Republic, Ethiopia, Italian East Africa, Italy, Panama, Paraguay, San Marino, Somalia, Uruguay, Vatican
Centime Algeria, Antwerp, Belgian Congo, Belgium, Cambodia, Cameroon, Cochin China, Comoro Islands, Djibouti, France, French Equatorial Africa, French Guiana, French Indochina, French Oceania, French Polynesia, French Somali Coast, French West Africa, Guadeloupe, Guinea, Haiti, Laos, Monaco, Morocco, New Caledonia, Reunion, Senegal, Switzerland, Togo, Tunisia, Vietnam, Westphalia, Yugoslavia, Zaire
Centimo Costa Rica, Mozambique, Paraguay, Peru, Philippines, Puerto Rico, St Thomas and Prince Islands, Spain, Venezuela
Centu Lithuania
Chervonetz (plural **Chervontzy**) Russia
Chetrum Bhutan
Cheun South Korea

Chiao   China, Formosa, Manchukuo
Chi'en   China
Chio   China
Chon   Korea
Chuckram   Travancore
Colon   Costa Rica, El Salvador
Condor   Chile, Colombia, Ecuador
Cordoba   Nicaragua
Corona   Austrian provinces of Italy, Naples
Cruzadinho   Brazil, Portugal
Cruzado   Brazil, Portugal
Cruzeiro   Brazil
Denar   Macedonia
Deutschemark   Germany
Dinar   Afghanistan, Algeria, Bahrain, Hejaz, Iraq, Kuwait, Morocco, Persia, Saudi Arabia, Serbia, Tunisia, Turkey, Yugoslavia
Diner   Andorra
Dinero   Peru, Spain
Dirham   Jordan, Libya, Morocco, United Arab Emirates
Dirhem   Dubai, Iraq, Morocco, Qatar
Dobra   Sao Tome e Principe
Dollar   Anguilla, Antigua and Barbuda, Australia, Bahamas, Belize, Bermuda, Canada, Cayman Islands, China, Cocos (Keeling) Islands, Cook Islands, East Caribbean Territories, Fiji, Great Britain, Grenada, Guyana, Hawaii, Hong Kong, Indonesia, Jamaica, Japan, Kiribati, Liberia, Malaysia, Mauritius, Montserrat, Newfoundland, New Zealand, Panama, St Kitts-Nevis, St Lucia, St Vincent, Scotland, Sierra Leone, Singapore, Solomin Islands, Straits Settlements, Trinidad and Tobago, Tuvalu, USA, Virgin Islands, Western Samoa, Zimbabwe
Dong   Annam, Vietnam
Drachma   Crete, Greece
Dram   Armenia
Ekuele   Equatorial Guinea
Emalangeni   Swaziland
Escudo   Angola, Argentina, Azores, Bolivia, Cape Verde Islands, Central American Republic, Chile, Colombia, Costa Rica, Ecuador, Guadeloupe, Guatemala, Guinea-Bissau, Madeira, Mexico, Mozambique, Peru, Portugal, Portuguese Guinea/India, St Thomas and Prince Islands, Spain, Timor
Forint   Hungary
Franc   Algeria, Belgian Congo, Belgium, Burundi, Cambodia, Cameroon, Central African Republic, Chad, Comoro Islands, Congo, Danish West Indies, Djibouti, Dominican Republic, Ecuador, France, French Colonies, Gabon, Guadeloupe, Guinea, Ivory Coast, Katanga, Luxembourg, Madagascar, Malagasy Republic, Mali, Martinique, Mauretania, Monaco, Morocco, New Caledonia, New Hebrides, Reunion, Ruanda-Urundi, Rwanda, St Pierre and Miquelon, Senegal, Switzerland, Togo, Tunisia, West African States
Franchi   Switzerland
Frang   Luxembourg
Frank(en)   Belgium, Liechtenstein, Saar, Switzerland
Franka Ara   Albania
Gersh   Ethiopia
Girsh   Hejaz, Nejd, Saudi Arabia, Sudan
Golde   Sierra Leone
Grivna (plural **Grivny**)   Ukraine
Grosz (plural **Grosze** or **Groszy**)   Poland

Grush   Albania
Guarani   Paraguay
Guerche   Egypt, Saudi Arabia
Gulden   Austria, Curacao, German States, Netherlands, Netherlands Indies, Swiss Cantons
Habibi   Afghanistan
Hryvnia   Ukraine
Hsien   China
Hwan   Korea
Imadi   Yemen
Jeon   Korea
Jiao   People's Republic of China
Kapeikas   Latvia, Belarus
Khoum   Mauritania
Kina   Papua New Guinea
Kip   Laos
Korona   Bohemia and Moravia, Hungary, Slovakia
Korun(a) (plural **Koruny** or **Koruncic**)   Czechoslo-vakia
Krajczar   Hungary
Kran   Iran, Persia
Kreu(t)zer   Austria, Austrian States, Czechoslovakia, German States, Hungary, Liechtenstein, Poland, Roumania, Swiss Cantons
Krona (plural **Kronor** or **Kronur**)   Iceland, Sweden
Krona (plural **Kroner** or **Kronen**)   Austria, Denmark, German States, Greenland, Liechtenstein, Norway
Kroon(i)   Estonia
Kuna (plural **Kune**)   Croatia
Kurus   Turkey
Kuta   Congo-Kinshasa, Zaire
Kwacha   Malawi, Zambia
Kwanza   Angola
Kyat   Burma, Myanmar
Lari   Georgia
Lati, Lats   Latvia
Lei   Roumania
Lek (plural **Leke** or **Leku**)   Albania
Lempira   Honduras
Leone   Sierra Leone
Leu (plural **Lei**)   Roumania
Lev(a)   Bulgaria
Li   Manchukuo
Licente   Lesotho
Likuta   Zaire
Lilangeni   Swaziland
Lion d'Or   Austrian Netherlands
Lira (plural **Lire**)   Eritrea, Italian East Africa, Italy, San Marino, Syria, Turkey, Vatican
Lira (plural **Lirot**)   Israel
Lisente   Lesotho
Litas (plural **Litai** or **Litu**)   Lithuania
Luhlanga   Swaziland
Lweis   Angola
Macuta   Angola
Makuta   Zaire
Maloti   Lesotho
Manat Azerbaijan   Turkmenistan
Mark   Germany, German States, German New Guinea, Norway, Poland, Sweden
Marka   Estonia
Markka   Finland
Metical   Mozambique
Milreis   Brazil
Mon   Japan, Ryukyu Islands
Mongo   Mongolia
Mun   Korea

Mung   Mongolia
Naira   Nigeria
Nafka   Eritrea
Ngultrum   Bhutan
Ngwee   Zambia
Omani   Oman
Ouguiya   Mauritania
Pa'anga   Tonga
Pahlavi   Iran
Pataca   Macau
Pengo   Hungary
Penni(a)   Finland
Perper(a)   Montenegro
Pesa   German East Africa
Peseta   Andorra, Equatorial Guinea, Peru, Spain
Pesewa   Ghana
Peso   Argentina, Bolivia, Cambodia, Chile, Colombia, Costa Rica, Cuba, Dominican Republic, El Salvador, Guatemala, Guinea-Bissau, Honduras, Mexico, Netherlands Antilles, Nicaragua, Paraguay, Peru, Philippines, Puerto Rico, Uruguay, Venezuela
Piastre   Annam, Cambodia, Cochin China, Cyprus, Denmark, Egypt, French Indochina, Hejaz, Iraq, Khmer, Lebanon, Libya, Nejd, Saudi Arabia, Syria, Sudan, Tonkin, Tunisia, Turkey, Vietnam, Yemen
Piso   Philippines
Pond   Transvaal
Pound   Ascension, Australia, Biafra, Cyprus, Egypt, Falkland Islands, Ghana, Gibraltar, Great Britain, Guernsey, Iran, Ireland, Isle of Man, Israel, Jersey, Malta, Nigeria, Rhodesia, St Helena, South Arabia, South Africa, Sudan, Syria
Pruta(ot)   Israel
Pul   Afghanistan, China, Turkestan
Pula   Botswana
Pya(t)   Burma
Qindar(ka)   Albania
Quetzal   Guatemala
Rand   South Africa
Real(es)   Argentina, Bolivia, Central American Republic, Chile, Colombia, Costa Rica, Dominican Republic, Ecuador, El Salvador, Venezuela
Reichsmark   Germany
Reis   Angola, Azores, Brazil, Madeira, Mozambique, Portugal, Portuguese India
Renminbi   People's Republic of China
Rentenmark   Germany
Rial   Iran, Morocco, Muscat and Oman, Oman, Persia, Yemen Arab Republic
Riel   Kampuchea
Ringgit   Malaysia
Riyal   Iran, Iraq, Saudi Arabia, United Arab Emirates, Yemen Arab Republic
Rouble   Russia, USSR
Rubel   German occupation of Russia
Ruble   Poland, Transnistria
Rublis   Latvia
Rufiyaa   Maldive Islands
Rupee   Afghanistan, Andaman Islands, Bhutan, Burma, China, Cocos Keeling Islands, India, Iran, Kenya, Mauritius, Nepal, Pakistan, Saudi Arabia, Seychelles, Sri Lanka, Tanzania, Tibet, United Arab Emirates, Yemen
Rupia   Portuguese India, Somalia
Rupiah   Indonesia
Rupie   German East Africa

Ryal   England, Hejaz, Iran, Muscat and Oman, Nejd, Oman, Persia, Quaiti State, Saudi Arabia, Yemen, Zanzibar
Saidi   Oman
Satang   Siam (Thailand)
Scellino   Somalia
Schilling   Austria, German States, Poland, Swiss Cantons
Shahi   Afghanistan, Iran, Turkestan
Shamil   Tatarstan
Sheqal(im)   Israel
Shilin   Somalia
Shilingi   Tanzania
Shilling   Australia, Biafra, British West Africa, Canada, Cyprus, East Africa, Fiji, Gambia, Ghana, Great Britain, Grenada, Guernsey, Ireland, Isle of Man, Jamaica, Jersey, Kenya, Malawi, Malta, New Guinea, New Zealand, Nigeria, Scotland, Somalia, South Africa, Trinidad and Tobago, Uganda, Zambia
Sol(es)   Argentina, Haiti, Peru,
Soldo (plural **Soldi**)   Italian States, Swiss Cantons, Papal States,
Som   Kyrgyr Republic
Som   Kyrgyzstan
Somalo   Somalia
Somoni   Tajikistan
Srang   Tibet
Sucre   Ecuador, Galapagos
Sueldo   Bolivia, Spain
Sum   Uzbekistan
Syli   Guinea
Tael   China, Laos
Taka   Bangladesh
Tala   Samoa, Tokelau
Talaro   Ethiopia
Taler   German States, Poland, Swiss Cantons
Tambala   Malawi
Tamlung   Siam
Tanga   Portuguese India
Tangka   Tibet
Tanka   Nepal
Tenge   Kazakhstan
Thaler   Austria, Austrian States, Courland, Czechoslovakia, German States, Hungary, Liechtenstein, Poland, Roumania, Switzerland
Thebe   Botswana
Thetri   Georgia
Tical   Cambodia, Thailand
Tiyin   Kazakhstan
Toea   Papua New Guinea
Tola   India, Nepal
Tolar   Slovenia
Toman   Iran, Persia, Azerbaijan
Tughrik   Mongolia
Vatu   Vanuatu
Venezolano   Venezuela
Wan   Korea
Wark   Ethiopia
Warn   Korean
Wen   China
Whan   Korea
Won   South Korea
Xu   Vietnam
Yen   Japan
Yeni kurus   Turkey
Yeni Turk Lirasi   Turkey
Yuan   China
Zaire   Zaire
Zalat   Yemen Arab Republic
Zloty (plural **Zlote** or **Zlotych**)   Poland

BANKNOTE TERMS

Glossary of

Allied Military Currency Notes produced by the British and American governments for the use of military personnel in territories occupied during the World War II.

Alteration A deliberate change in some feature of a note, usually of a fraudulent nature.

Assignat Type of paper money used in France, 1789–96, representing confiscated Church land assigned to the holders.

Asterisk Note Note issued in Canada and New Zealand since ther 1950s to replace a defective note and so-called on account of the asterisk in the serial number.

Authorised Circulation The amount of money in notes which Scottish banks were permitted to have in circulation, under the Bank Act of 1845, based on a twelve-month average for the period prior to the Act coming into force. Any amount above this had to be backed by gold and silver.

Auxiliary Payment Certificate Form of paper money intended for use by American military personnel in overseas countries. See also Baf, Behelfszahlungsmittel and Scrip.

Babel Note Nickname derived from the biblical Tower of Babel, given to the paper currency of the Russian Socialist Federated Republic (1919) because it bore the slogan "workers of the world unite" in seven languages.

Back The side of a note generally regarded as of lesser importance than the front, and otherwise known as the reverse or verso. In early notes the back was often left blank, but in more recent times it has been used for a florid representation of the national arms or vignettes of scenery and landmarks.

Baf Acronym from British Armed Forces, the popular name for the vouchers which could only be exchanged for goods in service canteens from 1945 onwards.

Banknote Form of paper money issued by banks and usually promising to pay the bearer on demand in coin of the realm.

Banknote Strictly speaking, this is a piece of paper money issued by a bank, although the term is often loosely applied to any form of paper in circulation as currency.

Bearer Cheque A piece of paper which looks like a cheque but actually payable for the stated sum to any person holding it (the bearer) without requiring endorsement. Some of the emergency money used in Italy in the late 1970s consisted of such cheques.

Behelfszahlungsmittel German term for auxiliary payment certificates used in occupied Europe from 1939 to 1945.

Bill of Credit An American term denoting the paper money of the Colonial and early Continental period, from which comes the common expression 'bill' meaning a paper note.

Bill of Exchange The law defines this as "an unconditional order in writing, addressed by one person to another, signed by the person giving it, requiring the person to whom it is addressed to pay on demand or at a fixed or determinable future time, a sum certain in money to or to the order of a specified person or to bearers". It is addressed to a person or company, rather than a bank. The earliest examples are entirely handwritten although examples from the 19th century onwards often had the stock formula printed, with the details inserted by hand.

Billet de Confiance French for "tickets of trust", signifying small-denomination notes of the French Revolution issued to meet a shortage of coin due to hoarding.

Block Number Tiny numerals often found in the corners of notes, denoting the block or plate from which the notes were printed.

Bogus A note which is entirely false, in that it purports to be the money of a non-existent bank or country.

Bon Pour French for "good for", inscribed on tokens, coupons and vouchers which circulated as cash during periods of shortage of coinage.

21

Bond   A certificate of intention to pay the holder a specified sum, with or without interest, on a specified date.

Bradbury   Popular name for the UK Treasury notes introduced in August 1914 when specie payments were suspended on the outbreak of World War I, from the Treasury official, Sir John Bradbury, who signed them.

Braille   A system of reading by means of patterns of raised dots, invented by Louis Braille. In recent years such dots have been embossed on many banknotes to help identification by the blind and partially sighted, as well as provide an additional security feature.

Branch Banknote   A note which includes in its inscription a reference to the particular branch of a bank which issued it. In the USA such notes even had quite distinctive designs, but in England the name of the town or city sufficed to distinguish such notes from those of the head office in London.

British Armed Forces Special Voucher   Note issued from 1945 onwards for use in NAAFI canteens operated all over the world on behalf of the British armed services. Denominated in sterling, they could not be used outside the camp area and thus prevented black market operations between servicemen and the local population.

Broken Banknote   Note issued by a bank which has failed, but often applied more generally to banknotes which have been demonetised.

Burele   French term indicating a network of intersecting curved lines used as a security underprint.

Cancelled   A note withdrawn from circulation and rendered worthless by means of an overprint or perforated inscription, generally the word CANCELLED or its equivalent in other languages, e.g. Annule (French), Annulado (Spanish) or Ausser Kurs (German). Such notes sometimes come on to the market at a fraction of their original face value.

Carton   A form of soft card, much thicker than conventional paper, which has been used occasionally for emergency money, notably the small notes in Mexico, 1914–17.

Cartouche   Oval or circular frame enclosing a portrait or armorial device, setting it apart from the rest of the design.

Changeling   A note or cheque whose colour is altered from the norm as a result of exposure to humidity, sunlight or chemical action.

Chartered Bank   A bank operating under charter from the government, as opposed to a private or commercial bank.

Cheque   (American Check) A written order directing a bank to pay money.

Cheque Form   A printed form issued by banks for the convenience of customers. Collectors use this term to denote an unused cheque (preferably with the counterfoil still intact).

Chop   From the Hindi word chap, it means a stamp or seal used in India, China and other countries of Asia to make an official mark. The earliest paper money, for example, bore the chop of the Khan of Cathay, applied in vermilion, and this tradition continues to this day in the paper money of China and Japan.

Clearing Bank   A bank which is a member of a Clearing House.

Clearing House   A banking institution where notes and cheques are exchanged between banks.

Clearing House Certificate   A form of emergency money backed by coin or bullion deposited with the clearing house through which banks exchanged notes and cheques. Specifically the term is applied to American issues of 1907-8 and the early 1930s, during periods of economic crises and runs on banks.

Coin Note   A note issued by the US Treasury in 1890–1, so-called because it was redeemable in coin. A special reserve of silver dollars was established to cope with the redemption of these notes.

College Currency   Imitation money used in simulated transactions by business schools and colleges, mainly in the USA.

Colonial Currency   Paper money issued by the thirteen American colonies in the period from 1690 to 1776 or even later in some cases, before the emergence of the United States.

Colour Shifting Ink   Ink which appears to change colour as the note is tilted at a different angle.

Column Sort Note   A type of replacement note used in the English series where errors occur at random in one or more columns in a sheet.

Commemorative   A note issued for the specific purpose of marking a current event or the anniversary of a historic event or personality. Apart from notes with distinctive designs, such notes may consist of an additional or overprinted inscription, or even cyphers and serial numbers arranged in the form of anniversary dates or initials.

Company Note   A note issued by a commercial undertaking rather than a bank and redeemable in goods from the company store rather than actual cash. Such notes were common in Britain before they were rendered illegal by the Truck Acts of the 1840s.

Compound Interest Note   Note issued during the American Civil War, so-called on account of the six per cent interest which was compounded every six months.

Concentration Camp Money Various forms of notes and vouchers produced immediately before and during the World War II in a number of Nazi concentration camps. These notes were intended to reward slave workers for their labour and were exchangeable for a limited range of goods, but more usually for such luxuries as the loan of library books or admission to camp concerts. Notes of this type are known to have been used in Oranienburg, Ravensbruck, Dachau, Sachsenhausen, Buchenwald, Mauthausen, Auschwitz, Westerburg, Gross-Rosen and Mittelbau-Dora as well as in the ghettoes of Warsaw, Lodz (Litzmanstadt), Bielsk-Podlavsky and Theresienstadt. Notes denominated in US currency were also used in Deggendorf, Feldafing and Scheinfeld, former Nazi concentration camps which were used as displaced persons' camps, mainly for survivors of the Holocaust, prior to their immigration to Palestine in 1945–46. The British authorities also provided canteen money for Jews interned at camps in Cyprus in 1946–48, after being turned back from Palestine as illegal immigrants.

Continental Currency Paper money authorised by the Continental Congress between 1775 and 1779 in the early stages of the American War of Independence.

Counterfeit The forgery or imitation of a note intended for circulation to deceive the public and defraud the state or the issuing bank.

Counterfoil The left-hand portion of a note or cheque, retained by the issuer as a record of the issue. It was usually divided from the main portion by some highly elaborate vertical design which, in the case of cheques especially, tended to become more pictorial in the 19th and early 20th centuries. From the 1840s the counterfoil was separated from the main part by some form of perforation, but earlier examples were cut apart by scissors, often in a serpentine or irregular line so that the two portions could be matched later on if required.

Coupon Term from French couper, to cut, denoting a piece of paper which may be exchanged for goods or services, hence a detachable ticket or voucher entitling the holder to something. In the notaphilic context it denotes a detachable portion of a share certificate entitling the holder to a dividend, and has also been used to signify small notes used as emergency money.

Crossed Cheque A cheque which bears parallel diagonal lines across the middle, either printed or handwritten, giving instructions to the paying bank to limit negotiability to the payee.

Crossing Stamp A brass or rubber stamp applied by hand across the face of a cheque by the negotiating bank.

Currency Notes intended to pass current in general circulation as money.

Current Note still in circulation.

Cut Note A note which has been officially cut into halves or quarters and re-issued, each part thereby serving as a note of appropriate value. As a rule, each portion bears an overprint signifying its new value.

Cypher Term for the combination of letters which serve as a prefix in the serial number. In recent years such cyphers have often been deliberately contrived to serve a quasi-commemorative purpose, eg RLS (Robert Louis Stevenson), AGB (Alexander Graham Bell), SP (Scottish Parliament) and G/AD Glasgow, City of Architecture and Design) on Scottish notes of the 1990s.

Darlehnskassen German for 'state loan note', a form of paper money issued during the World War I in an abortive bid to fill the shortage of coinage in circulation. These low-denomination notes failed to meet demand and were superseded by local issues of Notgeld in 1916.

Date In many cases the year, or even a full date, merely denotes the point in time at which a note was authorised or introduced, and may antedate the actual time or even the year of release. In other cases, however, the date signifies the actual time of issue.

Demand Notes Name generally given to the first series of paper money authorised by the US federal government by Act of Congress in 1861 at the beginning of the American Civil War, and so-called because the United States promised to pay the bearer on demand. The formula, of course, is widely used on the notes of many other countries and is by no means confined to the USA.

Demonetisation The withdrawal of notes from circulation and declaring them to be worthless.

Denomination The face value of a note, expressed in words of figures or often a combination of both.

Depression Scrip American term for temporary makeshifts issued in various parts of the USA during the Depression of the early 1930s.

Device Heraldic term for the pattern or emblem on banknotes.

Devil's Head Collectors' term for certain notes of Canada and the Seychelles in which an image of the Devil was fancifully detected in the hair of Queen Elizabeth.

Die Hardened piece of metal, usually steel but sometimes copper, bearing a positive image of the device to be transferred to the printing plate.

Die Proof An impression, usually pulled on soft carton or India paper, of an intaglio engraving of a banknote, usually taken during the progress of engraving in order to check the detail. Proofs of this nature usually consist of the portrait or some detail of the design, such as the border, rather than the complete motif.

Dividend Warrant A cheque issued in payment of a dividend to a shareholder, often attached to a document setting out the details of the dividend.

Dix Note Collectors' term for $10 notes of the Citizens' Bank of Louisiana in New Orleans, from the French word DIX (ten) inscribed on their backs. The widespread notion that this gave rise to the term 'Dixie' denoting the Southern States of the USA is utterly false. Apart from the fact that many Canadian notes are similarly inscribed, it should be stated that the term 'Dixie', first popularised by the patriotic song of 1859 by Daniel D. Emmett, comes from the Mason-Dixon Line which separated the states of the free North and slave-owning South, Charles Mason and Jeremiah Dixon being the surveyors who mapped the southern boundary of Pennsylvania in the late 18th century.

Double Note A note in which the front and back bear no relation to each other. This apparently first arose during the American Civil War when unfinished notes of a broken bank were pressed into service, with a new device on the blank side, by other banks as a result of a chronic shortage of paper.

Draft An alternative name for a cheque, sometimes used in the context of a bank draft.

Drawer The person drawing or issuing a cheque and whose signature appears on it.

Dual Currency Notes inscribed with values in two different currency systems. This situation sometimes arises during a period of transition from one currency to another, usually as a result of monetary reforms.

Educational Notes Name given to the US silver certificates of 1896 on account of the didactic nature of their designs.

Embossing A printing process which entails the use of male and female dies or matrices to raise a portion of the design above the normal surface. It is commonly found on old cheques and bills of exchange which bear an embossed device denoting the payment of stamp duty, but in many banknotes of recent vintage it is used as a security device and an aid to blind and partially sighted persons to identify the face value correctly.

Emergency Money Any form of money used in times of economic and political upheaval, when traditional kinds of currency are not available. In paper money this takes the form of all kinds of coupons, vouchers and scrip employed in military campaigns or in towns under siege, the Notgeld issued by many towns in Austria and Germany (1916–23), encased money, fractional currency, guerrilla notes, invasion, liberation and occupation money from the two world wars and minor campaigns. Among more recent examples may be cited the use of cheques in Italy (1976–77) and the issue of talons or coupons in many of the countries of the former Soviet Union pending the introduction of their own distinctive currencies.

Encased Money Postage and revenue stamps enclosed in small metal and mica-faced discs, circulated as small change in times of emergency. The device was invented by John Gault, a Boston sewing-machine salesman, during the American Civil War (1862). The face of the stamp was visible through the transparent window, while the back of the disc was embossed with firms' advertisements. This practice was revived during and after the World War I when there was again a shortage of small coins. Encased stamps have also been recorded from Austria, France, Germany, Monaco and Norway. See also Stamp Money.

Endorsement The signature of the payee on the back of a cheque.

Endorsement Guarantee A statement indemnifying the paying bank in the case of an incorrect endorsement on a cheque, usually indicated by means of a rubber handstamp.

Engine Turning An intricate pattern of spiral and curved lines created by the Rose Engine, patented by Jacob Perkins between 1811 and 1819 as part of the process of steel engraving or siderography which established the fortunes of the security printing firm variously known as Perkins, Fairman & Heath, Perkins, Bacon & Heath or Perkins, Bacon. The French term guilloche is sometimes used.

Engraving The art of cutting lines or grooves into a die for recess-printing (intaglio) or cutting away parts of the surface leaving the portion to be printed standing out (letterpress). See these terms for further details.

Error Mistakes in paper money may be caused at the design or engraving stage, or as a result of a fault in the production processes. In the first category come misspellings in text or inscriptions, but more usually mistakes or inaccuracies in details of the design. In the second category the back of a note may be printed upside down in relation to the front, or a part of the design may be doubly printed or misplaced. Faulty registration of the printing plates may result in one colour being out of alignment. Other errors include serial numbers partially or wholly omitted or printed upside down. The commonest error consists of miscut notes.

Essay (From the French essai, a trial piece). In paper money this refers to any design, from the original artwork to a preliminary printing, for the purpose of examination by parliamentary or financial bodies, prior to the authorisation of an actual issue of notes, the counterpart of patterns in coinage or medals.

Face The surface of a banknote, more usually referred to as the front, the recto or obverse.

Face Value The value inscribed in words and/or figures at which the note passes current.

Facsimile An imitation, usually authorised officially, of a note, perhaps created long after the original has been withdrawn from circulation. Such notes, usually marked in some way to indicate their true nature, were sometimes produced for exhibition purposes or to complete gaps in the bank's official collection, often utilising the original plates or dies.

Fantasy A note purporting to be the currency of a country which does not exist. Recent examples include the notes of the Hutt River Province which declared its independence of Western Australia.

Federal Reserve Bank Note Type of note issued by the Federal Reserve Bank of the USA between 1915 and 1933 and thus inscribed.

Federal Reserve Note A note issued by the Federal Reserve of the USA from 1914 to the present day and thus inscribed. These notes are backed by the federal government and not by individual banks.

Fei-ch'ien Chinese for "flying money", denoting the earliest form of paper money in the world and dating from the 7th–9th centuries.

Fiat Money Notes issued by a government but not redeemable in coin or bullion.

Fiduciary Issue Notes issued purely on trust, without the backing of gold or other securities.

Flying Money See Fei-ch'ien.

Forced Issue Paper money imposed on a populace without any backing and usually issued by the authority of an occupying power in time of war.

Forgery An unauthorised copy or imitation of a note, made with the intention of deceiving collectors. Forgeries intended to pass current for real notes are more properly termed counterfeits.

Foxing Unsightly spots, ranging from yellow to brown or dark red, caused by iron impurities in old paper. It is, in fact, a form of fungus which can spread across the paper or attack other paper with which it comes in contact. It can often be checked, if not always entirely eliminated, by treating the affected part with a very weak solution of a bleaching agent such as Chloramine-T. It is exacerbated by lack of air circulation and for that reason it is important that notes should be examined periodically and allowed to breathe.

Fractional Currency Emergency issue of small-denomination notes by the USA in 1863-65, following a shortage of coins caused by the Civil War. This issue was superseded by the Postage Currency notes, but bore the inscription "Receivable for all US stamps", alluding to the most popular medium of small change at that time. Denominations ranged from 3c to 50c.

Frame That part of the design forming the border, prevalent in note design until the 1960s when a much lighter, open style of design came into fashion. In many older notes the frame was elaborately engraved and ornamented to defeat counterfeiters.

Front The main side of a note, otherwise the obverse or recto, on which appears the name of the bank and/or country, together with signatures of bank officials, the date and place of issue and usually some form of promise to pay the bearer in coin of the realm.

Fund Raising Note A note produced by an exiled organisation to raise money for the campaign to gain independence. Good examples are the notes issued mainly in the USA by Irish and Hungarian nationalists in the 19th century.

Funeral Money Imitations of banknotes, used in China and Latin America in funeral ceremonies. See also Hell notes.

Gold Bank Note A note issued in the 1870s by nine banks in California and one in Boston, so-called because they promised to pay the bearer in gold coin.

Gold Certificate A series of nine issues in the USA between 1863 and 1922, redeemable in gold coin.

Gold Note Term generally applied to any note specifically redeemable in gold.

Goodfor Popular name for emergency money made of paper or card, from the inscription "Good for" or its equivalent in other languages (e.g. French bon pour or Dutch goed voor) followed by a monetary value. Notes of this type have been recorded from Europe, Africa and America during times of economic crises or shortage of coinage.

Granite Paper Type of security paper which has tiny coloured threads enmeshed in it.

Greenback Popular name for the paper money issued under the authority of the US government, from the predominant colour of the verso.

Guerrilla Money Money issued in areas under the control of guerrillas and partisans during wartime range from the veld ponds of the Boer War (1899–1902) to the notes issued by the Garibaldi Brigade in Italy and the anti-fascist notes of Tito's partisans in Yugoslavia. The most prolific issues were those produced in Luzon, Mindanao and Negros Occidental by the Filipino resistance (1942–45).

Guilloche French term signifying the intricate pattern of curved lines produced by the rose engine and used as a security feature in the production of banknotes, cheques, stocks and share certificates. See also engine turning.

Gutschein German word for voucher or coupon, denoting the paper money used aboard ships of the Imperial Navy during World War I. The last issue was made at Scapa Flow, Orkney, during the internment of the High Seas Fleet (1918–19). The term is also widely used in Germany nowadays for any giveaway, exchangeable for goods or services as part of a sales promotion.

Halved Note   A note which has been cut in half as a precaution during transmission by post. On the safe arrival of the first half being notified, the other half is then sent by post. This practice was widespread in the early 19th century when highway robbery was prevalent. The two halves were subsequently re-united, often using specially printed strips of gummed paper.

Handsigned Notes   which have been individually signed by hand, rather than by means of an engraved facsimile signature.

Hansatsu   Japanese term denoting notes of purely local validity, usually printed by woodblocks on soft, thick handmade paper, hence the derisive trerm "blotter money".

Hell Notes   Imitation paper money used in Chinese funeral ceremonies and buried with the dead to pay for services in the next world.

Holed   Term denoting notes which have either been pierced with pins or staples to attach them to each other or to documents, thereby detracting from their collectable condition, or notes which have been deliberately punched with small holes as a security precaution. The latter device is sometimes applied to specimen notes or printers' samples to prevent them getting into general circulation. See also perforated.

Hologram   A security device consisting of an image which changes colour or design depending on how it is tilted towards the light. It was first applied to credit cards in the early 1980s and to banknotes in 1988 (Australia), but has become much more widespread in very recent years.

Imitation Money   Also known as play money or toy money, it consists of notes produced for games of chance (like Monopoly), children's toy shops and post offices, as tourist souvenirs or for political satire (e.g. the shrinking pound or dollar). See also funeral money, hell notes and skit notes.

Imprint   Inscription on a note giving the name of the printer, usually found in the lower margin.

Indented   Description of an irregular edge on the left-hand side of a note, matching a corresponding pattern in the counterfoil, used in the 19th century as a precaution against forgery.

Inflation Money   Notes produced in Germany (1921–23), Austria (1923), Poland (1923), Hungary (1945–46), Greece (1946), China (1946–48) and many countries of Latin America and the former communist bloc since the 1980s and, most recently, by Angola and Turkey.

Hungary holds the record for the highest value of any note ever issued—one thousand million adopengos equivalent to no less than 20,000,00 0,000,000,000,000,000,000,000 pengos.

Inscription   Any kind of text printed on the back or front of a note.

Intaglio   In the production of paper money, intaglio engraving is still commonly practised. In this process the engraver cuts the design into a steel die and the printing ink lies in the grooves. The paper is forced into the grooves under great pressure where it takes up the ink and results in the ridges which are characeristic of this process.

Interest Bearing Note   A note whose promise to pay the bearer includes a reference to interest payable at the time of redemption.

Invasion Money   Notes prepared in advance of a military invasion, either solely for the use of the invading forces, or also extended forcibly to the civil population and thus employed as means of controlling the local economy. *See also* liberation and occupation money.

Jugate   (From Latin Jugum, a yoke). Heraldic term denoting the overlapping profiles of two or more persons portrayed on banknotes. A good recent example is provided by the notes of Thailand celebrating the Golden Wedding of the King and Queen, released in April 2000.

Kreditivsedlar   (Swedish for "credit notes"). The name given to the first issue of paper money made in the western world. Paper money of this type was the invention of Johan Palmstruch at Riga in 1652 but nine years elapsed before it was implemented by the Stockholm Bank. The notes were issued up to 1666 and were mainly redeemable in copper platmynt though latterly in silver coin.

Labour Note   A form of paper money devised by the industrialist and philanthropist Robert Owen and used to pay his employees at the textile mills in New Lanark, Scotland in the 1830s. The value was expressed in hours worked rather than any monetary terms. The concept spread briefly to England and America, but was generally frowned on as an abuse of the workers' rights to spend their money freely, rather than at the company store.

Latent Image   A security device on a banknote which takes the form of an image that only becomes apparent when the surface of the note is tilted in a particular direction, and thus was a precursor of the hologram as a safeguard against forgery.

Leather Money   Pieces of leather embossed with an official device have been used as money on several occasions, during the sieges of Faenza and Leiden and in the Isle of Man in the 15th and 16th centuries. Several towns in Austria and Germany produced lether tokens during and after World War I.

Legal Tender   Notes which are declared by law to be current money and which tradesmen and shopkeepers are obliged to accept in payment for goods or services. (*See* Banknotes and the Law).

Legend   The inscription on a banknote.

Letterpress   A printing process in which the ink is applied to the raised portions of a die or plate and then transferred to paper . It takes its name from the fact that this method was originally used in the printing of books and newspapers consisting mainly of lettering although from the outset it also included illustrations from woodblocks. This process is much cheaper and less secure than intaglio, and was used for many early banknotes. *See also* typeset.

Liberation Money   Paper money prepared for use in parts of Europe and Asia, formerly under Axis occupation. Liberation notes were used in France, Belgium and the Netherlands in 1944-45, while various Japanese and Chinese notes were overprinted for use in Hong Kong when it was liberated in 1945. Indian notes overprinted for use in Burma were issued in 1945-46 when that country was freed from Japanese occupation.

Lithography   A printing process patented by Alois Senefelder in 1795 and since widely used in the production of banknotes and cheques, mainly as an underprint, often in special fugitive inks. The name comes from the Greek lithos, a stone and graphein, to write, and alludes to the polished limestone slabs originally employed, although nowadays zinc or even paper plates are used instead. The image is laid down on the stone in greasy ink or by means of transfers. The printing ink adheres to the grease but is repelled by the blank areas of the plate.

Low Number   A note with a very low serial number, either one or two digits preceded by a string of noughts, is regarded by collectors as very desirable, indicating very early issue. Pandering to this, however, many banks now set aside the low-numbered notes for inclusion in presentation folders sold to collectors.

Mandat   Name given to a form of paper money issued in the period of the French Revolution. Like the assignat, which it replaced, the value of the mandat was theoretically backed by land confiscated from the Church and the aristocracy.

Margin   That portion of a note lying between the outer border of the design and the edge of the paper. Notes with regular margins on all four sides often command a premium, whereas notes with irregular margins are often discounted. Margins may be clean-cut (by guillotine), rough or even deckle-edged if produced from individual pieces of handmade paper instead of being printed in sheets.

Master Die   The original piece of steel or copper engraved by hand. It is then hardened chemically and an image taken by means of a transfer roller which, after hardening, transfers the image in reverse to the printing plate. Alterations to the master die, by means of punches or subsequent engraving, create secondary dies (often for the production of different denominations using the same basic design).

Metal Thread   A security device in the form of a thin strip of metal embedded in the paper pulp during manufacture.

Microprint   Printing in very tiny lettering, usually endlessly repeated, as a security precaution. It is often used in doubly fugitive ink on those parts of cheques where handwriting appears, to prevent attempts to alter or falsify details by washing, bleaching or chemical means.

Military Currency   Notes issued under military authority, mainly for the use of troops on active service.

Military Payment Certificate   A note produced by the US military authorities for the use of service personnel in PX (post exchange) canteens to prevent black market trading with local civilians.

Ming Note   A large-sized Chinese note issued during the Ming Dynasty (1368-1644), using paper made from mulberry bark. Now highly desirable as the earliest form of paper money available to the collector market.

Miscut   A note with very irregular margins, or even showing a portion of an adjoining note in the sheet, caused by misalignment of the blades cutting up the sheets of notes prior to issue. In some cases an additional piece of paper remains attached as a result of part of the wide sheet margin being accidentally folded over. Such errors in production are of curiosity interest rather than high monetary value, although they often command a premium.

Model   A mock-up of a banknote, produced at a preliminary stage of production, often incorporated the pasted-up portions of previously issued notes or a composite of different elements which may eventually form the complete design,

Moiré   French for "watering", denoting a security underprint of close wavy lines having the effect of watered silk.

Money Order   Certificate for a specific amount of money, which may be transmitted by post and encashed at a money order office or post office. This system was pioneered by Britain and the USA in the early 19th century and is now virtually worldwide. The term is now confined to certificates above a certain value, the terms postal order and postal note being used for similar certificates covering small amounts.

Moses Crowns   Popular name for the notes issued under the authority of the Jewish Council of Elders in Theresienstadt concentration camp during World War II, and so-called on account of the principal motif showing Moses holding up the Ten Commandments. *See also* concentration camp money.

Mule A note whose back and front are printed from plates which were not originally intended to be paired together.

Multilingual A note bearing inscriptions in many different languages. Apart from the so-called Babel notes of revolutionary Russia, good examples may be found in the issues of the Habsburg Empire, with values in up to eight languages and two scripts, or Indian notes with inscriptions in English and many different indigenous scripts. The Euro notes of the European Community bear the initials of the European Central Bank in the different languages and scripts of the member countries.

Multiple Denomination A note with values expressed in two or more different currencies, generally to facilitate exchange. *See also* dual currency.

National Bank Note American term applied specifically to the notes issued by banks, chartered by the federal government between 1863 and 1935, and backed by US Treasury bonds.

Negotiable Term applied to a banknote or cheque which can be readily converted into coin.

Notaphily Hybrid word from Latin nota (note) and Greek philos (love), coined in 1969 to denote the branch of numismatics devoted to the collection and study of paper money. *See also* syngraphics.

Note A piece of paper money. In former times the term was also loosely applied to cheques or IOUs.

Notgeld German word meaning "emergency money", applied to the various forms of currency, including notes, which circulated during the World War I when coinage disappeared from circulation, but rapidly overtaken by infinitely more prolific issues of paper money produced by shops, chambers of commerce, businesses and local authorities. Collectors distinguish between kleine Notgeld (small emergency money) in denominations from 10 to 50 pfennigs during and immediately after the war, and the large Notgeld whose denominations were in thousands, and later millions, of marks. Some 3,000 types appeared in 1922 and over 60,000 in 1923 alone. These quaint and colourful mementoes of the German hyperinflation ceased to circulate in 1924 when the currency was reformed.

Obsolete Term denoting a note which is no longer issued and has been withdrawn from circulation. Notes which are no longer issued but which may still be current during a brief overlapping period are more properly described as obsolescent.

Obverse The front of a note, equivalent to the "heads" side of a coin or medal, although the term recto is more appropriate for a piece of paper.

Occupation Money Any form of money, but usually notes or vouchers, issued in wartime by enemy forces in the territory which they invade and occupy.

Order Cheque A cheque payable to a specified person or to his or her order.

Out of Date Cheque A cheque which is considered by the paying bank to have been in circulation for "an unreasonable period of time". This is usually regarded as at least six months, although there is apparently no statutory limit.

Overprint Any form of printing added to a note or cheque after it was originally produced. Such a practice may be employed to alter the name of the issuing bank or authority or, in times of inflation and monetary reform, to convert the denomination to the reformed system. An overprint may also signify a change of government or regime, or even the name of the country.

Paid Cheque A cheque which has been honoured by a bank and the amount debited to the drawer's account.

Paid Stamp The handstamp applied to a cheque by the paying bank after debiting the sum to the drawer's account.

Paper Money Any form of currency based on paper.

Partisan Note A note produced by Tito's partisans operating in Serbia, Croatia and other parts of Yugoslavia after it was dismembered by the Axis during World War II, and used in those parts of the country which were effectively under their control.

Payee The person to whom a cheque is made payable.

Perforation A series of small holes punched out of paper. The earliest form, dating from the 1840s, was used to facilitate the separation of the cheque or banknote from its counterfoil, but later the punches were often arranged in the form of letters or numerals and could thus be applied to cheques to indicate the date on which they were presented for payment. In banknotes, perforation has sometimes been employed to mark them as Specimens intended for archival or publicity purposes and not valid for circulation. *See also* Cancelled.

Pilgrim Receipt A form of paper money overprinted for the use of people going on a religious pilgrimage. Notes of Pakistan, for example, are specially overprinted for use by pilgrims from that country making the haj to the Moslem holy places of Mecca and Medina in Saudi Arabia.

Pinhole A blemish on a banknote caused by it having been pinned or stapled to a document or another note. It should be noted, however, that certain notes only exist with this feature as they were put into circulation in batches stapled together for the sake of convenience.

Plain Back   A note which has no printing of any kind on the reverse. *See also* Uniface.

Plate Number   A small number incorporated in the design of some notes to indicate the plate from which it was printed.

Play Money   Imitations of banknotes produced for use in such games of chance as Monopoly or as part of children's toy outfits for shops and post offices. Of passing interest to notaphilists only in so far as the designs are often vaguely derived from actual notes.

Playing Card Money   A form of emergency money created in French Canada from 1685 onwards during shortages of coin supplied from France. Governor Duplessis hit upon using playing cards, with his signature and the denomination added in handwriting.

Polymer   A chemical compound containing repeating structural units and formed by chemical combination of many small molecules. In notaphily the term is applied to various plastic materials used in the manufacture of banknotes since the 1970s.

Postage Currency   Small notes in denominations of 5, 10, 25 and 50 cents, issued by the US federal government in 1862–63, were thus inscribed and had reproductions of postage stamps engraved on them—five 5c stamps on the 25c and five 10c stamps on the 50c notes. The earliest issue even had perforations in the manner of stamps, but this unnecessary device was soon dispensed with. *See also* stamp money.

Postal Notes or Orders   Low-value notes intended for transmission by post and encashable at post offices. Introduced by Britain in 1883, they were an extension of the earlier money order system and are now issued by virtually every country.

Post-dated   A cheque bearing a date subsequent to that on which it is presented for payment. As banks are not obliged to honour such cheques they are invariably handed back to the payee or returned to the drawer for re-presentation on or after the due date.

Prisoner of War Money   Under the terns of the Geneva Convention the belligerents on both sides during the world wars provided special issues of notes for use within prisoner of war camps. Similar provisions were also made for camps in which civilians were interned.

Promissory Note   A written promise to pay, either on demand or at some future time, a sum of money to a specified individual or to the bearer.

Proof   A preliminary test printing of the back or front of a note, taken from the master die or the printing plate before actual production, in order to ensure that every detail is correct.

Propaganda Note   A piece of paper money containing political slogans or a didactic element. During World War II for example, forgeries of German and Japanese notes were produced by the Allies and additionally inscribed or overprinted with slogans such as "Co-Prosperity Sphere—What is it worth?" (a reference to the Japanese occupied areas of Southeast Asia). Forged dollars with Anti-American propaganda were airdropped over Sicily by the Germans in 1943 and counterfeit pounds with Arabic propaganda over Egypt in 1942–43. Various anti-communist organisations liberated propaganda forgeries of paper money by balloon over Eastern Europe during the Cold War period.

Provincial Note   A note issued by a provincial bank or under the authority of a provincial government (as in Canada). Provincial banks in England were only permitted to issue notes so long as they did not have an office in London. The last of the English provincial banks was Fox, Fowler of Wellington Somerset, whose notes ceased in 1921 when the bank became part of the Lloyd's group.

Psywar Note   A note produced as part of a campaign of psychological warfare. Effectively this means some kind of imitation paper money dropped as a leaflet by aircraft over enemy-held territory with the intention of demoralising the enemy and boosting the morale of the people enduring occupation.

Punched   A note or cheque which bears the mark of a ticket punch to denote that it has been cancelled.

Rag Paper   Paper made of linen rags, sometimes with an admixture of cotton or other textile substances, to produce a very tough, hard-wearing material for the production of banknotes.

Raised Note   A note which has been revalued by means of an official overprint.

Reckoning Note   A form of paper money issued to German troops on the eve of an invasion and exchangeable for local currency, usually at a considerable disadvantage to the economy of the occupied country.

Recto   The proper term for the face or front of a note.

Refunding Certificate   The official name for a $10 note issued by the US government in 1879 and made more acceptable to the general public on account of the 4 per cent interest per annum for an unspecified period. These notes were called in in 1907 by which time they were worth $21.30.

Reichskreditkassen   German for State Credit Treasury, inscribed on certain notes intended for circulation in occupied territories of Europe during World War II.

Re-issue   A note issued again after an extended lapse of time.

Remainder A note from a bank or issuing authority which has never been circulated, due to inflation, political changes or bank failure. Such notes, sometimes in partial or unfinished state (e.g. missing serial numbers or signatures) are generally unloaded on to the numismatic market at a nominal sum and provide a good source of inexpensive material for the beginner.

Repaired A note which has suffered damage, usually tears or splitting, and bearing the evidence of having been restored. Unless they are very rare, such specimens are usually heavily discounted.

Replacement Note A note issued to replace a defective note of the same serial number but generally identified as such by the inclusion of an asterisk or star alongside the number. All the issuing authorities of the United Kingdom and Eire use designated prefixes for replacement notes and these are listed throughout the text.

Reprint A note produced from the original plates but long after production has been generally discontinued. Such notes often differ subtly from the originals, either in the type of paper used or, more often, in the shade of inks employed.

Revalidation The process of bringing back into use notes which had previously been withdrawn from circulation and declared invalid. This has sometimes happened as a result of changes in political regime, such as in Austria where the notes of the early postwar period were similar to those immediately before the Nazi takeover in 1938, identifiable only by their dates.

Revalue An overprint which alters the face value of a note.

Reverse The back of a note, more properly termed the verso.

Saddle Blanket Nickname for the very large notes of the United States in the 19th century.

Safe Conduct Pass A form of propaganda note airdropped behind enemy lines promising safe conduct to military personnel who decide to surrender.

Safety Paper A form of security paper which dramatically changes colour (usually deep blue) when exposed to water. It was formerly widely used in the production of cheques, in order to deter people from trying to alter signatures or other handwritten portions by washing off the ink.

Scrip Paper money of restricted validity or circulation, such as Bafs and other military notes used in service canteens and post exchanges.

Scripophily Term coined in the 1970s to denote the study and collection of stocks, bond and share certificates.

Seal A device, usually circular, which simulates the seal of a bank, a treasury or the state, formerly applied to documents in red sealing wax or embossed in metal foil, but now more generally applied by lithography or letterpress to the banknote design to enhance its official character. See also chop.

Sealskin Money Notes of 1818-30 issued by the Russian Company trading in Alaska, using a form of parchment derived from the skins of seals.

Secret Mark Any device concealed within the mass of engraving with the intention of tripping up the would-be counterfeiter. Such hidden marks, generally overlooked by forgers when fabricating notes, are known to the Secret Service (USA) and bank inspectors and are regarded as a test of genuineness.

Security Features Since 1820 various devices have been incorporated in the design and production of banknotes in order to obviate forgery. These include guilloche engraving, watermarks, metal threads, granite paper, latent images, images visible only under ultra-violet light, microprinting, colour shifting ink, embossing, lithographic underprinting, holograms and much more.

Segmented Security Thread Security device in the form of a line of dashes running across the back of a note, either as a metallic thread or a minute holographic image.

Serial The sequence of figures in numerical order which identifies each individual note. As a rule, numbers are combined with prefix and/or suffix letters which considerably extend the range of serials. As well as very low serial numbers, indicating early issue, collectors also take note of different styles or colours of figures and the presence of symbols (asterisks or stars) denoting replacement notes.

Series A set of different denominations more or less issued within a clearly definable period if not always simultaneously, which possess common features in inscription, style or design. In some cases the word SERIES actually appears on the notes, followed by the date of its introduction.

Share Certificate A piece of paper, often highly ornate or intricately printed, which certifies that the holder possesses a certain specified number of shares in a company.

Shinplasters Derisory term originally applied to the Continental currency notes issued during the American War of Independence, the fractional currency of the Civil War period and also the low-denomination notes of Canada between 1870 and 1935, but often applied indiscriminately to any other low-denomination, small-format notes.

Shoshi Adhesive stamps affixed to Japanese banknotes in the immediate postwar period in order to revalidate them.

Siderography   A printing process patented between 1811 and 1819 by Jacob Perkins and applied to the manufacture of printing plates for banknotes from 1820 onwards. From the Greek sideros, iron and graphein, to write.

Siege Note   A note produced by the defenders during the siege of a town, when supplies of normal currency are cut off. Notable examples include the notes issued at Venice during the Austrian siege of 1848 and by Mafeking in 1900 during the Boer War.

Sight Note   A type of promissory note, so-called on account of the formula "At . . . [number of days] after Sight, pay this to . . . Or Order, the Sum of . . ." Although in some cases the word "Sight" itself was inserted in manuscript, the period specified being usually 30 days.

Silk Thread   A security device patented in the 1830s by John Dickinson and incorporated into some banknotes of the mid-19th century as a precursor of the metallic thread.

Silver Certificate   Type of paper money introduced by the United States in 1878, redeemable by the Treasury in silver coin.

Signature   From the earliest times, bills, promissory notes, cheques and banknotes relied heavily on the signature of an individual or bank official. Handsigned notes survived in some instances until the late 19th century but from the 1820s onwards the vast majority of signatures have been engraved facsimiles. They are of importance to collectors as constituting a major variety in any series of notes, each change of signature constituting a collectable variant. One, two or even three signatures of different bank officials are the norm, although notes of the Austro-Hungarian Bank had three Austrian and three Hungarian signatures, on the front and back respectively.

Skit Note   A piece of paper masquerading as a banknote. It differs from a counterfeit in that its design parodies that of a genuine note, often for political, satirical or advertising reasons. Others were produced as April Fools' Day jokes or a form of Valentine (e.g. The Banks of Hearts or Lovers). In recent years they have been produced as advertising gimmicks or as coupons permitting a discount off the list price of goods. Also known as "Flash" notes.

Small Size Note   Collectors' term for the series of notes, in a reduced size from the preceding issues, which came into use in the USA in 1929 and are still in use.

Special Cheque   A cheque drawn on a form specially printed for the drawer and not of the standard design. Such cheques usually give far greater prominence to the names of the drawers (usually a company or institution) and may even be embellished with pictures of factories, premises or products. For this reason they are of immense interest to local historians.

Specie   Money in coin. Many issues of paper owe their existence to the suspension of specie payment in time of war or monetary crisis.

Specimen   Term generally used to denote a single item but more specifically applying to a note intended for circulation between banks or for press publicity and distinguished from the generally issued version by zero serial numbers, punch holes or a security overprint, usually the word SPECIMEN or its equivalent.

Stage Money   Notes specially printed for use in dramatic productions, on stage, screen or television, sometimes in vague imitation of real notes but often completely different to avoid any charge of counterfeiting.

Stamp Duty   A government tax on transactions involving money, and therefore applied in Britain to cheques between the beginning of the 19th century and 1962. The earliest duty was denoted by a colourless embossed stamp, followed in 1853-81 by various adhesive revenue stamps, then the small upright oval embossed stamps in red (1d) or blue (2d) and finally by the small circular crowned medallion stamps printed in black. Similar systems applied in many other countries. In the USA, for example, the duty could be denoted by a variety of adhesive stamps or by a device printed in orange-yellow across the middle of the cheque.

Stamped   Banknotes to which have been affixed adhesive stamps, either to denote the payment of a tax or to authenticate them. The latter practice has sometimes been used in lieu of an overprint to alter the validity of notes.

Stamp Money   Both postage and revenue stamps have circulated as money during shortages of coins, from the American Civil War onwards. Encased postage stamps were used in the USA (1861–62) before they were superseded by Postage Currency notes, but the same expedient was adopted by many other countries immediately after the World War I. Stamps affixed to special cards have circulated as money in Rhodesia (now Zimbabwe) in 1900, the French colonies and Turkey during the World War I, in Spain during the Civil War (1936–39) and the Philippines during the Japanese occupation (1942–45). Stamps printed on thick card, with an inscription on the reverse signifying their parity with silver coins, were issued in Russia (1917–18) and also in Armenia, the Crimea and the Ukraine (1918–20). During World War II Ceylon (which is now Sri Lanka) and several Indian states issued small money cards with contemporary stamps printed on them.

Star Note   A replacement note issued in the USA, so-called on account of the five-pointed star before or after the serial number.

State Bank Note   A note issued by a bank chartered by one of the states in the USA, as opposed to the issues of the Treasury, Federal Reserve or other agencies of the federal government.

State Note A note issued in the early 19th century by one of the states in the USA.

Stopped Cheque A cheque on which payment has been countermanded by the drawer before it is presented at the paying bank.

Stub Another term for the counterfoil, retained as a record of a bank transaction.

Subject Term indicating an individual note which is part of a sheet. Thus a 20-subject sheet would contain 20 impressions of the note.

Surface Printing An alternative name for letterpress, the printing process mainly employed in the production of banknotes before 1820.

Sutlers' Notes A form of scrip issued by US army canteen-keepers for use on military posts and redeemable in merchandise. They were mainly issued during the late 19th century.

Syngraphics Term coined in the 1970s, from the Greek syn (together) and graphein (to write) to denote the study and collection of cheques.

Travellers' Cheques (American, Travelers' Checks) Notes in various denominations issued by Thomas Cook, American Express and many banks which can be converted into cash by tourists and businessmen when travelling abroad. They are validated by the traveller who signs each note in the presence of the issuing agent and then signs them again at the point of encashment. They are issued in sterling, US dollars or some other widely recognised currency but can then be converted into the equivalent in local money. Since the advent of credit cards and bank cards, however, the use of travellers' cheques has dropped very dramatically.

Treasury Note Paper money worth 10 shillings or one pound, issued by the British treasury on the outbreak of the World War I when specie payments were suspended, and continuing till 1928 when the Bank of England took over responsibility for note-issuing. They were popularly known as Bradburys, from the signature of the Treasury official, Sir John Bradbury, engraved on them.

Type A major design.

Typeset A note in which the design is entirely composed of lettering, ornament being confined to printer's rule and the use of conventional symbols, usually to create a border.

Uncirculated A note which is in the most perfect condition, as received at the bank from the printer and never passed from hand to hand.

Uncut A sheet or part of a sheet in which two or more notes are still unsevered.

Underprint The background to the principal motif and inscriptions of a banknote, generally printed by a different process (e.g. lithography instead of intaglio) and in contrasting, lighter colours incorporating security features such as microprinting and latent images.

Uniface A note which has printing on one side only.

Upham A Philadelphia printer whose patriotism during the Civil War led him to produce facsimiles of Confederate notes. The reproduction was excellent and the imitations could only be readily distinguished by Upham's imprint and advertisement in the bottom margin. Unfortunately most of his notes had the advert trimmed off and swiftly found their way to the Confederacy where they were promptly circulated as genuine. As a result, Upham facsimiles with the imprint still intact are now relatively scarce, and certainly rarer than the notes they imitated.

Validating Stamp A handstruck mark applied to notes either at the time of issue to render them valid or subsequently applied to extend their usage.

Varible Optical Ink Ink which appears to change colour or density depending on the angle at which the note is viewed.

Variety Variation in, or modification of type, effigy or inscription.

Verso The proper term for the reverse or back of a note.

Victory Note A banknote of the Philippines overprinted VICTORY from October 20, 1944 onwards to celebrate the liberation of the islands after almost three years of Japanese rule.

Vignette Strictly speaking the pictorial element of a note, shading off into the surrounding unprinted paper rather than having a clearly defined border or frame, but nowadays applied generally to the picture portion of a banknote, as opposed to the portrait, armorial or numeral elements.

Voucher A piece of paper exchangeable for goods or services of a specified value and therefore regarded as a form of paper money.

War Lord Note A note issued by one of the many tuchuns or war lords who operated in various parts of China in the period between the fall of the Manchu Dynasty and the communist takeover in 1949. Seldom, if ever, backed by gold or collateral other than the barrel of the gun, these notes were often well designed and printed (employing the leading security printers of Europe and America to lend them respectability), but rendered worthless as the fortunes of civil war ebbed and flowed. They have left a rich legacy of relatively cheap but colourful material for the collector market.

Watermark A security device, generally visible when the note is held up to the light, and ranging from an overall geometric or curvilinear pattern to state emblems and even portraits, the lastnamed often set within a circular or oval cartouche. The watermark derives its name from the fact that it is created at the wet pulp stage in the manufacture of the paper, in which the pressure from brass wires or "bits" of the required pattern causes a slight thinning in the paper. In some cases notes have been printed on paper bearing the papermaker's name or trademark, only a portion of which is visible on any one note.

White Note Collector's term for the early notes of the Bank of England which were printed in black ink on white paper, using a relatively large format. This tradition, dating from 1695, continued as late as 1957 when the "white fiver" was superseded by a £5 note of more conventional design. These white notes were deceptively simple, which may have encouraged the Germans, under Operation Bernhard, to forge them during the World War II, using skilled counterfeiters in prisons and concentration camps for the purpose. But in fact the secret of these notes lay in the quality of paper used, with its extremely intricate watermark pattern, and it was the failure to secure paper of the right quality which defeated the forgers in the long run.

Wildcat Notes Notes issued in the USA and Canada in the early 19th century by unscrupulous persons who purported to act on behalf of non-existent banks. Poor communications and lax banking laws enabled them to get away with these frauds for a short time before their notes were unmasked as false and worthless. Nevertheless they are not without considerable interest on account of their colourful designs and their role in the rather freewheeling commerce of the period.

Withdrawn Note A note which has been taken out of circulation. Sometimes, though by no means always, such notes are overprinted, perforated or punched in some way to indicate that they have no legal tender status or any actual worth.

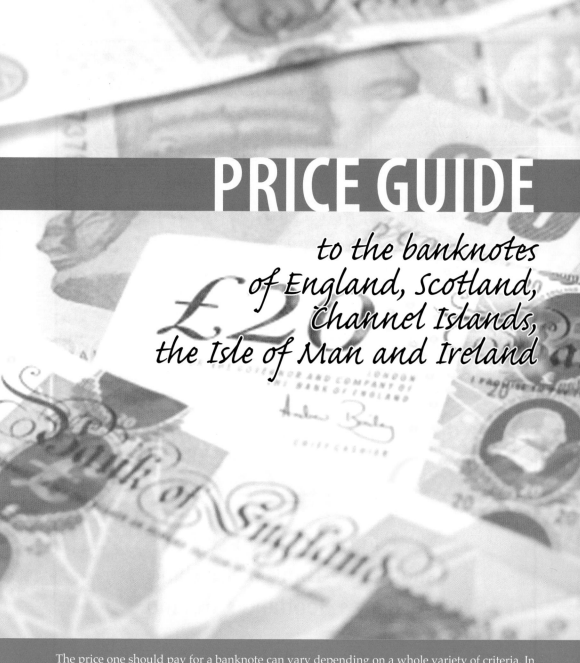

PRICE GUIDE

to the banknotes of England, Scotland, Channel Islands, the Isle of Man and Ireland

The price one should pay for a banknote can vary depending on a whole variety of criteria. In this price guide the figures given are intended as a *guide only* to prices that one should expect to pay for notes in the condition noted at the top of each column—the grading is as explained in the grading table on page 14. Notes in lower grades would obviously cost far less and notes in exceptional condition can command higher prices than those given. The notes listed are ordinary circulating examples.

To comply with current legislation illustrations of all modern English notes have been endorsed with the word SPECIMEN—this, of course, does not appear on the notes themselves. Proofs, specimen printings and other varieties are beyond the scope of this publication—for further information the reader is referred to the relevant specialist book as listed in the Bibliography in the Directory section at the end of this book.

EARLY BANK OF ENGLAND NOTES

BY the close of the 17th century London was becoming one of the most important trading and commercial centres of the world. Its rich merchants and goldsmiths, many of whom are remembered to this day in the names of the banks such as Martins, Lloyds, Barclays and Glyn Mills, had been issuing promissory notes and receipts for valuables for many years and these pieces of paper were accepted as if they were actually money. By 1680 there were about fifty of these merchants whose promissory notes were readily acceptable. With the rapid development of England as a trading nation it became necessary to establish some sort of national bank. In 1694, the Bank of England was founded by William Paterson, a Scotsman whose proposals were readily endorsed by Charles Montagu, the Chancellor of the Exchequer at the time. In the year of its foundation the Bank issued only a few notes, for £20 and £50, and these were entirely hand-written like the merchants' notes.

The first printed notes were released on June 5, 1695 but had a very short life, being hurriedly withdrawn when a cunning forger obtained a quantity of paper from the same supplier as the Bank and then produced excellent counterfeits. The Bank got around this problem by using a different type of paper, with a marbled pattern. As a further precaution against fraud, these marbled notes were cut in half and only one half given to the customer. When the note came back to the bank it could be checked against the other half to prove that it was genuine. None of these marbled notes has survived, but the practice of cutting notes in half continued for some time. Later notes may be found with curved cuts between the two halves as well as a printed design.

A watermark was adopted as a security feature in 1697 and specially watermarked paper has been used for all Bank of England notes since then. The notes from 1696 to 1725 had the amounts written in by hand and could be issued for any odd amount from £10 upwards. Regular denominations were re-introduced in 1725 and were issued in values from £20 to £1000. In 1759 notes for £10 and £15 were added, and six years later a £25 was introduced. The Bank of England did not issue notes of lower value, and it was left to the many private banks to fill the gap. The first £5 notes appeared in 1793, a year when many private banks crashed as a result of the outbreak of war with Revolutionary France.

During a shortage of gold coin during the Napoleonic Wars, notes of £1 and £2 were added to the series and these continued until 1821, but thereafter (except for £1 notes reissued during the bank crisis of 1825-6) the Bank reverted to notes from £5 to £1000 only. All of these 19th century notes are of the greatest rarity. They are generally grouped according to the signature of the Chief Cashier which appears on them. At various times from 1826 onwards branches of the Bank of England were opened in a number of provincial cities, resulting in notes specifically inscribed. Our listing of Bank of England notes is confined to the notes issued in London which are available in collectable condition. Included are the notes issued by the Treasury following the outbreak of World War I. The Bank of England, at that time was only empowered to issue notes of £5 and over and due to the predicted restrictions on gold, Treasury notes were issued in denominations of ten shillings and one pound with the intention of replacing the sovereign and half sovereign.

BANK OF ENGLAND
Pre 1925

All of the black and white notes (commonly known as "White" notes) issued before 1913 are rare and only the £1 Hase is offered with any regularity by dealers and then only occasionally. All of the "White" notes were issued from London and most were also issued from branch offices in Birmingham, Bristol, Hull, Leeds, Liverpool, Manchester, Newcastle, Plymouth and Portsmouth. These branch notes are usually scarcer than the London issues and most are beyond the scope of this yearbook. Occasionally, however, a branch issue is either commoner than the corresponding London note or available in sufficient quantities to warrant a listing.

These notes were all printed in black on white paper in sheets of two notes (except for the smaller £1 and £2 values which were printed in sheets of four) which were then cut up to give one straight edge and three uncut (deckled) edges.

Later issues of the famous "White" notes are found under "Bank of England issues from 1928".

ONE POUND

BE1

Note: This note was discovered in 2008 inside an 18th century book in the library of a Lincolnshire mansion. — Ed.

(1803-07)		*F*	*VF*
BE1	Chief Cashier: A. Newland		
	Handwritten date and serial numbers..............................	£6000	£10,500

BE2a

		F	VF
(1808-21)			
BE2a	*Chief Cashier: H. Hase*		
	Printed date and serial numbers...	£2000	£3500
(1825-26)			
BE2b	*Chief Cashier: H. Hase*		
	Printed date and serial numbers, emergency issue	£2000	£3500

TWO POUNDS

(1805-07)			
BE3	*Chief Cashier: A. Newland*		
	Handwritten date and serial numbers	£12,000	£18,000

BE3A

(1808-21)			
BE3A	*Chief Cashier: H. Hase*		
	Printed date and serial numbers	£7500	£12,000

FIVE POUNDS

BE4

<table>
<tr><td></td><td>F</td><td>VF</td></tr>
</table>

(1793-1807)

BE4   *Chief Cashier: A. Newland*
Handwritten date and serial numbers £17,500   £28,000

BE4A

(1808-29)
BE4A   *Chief Cashier: H. Hase*
Printed date and serial numbers £12,000   £20,000

BE4B

	F	VF

(1829-35)
BE4B   *Chief Cashier: T. Rippon*
Handwritten signature of authorised clerks £11,000   £17,500

BE5a

(1835-55)
BE5a   *Chief Cashier: M. Marshall*
Handwritten or printed signature of authorised clerks £7000   £11,000

BE5b

	F	VF
(1855-64)		
BE5b *Chief Cashier: M. Marshall*		
Watermark signature of Marshall and new Maclise Britannia	£7000	£11,000
(1864-66)		
BE6 *Chief Cashier: W. Miller*		
Printed signature of authorised clerks	£18,000	£30,000
(1866-70)		
BE7a *Chief Cashier: G. Forbes*		
Printed signature of authorised clerks	£7500	£12,000
(1868-73)		
BE7b *Chief Cashier: G. Forbes*		
Printed signature of Geo. Forbes...	£14,000	£22,000

BE8

(1873-93)		
BE8 *Signature: F. May*		
London	£4000	£6,500

BE9

		F	VF
(1893-1902)			
BE9	*Signature: H G. Bowen*		
	London	£4000	£6500

		F	VF	EF
(1902-18)				
BE10	*Signature: J. G. Nairne*			
	London	£325	£550	£900

BE11

		F	VF	EF
(1918-25)				
BE11	*Signature: E. M. Harvey*			
	London	£225	£385	£650

TEN POUNDS

BE12

(1902-18)		F	VF	EF
BE12	*Signature: J. G. Nairne*			
	London	£550	£900	£1400

(1918-25)				
BE13	*Signature: E. M. Harvey*			
	London	£300	£500	£850

TWENTY POUNDS

(1902-18)				
BE14	*Signature: J. G. Nairne*			
	Manchester..	£1750	£3000	£5000

BE15

(1918-25)				
BE15	*Signature: E. M. Harvey*			
	London	£2500	£4000	£7000

FIFTY POUNDS

BE16

(1902-18)		F	VF	EF
BE16	*Signature: J. G. Nairne*			
	Manchester	£2000	£3250	£5500

(1918-25)				
BE17	*Signature: E. M. Harvey*			
	London	£1000	£1750	£2850

ONE HUNDRED POUNDS

BE18

(1902-18)				
BE18	*Signature: J. G. Nairne*			
	Manchester..	£1800	£2750	£4500

N.B. The above prices for Nairne notes are for the later issues. Those issued before 1913 are much scarcer and are likely to command a significant premium.

(1918-25)				
BE19	*Signature: E. M. Harvey*			
	London	£1100	£1850	£3200

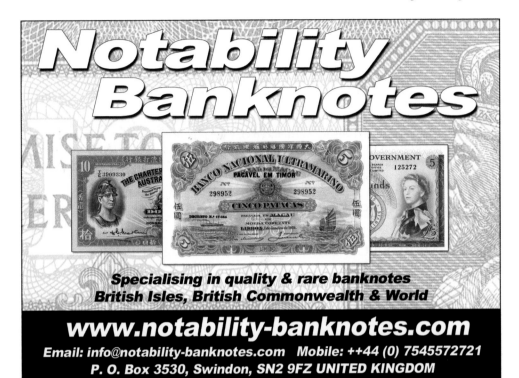
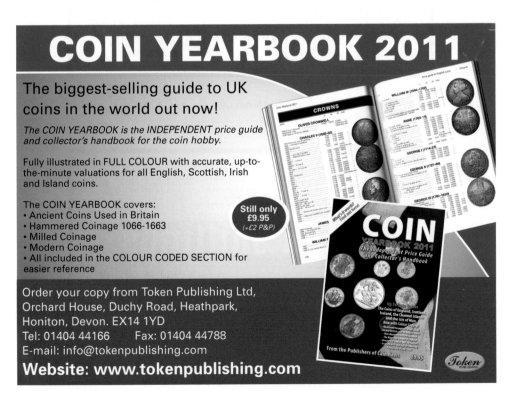

TREASURY NOTES

Notes of one shilling (1/-), two shillings and sixpence (2/6) and five shillings (5/-) signed by John Bradbury and Norman Fenwick Warren Fisher, were produced between December 1917 and November 1919 but were never issued. However, a few notes survived destruction and, along with some examples of proof status, somehow escaped. They very occasionally come onto the market and command very high prices.

TEN SHILLINGS

FIRST (EMERGENCY) BRADBURY ISSUE (August 1914)

Red. 127 x 63mm. Blank reverse
Signature: John Bradbury

TR1a

		VF	EF	UNC
TR1a	Prefix A. N<u>o</u> (*with **dash***) followed by letter over number followed by 6 serial numbers	£425	£700	£1150

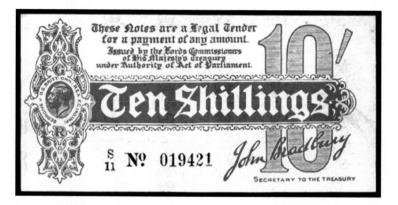

TR1b

		VF	EF	UNC
TR1b	Prefix S and T. Letter over number followed by *No.* (*with **dot***) followed by 6 serial numbers	£650	£1100	£1750

TR1c

		VF	*EF*	*UNC*
TR1c	Prefix B and C. Letter over number followed by *No.* (*with* ***dot***) followed by 5 serial numbers	£750	£1350	£2500

SECOND BRADBURY ISSUE (January 1915)

Red. 136 x 76mm. Blank reverse.De La Rue printing
Signature: John Bradbury

TR2a

TR2a	Prefix A-M. Letter over number followed by 5 serial numbers	£285	£525	£875
TR2b	Prefix A1-M1. Letter and figure 1 over number followed by 5 serial numbers	£300	£550	£900
TR2c	Prefix A2-C2. Letter and figure 2 over number followed by 5 serial numbers	£350	£600	£1000

Red. 136 x 76mm. Blank reverse.Waterlow printing
Signature: John Bradbury

TR3a

		VF	EF	UNC
TR3a	Prefix N-Z. Letter over number followed by .... 6 serial numbers..	£350	£600	£1000
TR3b	Prefix O1-Z1. Letter and figure 1 over number followed by 6 serial numbers...	£350	£600	£1000

SECOND BRADBURY ISSUE DARDANELLES OVERPRINT (May 1915)

Overprint in Turkish "60 silver piastres" on TR3a above for the use of the British Expeditionary Forces in Turkey in 1915

		F	VF	EF

TR4

		F	VF	EF
TR4	Prefix Y and Z. Letter over number followed by 6 serial numbers	£550	£850	£1600

THIRD BRADBURY ISSUE
(October 1918)

Green, brown and purple. 138 x 78mm.
Signature: John Bradbury

TR5a

		VF	EF	UNC
TR5a	Prefix A. Letter over number followed by *No.* (*with **dot***) and serial numbers in black	£425	£700	£1150

TR5b

		VF	EF	UNC
TR5b	Prefix A. Letter over number followed by *No* (*with **dash***) and serial numbers in black	£450	£750	£1200

(December 1918)

TR6a

		VF	EF	UNC
TR6a	Prefix B and C. Letter over number followed by *No.* (*with **dot***) and serial numbers in red.. £1250		—	—

TR6b

TR6b	Prefix B and C. Letter over number followed by *No* (*with **dash***) and serial numbers in red... £350	£600	£1000

FIRST FISHER ISSUE
(September 1919)
Green, brown and purple. 138 x 78mm.
Signature: N. F. Warren Fisher

		VF	EF	UNC
TR7a	Prefix D-H. Letter over number followed by *No.* (*with **dot***) and serial numbers in red...	£185	£375	£650

TR7b

TR7b	Prefix D-H. Letter over number followed by *No_* (*with **dash***) and serial numbers in red...	£175	£350	£600

SECOND FISHER ISSUE
(November 1922)
Green, brown and purple. 138 x 78mm.
Signature: N. F. Warren Fisher

TR8

TR8	Prefix J-S. Letter over number followed by serial numbers	£150	£300	£525

THIRD FISHER ISSUE ("NORTHERN" ADDED TO TITLE)
(July 1927)
Green, brown and purple. 138 x 78mm.
Signature: N. F. Warren Fisher

TR9

		VF	EF	UNC
TR9	Prefix T, U, W. Letter over number followed by serial numbers	£150	£300	£525

ONE POUND

FIRST (EMERGENCY) BRADBURY ISSUE (August 1914)
Black. 127 x 63mm. Blank reverse
Signature: John Bradbury

TR10a

		F	VF	EF
TR10a	Prefix A., B. and C. (*with dot*) followed by 6 serial numbers	£700	£1200	£2400
TR10b	Prefix A, B and C (*without dot*) followed by 6 serial numbers	£1000	£1800	£3600
TR10c	Prefix G (possibly others) Letter over number followed by *No.* (*with dot*) and 4 serial numbers	£850	£1350	£3000

		VF	EF	UNC
TR10d	Prefix B-W (not inclusive). Letter over number followed by *No.* (*with dot*) and 5 serial numbers	£600	£1100	£1850

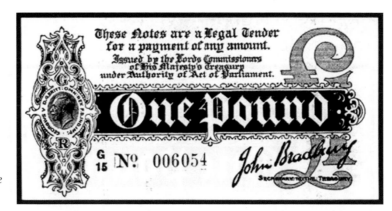

TR10e

	VF	EF	UNC
TR10e	Prefix A-**X**. Letter over number followed by *No.*(*with **dot***) and 6 serial numbers	£550	£950	£1700

	F	VF	EF
TR10f	Prefix B (possibly others). Letter over number followed by *No.* (*with **dot***) and 7 serial numbers	£750	£1200	£2600

TR11a

	VF	EF	UNC
TR11a	Prefix L (possibly others). Letter over number followed by *No* (*with **dash***) and 4 serial numbers..	£850	£1500	£3250
TR11b	Prefix E, J, K and L (possibly others). Letter over number followed by *No* (*with **dash***) and 5 serial numbers...............	£500	£850	£1650

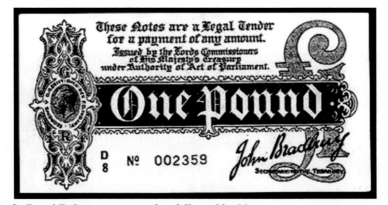

TR12a

	VF	EF	UNC
TR12a	Prefix B and D. Letter over number followed by *No* (*with **dash***) and 6 serial numbers in smaller type................	£525	£900	£1750

	F	VF	EF

TR12b   Prefix B (possibly others). Letter over number followed by *No.*
(*with* **dot**) and 7 serial numbers in smaller type £850   £1500   £2800

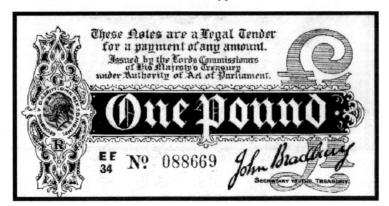

TR13a

TR13a   Prefix AA-LL. Double letter over number followed by *No.*
(*with* **dot**) and 6 serial numbers £450   £850   £1600

TR13b

TR13b   Prefix LL. Double letter over number followed by *No.*
(*with* **dot**) and 4 serial numbers ....   —   Rare   —

SECOND BRADBURY ISSUE (October 1914)

Black. 149 x 85mm. Blank reverse
Signature: John Bradbury

VF   EF   UNC

TR14a

TR14a   Prefix A-Z. Letter over number followed by 5 serial
numbers.. £375   £650   £1100

TR14b

TR14b   Prefix A1-L1. Letter and figure 1 over number followed by.
5 serial numbers £375   £650   £1100

SECOND BRADBURY ISSUE DARDANELLES OVERPRINT
(May 1915)
Overprint in Turkish "120 silver piastres" on TR14a above for the use of the British Expeditionary Forces in Turkey in 1915

TR15

		VG	F	VF
TR15	Prefix F, J, M, Y. Letter over number followed by 5 serial numbers	£2000	£3250	£5500

THIRD BRADBURY ISSUE
(January 1917)
Green, brown and purple.151 x 84mm.
Signature: John Bradbury

		VF	EF	UNC
TR16a	Prefix A. Letter over number followed by serial numbers	£150	£285	£525

TR16b

TR16b	Prefix B-H. Letter over number followed by serial numbers	£130	£250	£475

		VF	EF	UNC
TR16c	Prefix Z. Letter over number followed by serial numbers.	£160	£300	£550
TR16d	Prefix A and B. Variety with small anchor beneath Big Ben on reverse	£1250	£2500	—

FIRST FISHER ISSUE
(September 1919)
Green, brown and purple. 151 x 84mm.
Signature: N. F. Warren Fisher

TR17a	Prefix K. Letter over number followed by serial numbers	£95	£175	£300

TR17b

TR17b	Prefix L-Y. Letter over number followed by serial numbers	£85	£160	£275
TR17c	Prefix Z. Letter over number followed by serial numbers.	£100	£185	£325

SECOND FISHER ISSUE
(February 1923)
Green, brown and purple. 151 x 84mm.
Signature: N. F. Warren Fisher

		VF	EF	UNC
TR18a	Prefix A1. Letter and figure 1 over number followed by *No.* and serial numbers	£95	£175	£300
TR18b	Prefix B1-R1. Letter and figure 1 over number followed by *No.* and serial numbers	£85	£160	£275

TR18c

TR18c	Prefix Z1. Letter and figure 1 over number followed by *No.* and serial numbers	£100	£185	£325

TR18d

TR18d	Prefix H1-R1. As *TR18b* but with square dot below	£185	£350	—
TR18e	Prefix Z1. As *TR18c* but with square dot below	£225	£425	—

THIRD FISHER ISSUE
("NORTHERN" ADDED TO TITLE)
(July 1927)

Green, brown and purple. 151 x 84mm.
Signature: N. F. Warren Fisher

		VF	EF	UNC
TR19a	Prefix S1. Letter and figure 1 over number followed by *No.* and serial numbers..	£110	£200	£400

TR19b

TR19b	Prefix T1-X1. Letter and figure 1 over number followed by *No.* and serial numbers..	£95	£180	£350
TR19c	Prefix Z1. Letter and figure 1 over number followed by *No.* and serial numbers..	£120	£225	£450
TR19d	Prefix S1-X1. As *TR19b* but with square dot below.............	£200	£375	—

TR19e

TR19e	Prefix Z1. As *TR19c* but with square dot below	£240	£450	—

BANK OF ENGLAND
From 1928

TEN SHILLINGS
SERIES "A" BRITANNIA ISSUE

(November 1928)
Red-brown. 138 x 78mm
Signature: C. P. Mahon

Prefix sequence: Letter/Number/Number

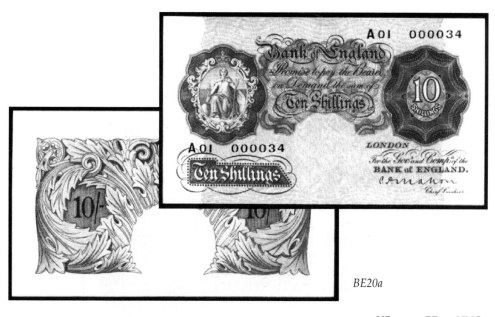

BE20a

		VF	EF	UNC
BE20a	Prefix A01 followed by serial number	£550	£950	£1350
BE20b	Prefix Z01	£400	£650	£1000
BE20c	Prefix Z- -	£150	£285	£450
BE20d	Prefix Y- -, X- -, W- -	£130	£250	£400
BE20e	Prefix V- - (*traced to V13*)	£550	£950	—

(July 1930)
Red-brown. 138 x 78mm
Signature: B. G. Catterns

Prefix sequence: Letter/Number/Number

BE21a

		VF	EF	UNC
BE21a	Prefix V- - followed by serial number (*traced from V14*)	£90	£190	£325
BE21b	Prefix U- - to L- -	£45	£85	£165
BE21c	Prefix K- - (*traced to K99*)	£80	£175	£295

October 1934)
Red-brown. 138 x 78mm
Signature: K .O. Peppiatt

Prefix sequence: Letter/Number/Number

BE22a	Prefix J01 followed by serial number	£400	£850	—

BE22b

BE22b	Prefix J- -	£65	£130	£240
BE22c	Prefix H- - to B- -	£45	£85	£160
BE22d	Prefix A- - (*traced to A99*)	£65	£130	£240

Prefix sequence: Number/Number/Letter

		VF	EF	UNC
BE23a	Prefix 01Z followed by serial number	£300	£650	—

BE23b

BE23b	Prefix - -Z	£70	£135	£260
BE23c	Prefix - -Y to - -R	£35	£70	£115
BE23d	Prefix - -O (*traced to 42/49O*)	£60	£110	£185

(October 1940)

Mauve (shades). 138 x 78mm. With metal security thread
Signature: K .O. Peppiatt

Prefix sequence: Letter/Number/Number/Letter

BE24a

BE24a	Prefix Z01D followed by serial number	£200	£400	£650
BE24b	Prefix Z- -D	£40	£75	£130
BE24c	Prefix Y- -D to B- -D	£35	£65	£100
BE24d	Prefix A- -D (*traced to A99D*)..	£40	£75	£130
BE24e	Prefix Z- -E, Y- -E	£35	£70	£110
BE24f	Prefix X- -E (*traced to X17E*)	£90	£160	£285
BE24g	Prefix X21E..	£200	£400	—

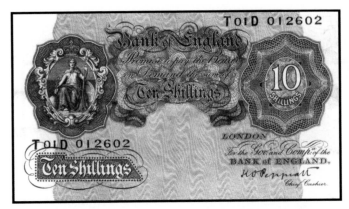

BE24Aa

		VF	EF	UNC
BE24Aa	Prefix T01D Replacement note	£450	£800	—
BE24Ab	Prefix T- -D Replacement note (traced to T12D)	£275	£500	—

(June 1948)

Red-brown. 138 x 78mm. Without metal security thread

Signature: K .O. Peppiatt

Prefix sequence: Number/Number/Letter

BE25a

BE25a	Prefix - -O (*traced from 42/49O-70O*) followed by serial number	£70	£150	£275
BE25b	Prefix - -L (*traced from 05L-71L*)	£65	£135	£250

(October 1948)

Red-brown. 138 x 78mm. With metal security thread

Signature: K .O. Peppiatt

Prefix sequence: Number/Number/Letter

BE26a

		VF	EF	UNC
BE26a	Prefix - -L followed by serial number (*traced from 71L*)	£110	£250	£400
BE26b	Prefix - -K, - -J, - -H	£25	£55	£90
BE26c	Prefix - -E (*traced to 91E*)...	£35	£80	£125
BE27a	Prefix 01A Replacement note	£750	£1300	£2200
BE27b	Prefix 02A Replacement note	£500	£900	£1500

BE27c

BE27c	Prefix 03A Replacement note	£600	£1100	£1750

(March 1950)
Red-brown. 138 x 78mm. With metal security thread
Signature: P. S. Beale

Prefix sequence: Number/Number/Letter

		VF	EF	UNC
BE28a	Prefix 92E followed by serial number	£250	£600	£1000

BE28b

BE28b	Prefix – – E..	£70	£150	£275
BE28c	Prefix - -D, - -C...	£18	£40	£70
BE28d	Prefix - -B (*traced to 99B*)..	£20	£45	£80
BE29a	Prefix 04A Replacement note	£400	£750	£1250

BE29b

BE29b	Prefix - -A Replacement note (*traced to 35A*)	£85	£175	£325

Prefix sequence: Letter/Number/Number/Letter

		VF	EF	UNC
BE30a	Prefix Z01Z followed by number...	£225	£400	£700

BE30b

BE30b	Prefix Z- -Z	£18	£35	£65
BE30c	Prefix Y- -Z to E- -Z	£12	£25	£50
BE30d	Prefix D- -Z *(traced to D85Z)*	£18	£35	£70

(November 1955)

Red-brown. 138 x 78mm.
Signature: L. K. O'Brien

Prefix sequence: Letter/Number/Number/Letter

BE31a	Prefix D86Z followed by serial number..............................	£125	£225	£400
BE31b	Prefix D- -Z...	£45	£80	£150
BE31c	Prefix C- -Z, B- -Z...	£8	£18	£35
BE31d	Prefix A- -Z...	£10	£22	£40
BE31e	Prefix Z- -Y...	£10	£22	£40
BE31f	Prefix Y- -Y to B- - Y..	£7	£16	£30
BE31g	Prefix A- -Y...	£10	£22	£40
BE31h	Prefix Z - -X...	£10	£22	£40
BE31i	Prefix Y- -X	£14	£30	£55

BE31j

BE31j	Prefix Y25X *(last prefix of Britannia Series "A"10/-)*..............	£85	£185	£350

BE32

		VF	EF	UNC
BE32	Prefix - -A Replacement note (*traced from 35A-69A*)............	£55	£120	£225

SERIES "C" PORTRAIT ISSUE

(October 1961)
Red-brown. 140 x 66.7mm.
Signature: L. K. O'Brien

Prefix sequence: Letter/Number/Number

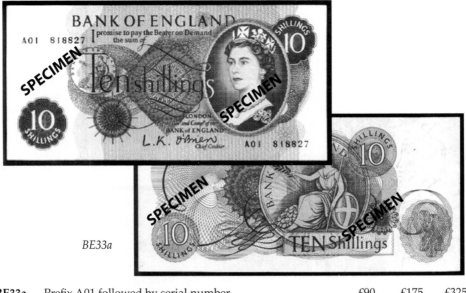

BE33a

BE33a	Prefix A01 followed by serial number	£90	£175	£325
BE33b	Prefix A- -.	£4	£8	£15
BE33c	Prefix B- - to J- -	£3	£6	£10
BE33d	Prefix K- - (*traced to K64*)	£8	£16	£30
BE34a	Prefix M01 Replacement note	£125	£240	£450

BE34b

		VF	EF	UNC
BE34b	Prefix M- - *(traced to M18)*	£28	£65	£120

(April 1963)

Signature: J. Q. Hollom

Prefix sequence: Letter/Number/Number

BE35a

BE35a	Prefix K65 followed by serial number	£95	£185	£350
BE35b	Prefix K- -.	£9	£18	£35
BE35c	Prefix L- - to Y- -.	£2	£4	£8
BE35d	Prefix Z- -	£7	£14	£25
BE35e	Prefix Z99	£80	£150	£275
BE36a	Prefix M19 Replacement note...	£90	£175	£325

BE36b

BE36b	Prefix M- - Replacement note...	£18	£35	£75
BE36c	Prefix M55 Replacement note...	£85	£160	£285

Prefix sequence: Number/Number/Letter

		VF	EF	UNC
BE37a	Prefix 01A followed by serial number	£100	£190	£375

BE37b

BE37b	Prefix - -A	£4	£7	£15
BE37c	Prefix - -B to - -N	£2	£4	£7
BE37d	Prefix - -R (*traced to 26R*).	£8	£18	£40

(February 1967)
Signature: J. S. Fforde

Prefix sequence: Number/Number/Letter

BE38a	Prefix 26R followed by serial number	£180	£300	—

BE38b

BE38b	Prefix - -R..	£6	£12	£25
BE38c	Prefix - -S to - -Y	£2	£4	£7
BE38d	Prefix - -Z	£4	£7	£12
BE38e	Prefix 99Z	£140	£240	—

		VF	*EF*	*UNC*

Prefix sequence: Letter/Number/Number/Letter

		VF	*EF*	*UNC*
BE39a	Prefix A01N followed by serial number.	£60	£100	£190
BE39b	Prefix A- - N.	£5	£10	£18
BE39c	Prefix B- -N, C- -N.	£2	£4	£7
BE39d	Prefix D- -N	£4	£7	£12

BE39e

BE39e	Prefix D38N (*last prefix of Portrait Series "C"10/-*).	£18	£35	£70
BE40a	Prefix M56 Replacement note	£70	£125	£240
BE40b	Prefix M- -.	£12	£8	£14

BE40c

BE40c	Prefix M80 (Last re*placement prefix of Portrait Series "C"10/-*)	£12	£22	£40

ONE POUND
SERIES "A" BRITANNIA ISSUE
(November 1928)

Green. 150.7 x 84.4mm
Signature: C. P. Mahon

Prefix sequence: Letter/Number/Number

BE41a

		VF	EF	UNC
BE41a	Prefix A01 followed by serial number	£550	£950	£1350
BE41b	Prefix A- -	£80	£150	£265
BE41c	Prefix B- - to G- -...	£65	£120	£200
BE41d	Prefix H- - (*traced to H32*)	£95	£185	£350

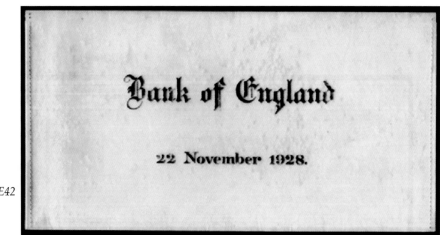

BE42

		VF	EF	UNC
BE42	Presentation set of Ten Shillings and One Pound notes with matching A01 serial numbers in special Bank of England parchment envelope dated 22 November 1928. Only 125 sets were issued numbered A01 000001 to A01 000125..............	—	£4800	£7500

(July 1930)
Green. 150.7 x 84.4mm
Signature: B. G. Catterns

Prefix sequence: Letter/Number/Number

BE43a

		VF	EF	UNC
BE43a	Prefix H- - followed by serial number (*traced from H33*)	£50	£110	£170
BE43b	Prefix J- - to Y- -	£25	£60	£95
BE43c	Prefix Z- - (*traced to Z99*)	£35	£75	£120

		VF	EF	UNC

Prefix sequence Number/Number/Letter

BE44a   Prefix 01A .... £300 £550 —

BE44b

BE44b   Prefix - -A £90 £185 £275

(October 1934)
Green. 150.7 x 84.4mm
Signature: K .O. Peppiatt

Prefix sequence: Number/Number/Letter

BE45a   Prefix 01B followed by serial number .... £550 £1000 —
BE45b   Prefix - -B £30 £70 £120
BE45c   Prefix - -C to - -Y £20 £45 £75

BE45d

BE45d   Prefix - -Z *(traced to 99Z)* £25 £60 £100

		VF	EF	UNC

Prefix sequence Letter/Number/Number/Letter

		VF	EF	UNC
BE46a	Prefix A01A followed by serial number …	£850	—	—
BE46b	Prefix A -A …	£25	£60	£95
BE46c	Prefix B- -A to K- -A	£14	£35	£65

BE46d

		VF	EF	UNC
BE46d	Prefix L- -A ...…..	£20	£45	£75
BE46e	Prefix L39A ...…...	£135	£250	£400

(March 1940)

Blue (various shades). 150.7 x 84.4mm. With metal security thread
Signature: K .O. Peppiatt

Prefix sequence: Letter/Number/Number/Letter

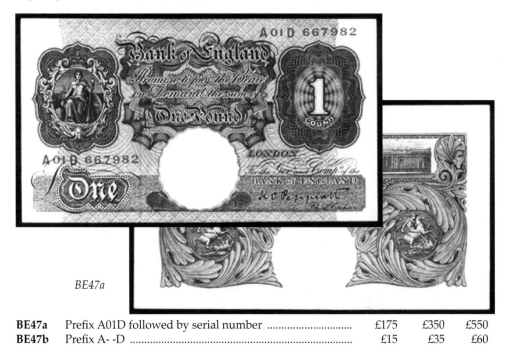

BE47a

		VF	EF	UNC
BE47a	Prefix A01D followed by serial number	£175	£350	£550
BE47b	Prefix A- -D	£15	£35	£60

		VF	EF	UNC
BE47c	Prefix A- -E, A- -H	£9	£25	£45
BE47d	Prefix B- -D to Y- -D	£8	£20	£30
BE47e	Prefix Z- -D	£9	£25	£45
BE47f	Prefix Z87D	—	—	—
BE47g	Prefix B- -E to U- -E...	£8	£20	£30
BE47h	Prefix W- -E..	£9	£25	£45
BE47i	Prefix W48E..	£250	£450	£650
BE47j	Prefix B- -H to W- -H	£8	£20	£30
BE47k	Prefix X- -H	£15	£40	£70
BE47l	Prefix X96H	£250	£450	—
BE47Aa	Prefix S01D Replacement note	£250	£450	£750
BE47Ab	Prefix S- -D Replacement note *(traced to S16D)*....................	£175	£300	£500
BE47Ac	Prefix S- -E Replacement note *(traced from S03E to S09E)*...	£175	£300	£500

BE47Ad

Note: This is an example of the rare pale straw shade of underprint on a replacement note. — Ed.

		VF	EF	UNC
BE47Ad	Prefix S01H Replacement note...	£225	£400	£650
BE47Ae	Prefix S- -H Replacement note *(traced to S13H)*	£175	£300	£500

THE STATES OF GUERNSEY OVERPRINTS
(September 18th 1941)

Green. 150.7 x 84.4mm. Without metal security thread
Signatures: C. P. Mahon, B. G. Catterns and K .O. Peppiatt

Overprinted "Withdrawn from circulation September 18th, 1941." With stop after 1941 on front but not on back

Prefix sequence: Various

		VF	EF	UNC
BE48a	Signature Mahon. Prefix A- - to H- - (*48 known*)	£750	£1350	—
BE48b	Signature Catterns. Prefix H- - to Z- - (*69 known*)	£600	£1000	—
BE48c	Signature Catterns. Prefix - -A (*5 known*).............................	£3500	£6000	—
BE48d	Signature Peppiatt. Prefix - -B to - -Z (*330 known*)...............	£400	£750	—

BE48e

BE48e Signature Peppiatt. Prefix A- -A to L- -A (*1,885 known*)........... £200 £385 £600

(September 18th 1941)
Blue (various shades). 150.7 x 84.4mm. With metal security thread
Signature: K .O. Peppiatt
Overprinted "Withdrawn from circulation September 18th, 1941." With stop after 1941 on front but not on back

Prefix sequence: Letter/Number/Number/Letter

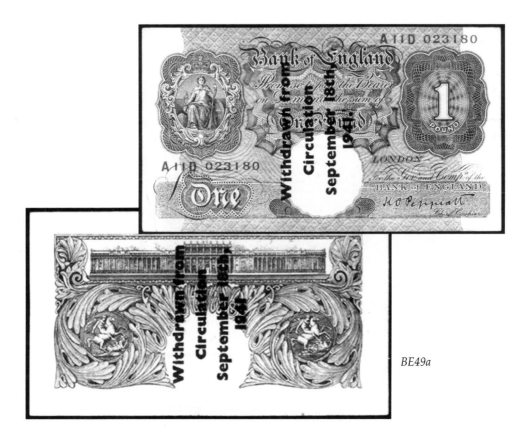

BE49a

		VF	EF	UNC
BE49a	Prefix A- -D *(35 known)*	£850	£1400	—
BE49b	Prefix C- -D *(85 known)*	£450	£700	£1000

(November 10th 1941)

Green. 150.7 x 84.4mm. Without metal security thread
Signature: K .O. Peppiatt
Overprinted "Withdrawn from circulation November 10th, 1941."

Prefix sequence: Letter/Number/Number/Letter

BE50a

		VF	EF	UNC
BE50a	Prefix E03A. With stop after 1941 front and back *(75 known)*	£375	£650	£900
BE50b	Prefix E15A. With stop after 1941 back only *(403 known)* ..	£275	£450	£700

(June 1948)

Green. 150.7 x 84.4mm. Without metal security thread
Signature: K .O. Peppiatt

Prefix sequence: Letter/Number/Number/Letter

BE51a	Prefix R01A followed by serial number................................	£75	£175	£300
BE51b	Prefix R- -A	£18	£40	£60

BE51c

BE51c Prefix S- -A *(traced to S48A)*	£20	£45	£70

(September 1948)
Green. 150.7 x 84.4mm. Withmetal security thread
Signature: K .O. Peppiatt

Prefix sequence: Letter/Number/Number/Letter

BE52a

		VF	EF	UNC
BE52a	Prefix S- -A (*traced from S39A*) followed by serial number.	£22	£50	£80
BE52b	Prefix T- -A to Y- -A..	£9	£16	£28
BE52c	Prefix Z- -A (*traced to Z99A*)	£20	£35	£50
BE52d	Prefix A- -B (*traced from A01B*)...................................	£20	£35	£50
BE52e	Prefix B- -B to E- -B	£9	£16	£28
BE52f	Prefix H- -B	£22	£40	£60
BE52g	Prefix H36B	£85	£160	£300
BE53a	Prefix S01S Replacement note	£285	£475	£750

BE53b

BE53b	Prefix S- -S Replacement note	£135	£250	£450
BE53c	Prefix S09S Replacement note	£200	£375	£650

(March 1950)
Green. 150.7 x 84.4mm.
Signature: P .S. Beale

Prefix sequence: Letter/Number/Number/Letter

		VF	EF	UNC
BE54a	Prefix H37B followed by serial number................................	£175	£300	£525

BE54b

BE54b	Prefix H- -B..	£12	£25	£40
BE54c	Prefix J- -B to Y- -B	£5	£9	£16
BE54d	Prefix Z- -B *(traced to Z99B)*	£7	£12	£25
BE54e	Prefix A- -C *(traced from A01C)*	£7	£12	£25
BE54f	Prefix B- -C to Y- -C	£5	£9	£16
BE54g	Prefix Z- -C *(traced to Z99C)*......................................	£7	£12	£25
BE54h	Prefix A- -J *(traced from A01J)*	£7	£12	£25
BE54i	Prefix B- -J to K- -J	£5	£9	£16
BE54j	Prefix L- -J...	£12	£25	£40
BE54k	Prefix L63J	£75	£140	£275
BE55a	Prefix S10S Replacement note	£140	£240	£400

BE55b

BE55b	Prefix S- -S Replacement note	£25	£48	£80
BE55c	Prefix S70S Replacement note	£150	£275	£550

(November 1955)
Green. 150.7 x 84.4mm.
Signature: L .K. O'Brien

Prefix sequence: Letter/Number/Number/Letter

		VF	EF	UNC
BE56a	Prefix L64J followed by serial number...............................	£90	£175	£300
BE56b	Prefix L- -J...	£8	£15	£30
BE56c	Prefix M- -J to Y- -J	£3	£7	£15
BE56d	Prefix Z- -J *(traced to Z99J)*	£6	£12	£25
BE56e	Prefix A- -K *(traced from A01K)*	£8	£15	£30
BE56f	Prefix B- -K to Y- -K	£3	£7	£15
BE56g	Prefix Z- -K *(traced to Z99K)*	£6	£12	£25
BE56h	Prefix A- -L *(traced from A01L)*................................	£8	£15	£30
BE56i	Prefix B- -L to J- -L	£3	£7	£15
BE56j	Prefix K- -L	£22	£40	£70

BE56k

BE56k	Prefix K13L *(last prefix of Britannia Series "A" £1)*	£140	£275	£450
BE57a	Prefix S71S Replacement note	£110	£200	£375
BE57b	Prefix S- -S Replacement note *(traced to S99S)*	£20	£45	£70
BE58a	Prefix S01T Replacement note...	£120	£220	£400

BE58b

BE58b	Prefix S- -T Replacement note *(traced to S23T)*	£22	£50	£80

SERIES "C" PORTRAIT ISSUE
(March 1960)
Green. 151 x 71.8mm.
Signature: L .K. O'Brien

Prefix sequence: Letter/Number/Number

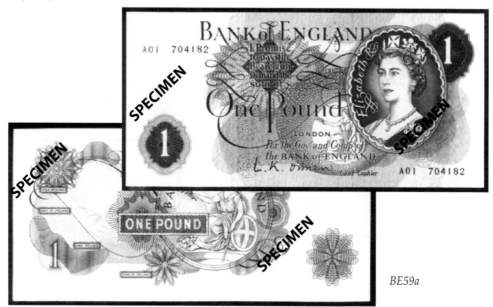

BE59a

		VF	EF	UNC
BE59a	Prefix A01 followed by serial number	£110	£200	£350
BE59b	Prefix A- -	£6	£10	£18
BE59c	Prefix B- - to Y- -..	£3	£5	£9
BE59d	Prefix Z- - (*traced to Z99*).	£5	£10	£18
BE59e	Prefix Z99.	£110	£200	£350

BE60a

BE60a	Prefix M01 Replacement note	£125	£240	£450
BE60b	Prefix M- - Replacement note (*traced to M68*)	£10	£18	£35

Prefix sequence: Number/Number/Letter

		VF	EF	UNC
BE61a	Prefix 01A followed by serial number	£120	£225	£400
BE61b	Prefix - -A	£6	£10	£18
BE61c	Prefix - -B to - - Y	£3	£5	£9
BE61d	Prefix - -Z	£5	£10	£18
BE61e	Prefix 99Z	£110	£200	£350

Experimental printing on a research machine
Prefix sequence: Letter/Number/Number/Letter

BE62a

BE62a	Prefix A01N (*small long tail 'R' on reverse for research*)	£120	£200	£500
BE62b	Prefix A05N (*small short tail 'R' on reverse*)	£130	£225	£550
BE62c	Prefix A06N (*small short tail 'R' on reverse*)	£135	£250	£600

Prefix sequence: Letter/Number/Number/Letter

BE63a	Prefix B01N	£75	£130	£275
BE63b	Prefix B- -N	£8	£15	£30
BE63c	Prefix B76N	£125	£225	£400

(February 1963)
Green. 151 x 71.8mm.
Signature: J .Q. Hollom

Prefix sequence: Letter/Number/Number/Letter

BE64a	Prefix B77N followed by serial number	£140	£250	—

BE64b

BE64b	Prefix B- -N	£20	£45	£85

		VF	EF	UNC
BE64c	Prefix C- -N to L- -N, A- -R to L- -R, A- -S to L- -S, A- -T to L- -T, A- -U to L- -U, A- -W to L- -W, A- -X to K- -X, A- -Y	£2	£4	£7
BE64d	Prefix B- -Y (*last series traced to B10Y*)	£22	£50	£100

Prefix sequence: Letter/Number/Number

BE65a	Prefix M68 Replacement note	£55	£100	£225
BE65b	Prefix M- - Replacement note	£14	£28	£50
BE65c	Prefix M99 Replacement note	£85	£180	—

Prefix sequence: Number/Number/Letter

BE66a	Prefix 01M Replacement note...	£65	£140	£300

BE66b

BE66b	Prefix - -M Replacement note (traced to 99M).....................	£9	£20	£40

Prefix sequence: Letter/Number/Number/Letter

BE67a	Prefix M01R Replacement note..	£90	£200	£450

BE67b

BE67b	Prefix M- -R Replacement note (*traced to M08R*)	£50	£125	£225

With small 'G' on reverse (indicating that note printed on a Goebel Machine)
Prefix sequence: Letter/Number/Number/Letter

BE68a

		VF	EF	UNC
BE68a	Prefix A- -N (*traced from A09N*)	£7	£14	£28
BE68b	Prefix D- -T, C- -W.	£4	£8	£16
BE68c	Prefix L01X	£10	£20	£45
BE68d	Prefix L- -X (*traced to L33X*)	£5	£9	£20
BE69a	Prefix M01N Replacement note.	£75	£160	£375

BE69b

BE69b	Prefix M- -N Replacement note (*traced to M28N*)	£15	£32	£75

(February 1967)

Green. 151 x 71.8mm.
Signature: J .S. Fforde

Prefix sequence: Letter/Number/Number/Letter

BE70a

		VF	EF	UNC
BE70a	Prefix B11Y followed by serial number	£120	£250	£600
BE70b	Prefix B- -Y	£15	£35	£60
BE70c	Prefix C- -Y to L- -Y, A- -Z to J- -Z	£2	£5	£12
BE70d	Prefix L- -Z *(traced to L99Z)*	£7	£15	£35
BE71a	Prefix M09R Replacement note	£200	£350	—

BE71b

		VF	EF	UNC
BE71b	Prefix M- -R Replacement note *(traced from to M50R)*	£20	£45	£85
BE72a	Prefix N01A	—	—	—
BE72b	Prefix N- -A	£25	£55	£100
BE72c	Prefix N- -B to N- -L, R- -A to R- -K, S- -L, T- -A to T- -L, U- -A to U- -H, W- -A to W- -D, X- -B.	FV	£3	£6
BE72d	Prefix S87L, S88L, S89L, S90L *(Overlaps with Page BE78a,b below)*	£15	£35	£70

		VF	EF	UNC
BE72e	Prefix X- -C	£14	£30	£50

BE72f

		VF	EF	UNC
BE72f	Prefix X42C	£225	£400	—
BE73a	Prefix R01M Replacement note.............................	£70	£200	£600
BE73b	Prefix R- -M Replacement note *(traced to R54M)*	£7	£15	£25
BE73c	Prefix S01M Replacement note	£90	£225	—
BE73d	Prefix S- -M Replacement note *(traced to S78M)*	**£7**	£15	£25
BE73e	Prefix T01M Replacement note.............................	£160	£350	£600
BE73f	Prefix T- -M Replacement note *(traced to T04M)*..	£100	£225	£400

BE73g

		VF	EF	UNC
BE73g	Prefix U01M Replacement note *(traced in U01M only)*........	£160	£350	£600

With small 'G' on reverse (indicating that note printed on a Goebel machine)

		VF	EF	UNC
BE74a	Prefix E01Y..	£85	£175	—
BE74b	Prefix E- -Y *(traced to E99Y)*.....................................	£3	£7	£12
BE74c	Prefix K01Z..	£85	£175	—
BE74d	Prefix K- -Z *(traced to K99Z)*.....................................	£3	£7	£12

BE75a

		VF	EF	UNC
BE75a	Prefix M29N Replacement note	£85	£175	£400
BE75b	Prefix M- -N Replacement note...	£18	£40	£75
BE75c	Prefix M42N Replacement note.	£75	£160	£375
BE76a	Prefix R01B..	£130	£275	—
BE76b	Prefix R—B *(traced to R99B)*	£3	£7	£14
BE76c	Prefix R01L	£50	£95	£160
BE76d	Prefix R- -L *(traced to R99L)*	£3	£7	£14
BE76e	Prefix U01E	£55	£100	£180
BE76f	Prefix U- -E	£4	£8	£15
BE76g	Prefix U45E	£150	£325	—
BE77a	Prefix N01M Replacement note	£185	£300	£500
BE77b	Prefix N- -M Replacement note	£35	£75	£140
BE77c	Prefix N14M Replacement note	£70	£150	£275

BE77d

BE77d	Prefix T29M Replacement note	£45	£95	£185
BE77e	Prefix T- -M Replacement note	£55	£120	£225
BE77f	Prefix T32M Replacement note	£120	£250	£450

(1970 – date unknown)

Green. 151 x 71.8mm.
Signature: J .B. Page

Prefix sequence: Letter/Number/Number/Letter

BE78a	Prefix S87L followed by serial number.................................	£750	£1250	£2000
BE78b	Prefix S89L and S90L only..	£500	£850	£1300

		VF	EF	UNC
BE78c	Prefix T- -B to T- -L, U- -A to U- -H, W- -A to W- -H (*traced to W99H*)	FV	£4	£6
BE78d	Prefix X- -A to X- -L, Y- -A to Y- -L, Z- -A to Z- -K	FV	£4	£6
BE78e	Prefix Z- -L (*traced to Z84L*)	£6	£14	£25
BE79a	Prefix R- -M Replacement note (*traced from R44M to R99M*)	£9	£22	£55
BE79b	Prefix S- -M Replacement note (*traced from S32M*)..............	£6	£14	£25

BE79c

BE79c	Prefix S98M Replacement note	£90	£175	£325
BE79d	Prefix W01M Replacement note	£45	£85	£190
BE79e	Prefix W- -M Replacement note (*traced to W84M*)..............	£5	£12	£20
BE79f	Prefix X01M Replacement note...	£65	£120	£225
BE79g	Prefix X- -M Replacement note (*traced to X60M*).................	£5	£12	£20

BE80

BE80	Pair of consecutively numbered notes with signatures of J. S. Fforde and J. B. Page (*traced in prefixes S- -L, T- -D, T- -H, T- -K, T- -L, U- -C, U- -D, W- -A, W- -B, W- -C, X- -B, X- -C, R- -M and S- -M*).£150		£275	£475
BE81a	Prefix AN01 followed by serial number	£70	£130	£275
BE81b	Prefix AN- -	£3	£6	£10
BE81c	Prefix AR- - to AZ- -, BN- - to BZ- -, CN- - to CZ- -, DN- - to DZ- -, EN- - to EZ- -, HN- - to HY- -	FV	£3	£5
BE81d	Prefix HZ- -	£3	£6	£10
BE81e	Prefix HZ63 (*last prefix of Portrait Series "C" £1*)	—	—	—

BE82a

		VF	EF	UNC
BE82a	Prefix MR01 Replacement note.	£80	£140	£300
BE82b	Prefix MR- - Replacement note (*traced to MR48*)	£7	£15	£35
BE82c	Prefix MS01 Replacement note.	£40	£70	£135
BE82d	Prefix MS- - Replacement note (*traced to MS84*)	£3	£6	£12
BE82e	Prefix MT01 Replacement note.	£40	£70	£135
BE82f	Prefix MT- - Replacement note (*traced to MT23*)	£3	£6	£12
BE82g	Prefix MU01 Replacement note.	£15	£28	£50
BE82h	Prefix MU- - Replacement note (*traced to MU19*).	£3	£6	£12
BE82i	Prefix MW01 Replacement note.	£30	£55	£120
BE82j	Prefix MW- - Replacement note.	£3	£6	£12

BE82k

BE82k	Prefix MW19 Replacement note	£45	£85	£160

SERIES "D" PICTORIAL ISSUE
(February 1978)
Green and multicoloured. 134.5 x 66.7mm.
Reverse depicting Isaac Newton
Signature: J .B. Page

Prefix sequence: Letter/Number/Number

BE83a

		VF	EF	UNC
BE83a	Prefix A01 followed by serial number.......	£3	£7	£16
BE83b	Prefix A- -................................	FV	£4	£7
BE83c	Prefix B- - to Y- -........................	FV	£3	£6
BE83d	Prefix Z- -................................	£3	£7	£16
BE83e	Prefix Z80.................................	£100	£185	£350

BE84

BE84	Prefix M01 Replacement note	£160	£300	£475

Prefix sequence: Number/Number/Letter

BE85a	Prefix 01A followed by serial number ...	£15	£30	£55
BE85b	Prefix - -A	£2	£5	£8

		VF	EF	UNC
BE85c	Prefix - -B to - -X .	FV	£3	£6
BE85d	Prefix - -Y	£3	£7	£16
BE85e	Prefix 80Y	£125	£225	—
BE85f	Prefix 81A	£190	£350	£600
BE85g	Prefix 81B, C, D, E, H, K, L, N, R, S, T, U, W, X, Y	£150	£275	£450

BE85h

BE85h	Prefix 81Z	£175	£325	£575

BE85i

N.B. It is thought less than ten copies are known.

BE85i	Prefix 82J, 82K	£400	£700	—

Prefix sequence: Letter/Number/Number/Letter

BE86a	Prefix A01N followed by serial number.	£15	£35	£65
BE86b	Prefix A- -N	£3	£7	£16
BE86c	Prefix B- -N to D- -N	FV	£3	£6
BE86d	Prefix E- -N (*traced to E84N*)	£4	£9	£20

(March 1981)

Green and multicoloured with enhanced background colours. 134.5 x 66.7mm.
Printed by web- offset with small "W" at lower left on reverse
Signature: D. H. F. Somerset

Prefix sequence: Letter/Letter/Number/Number

BE87a

		VF	EF	UNC
BE87a	Prefix AN01 followed by serial number.	£14	£32	£60
BE87b	Prefix AN- -.	£2	£4	£8
BE87c	Prefix AR- - to DY- -.	FV	£3	£5
BE87d	Prefix DY21 *(last prefix of Pictorial Series "D" £1)*..	£8	£20	£45
BE88	Prefix MN- - Experimental note (traced from MN03 to MN18)	£1750	£3000	—

FIVE POUNDS

BLACK AND WHITE SERIES (continued)

BE89

		F	VF	EF
(1925-29)				
BE89	*Signature: C. P. Mahon*			
	London	£260	£425	£700
(1929-34)				
BE90	*Signature: B. G. Catterns*			
	London	£300	£550	£900

BE91

	VF	EF	UNC

(1934-44)

BE91   *Signature: K. O. Peppiatt*

London £190 £340 £575

NB. There are deceptive German World War II forgeries of the White £5 note, almost all of these being forgeries of BE90 and BE91.

(1944-45—issued 1945)

Thicker paper. With metal security thread
Signature: K. O. Peppiatt

Prefix sequence: Letter/Number/Number

BE92a

		VF	EF	UNC
BE92a	Prefix E- - followed by serial number	£130	£220	£325
BE92b	Prefix H- - to K- -	£110	£185	£285
BE92c	Prefix L- - *(traced to L02)*	£250	£425	£650

(1947 issued 1948)
Thinner paper. With metal security thread
Signature: K. O. Peppiatt

Prefix sequence: Letter/Number/Number

		VF	EF	UNC
BE93a	Prefix L- - followed by serial number (*traced from L03*)	£100	£170	£275

BE93b

BE93b	Prefix M- - (*traced to M71*)	£100	£170	£275

(1949-52)
Thinner paper. With metal security thread
Signature: P. S. Beale

Prefix sequence: Letter/Number/Number

BE94a	Prefix M- - followed by serial number (*traced from M72*) ...	£100	£170	£275
BE94b	Prefix N- - to X- -	£95	£150	£240

BE94c

BE94c	Prefix Y- - (*traced to Y70*)	£100	£170	£275

(1955-56)

Thinner paper. With metal security thread
Signature: L. K. O'Brien

Prefix sequence: Letter/Number/Number

		VF	EF	UNC
BE95a	Prefix Y- - followed by serial number (*traced from Y71*).......	£100	£170	£275
BE95b	Prefix Z- - (*traced to Z99*)	£95	£150	£240

Prefix sequence: Letter/Number/Number/Letter

BE96a

BE96a	Prefix A- -A followed by serial number................................	£100	£170	£275
BE96b	Prefix B- -A and C- -A..	£95	£150	£240
BE96c	Prefix D- -A (*traced to D99A*)..	£100	£170	£275

SERIES "B" HELMETED BRITANNIA ISSUE
(February 1957)
Blue on multicoloured underprint. Shaded £5 symbols on reverse. 159 x 89mm
Signature: L. K. O'Brien

Prefix sequence: Letter/Number/Number

shaded £5 symbol

unshaded £5 symbol

BE97a

		VF	EF	UNC
BE97a	Prefix A01 followed by serial number	£140	£275	£475
BE97b	Prefix A- -	£20	£45	£90
BE97c	Prefix B- - to D- -	£18	£40	£80
BE97d	Prefix E- -	£22	£50	£110
BE97e	Prefix E37...	£150	£285	£500

(July 1961)
Blue on multicoloured underprint. Unshaded £5 symbols on reverse. 159 x 89mm
Signature: L. K. O'Brien

Prefix sequence: Letter/Number/Number

BE98a	Prefix H01 followed by serial number	£375	£650	£1100
BE98b	Prefix H- -	£20	£45	£90
BE98c	Prefix J- -...	£18	£40	£110

BE98d

		VF	EF	UNC
BE98d	Prefix K- -	£22	£50	£110
BE98e	Prefix K45 (*last prefix of Helmeted Britannia Series "B" £5*)...	£240	£425	£750

SERIES "C" PORTRAIT ISSUE
(February 1963)

Blue 140 x 85mm.
Signature: J .Q. Hollom

Prefix sequence: Letter/Number/Number

BE99a

BE99a	Prefix A01 followed by serial number	£55	£100	£185

		VF	EF	UNC
BE99b	Prefix A- -	£12	£25	£45
BE99c	Prefix B- - to N- -	£10	£22	£40
BE99d	Prefix R- -(*traced to R19*)..	£25	£55	£100
BE100a	Prefix M01 Replacement note..	£260	£475	—

BE100b

BE100b	Prefix M- - Replacement note (*traced to M15*)	£150	£285	£525

(January 1967)
Blue 140 x 85mm.
Signature: J .S. Fforde

Prefix sequence: Letter/Number/Number

BE101a

		VF	EF	UNC
BE101a	Prefix R20 followed by serial number....................................	£75	£140	£300
BE101b	Prefix R- -..	£15	£28	£60
BE101c	Prefix S- - to Y- -	£12	£22	£40
BE101d	Prefix Z- -	£14	£25	£50
BE101e	Prefix Z99	£100	£185	£350
BE102	Prefix M- - Replacement note (*traced from M08 to M38*)	£110	£200	£420

Prefix sequence: Number/Number/Letter

		VF	EF	UNC
BE103a	Prefix 01A followed by serial number	£150	£275	—
BE103b	Prefix - -A	£14	£25	£50
BE103c	Prefix - -B to - -K (*overlaps with Page BE105b, c, d below*)	£12	£20	£40
BE103d	Prefix - -L(*traced to 40L*)..	£75	£135	£250
BE104a	Prefix 01M Replacement note...	£200	£360	—

BE104b

BE104b	Prefix - -M Replacement note (*traced to 15M*)	£90	£170	£350

Signature: J .B. Page
Prefix sequence: Number/Number/Letter

		VF	EF	UNC
BE105a	Prefix 03C followed by serial number	£170	£300	—
BE105b	Prefix - -C (*overlaps with Fforde BE103c above*)	£25	£45	£80
BE105c	Prefix - -D and - -E (*overlaps with Fforde BE103c above*)	£15	£28	£50
BE105d	Prefix - -H (*overlaps with Fforde BE 103c above*).....................	£75	£140	£275

BE105e

BE105e	Prefix 41H (*last reported prefix of Portrait Series "C" £5*).......	£200	—	—
BE106	Prefix - -M Replacement note (*traced from 04M to 18M*)	£120	£210	£440

BE107

	VF	EF	UNC
BE107 Pair of consecutively numbered notes with signatures of J. S. Fforde and J. B. Page (*traced in prefixes - - C , - -D, and - -E*)	—	£500	£750

SERIES "D" PICTORIAL ISSUE
(November 1971)
Blue and multicoloured. 145.5 x 78mm.
Reverse depicting the Duke of Wellington
Signature: J .B. Page

Prefix sequence: Letter/Number/Number

BE108a

		VF	EF	UNC
BE108a	Prefix A01 followed by serial number	£100	£180	£375
BE108b	Prefix A- -	£10	£18	£40
BE108c	Prefix B- - to K- -..	£8	£15	£32
BE108d	Prefix L- -(*traced to L94*)...	£32	£70	£120
BE109a	Prefix M01 Replacement note..................................	£185	£350	£600

BE109b

BE109b	Prefix M- - Replacement note (*traced to M05*)	£100	£185	£350

(August 1973)
Blue and multicoloured. 145.5 x 78mm. Reverse printed by lithography. Small "L" on reverse
Signature: J. B. Page

Prefix sequence: Number/Number/Letter

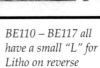

*BE110 – BE117 all
have a small "L" for
Litho on reverse*

BE110a

		VF	EF	UNC
BE110a	Prefix 01A followed by serial number	£85	£160	£350
BE110b	Prefix - -A	£10	£18	£40
BE110c	Prefix - -B to - -Y	£8	£15	£32
BE110d	Prefix - -Z	£12	£25	£45
BE110e	Prefix 96Z	£125	—	—
BE111a	Prefix 01M Replacement note	£175	£300	£550
BE111b	Prefix - -M Replacement note *(traced to 08M)*	£90	£175	£325

Prefix sequence: Letter/Letter/Number/Number

BE112a

BE112a	Prefix AN01 followed by serial number	£100	£185	£385
BE112b	Prefix AN- -	£9	£16	£35
BE112c	Prefix AR- - to CX- -	£7	£14	£30
BE112d	Prefix EZ- - *(last series traced from EZ01-EZ56)*	£28	£55	£100

(June 1980)

Blue and multicoloured. 145.5 x 78mm. Reverse printed by lithography. Small "L" on reverse
Signature: D. H. F. Somerset

Prefix sequence: Letter/Letter/Number/Number

BE113a

		VF	EF	UNC
BE113a	Prefix DN01 followed by serial number	£50	£95	£200
BE113b	Prefix DN- -..	£7	£14	£25
BE113c	Prefix DR- - to LY- -...	FV	£9	£20
BE113d	Prefix LZ- -	£12	£25	£50
BE113e	Prefix LZ90	£75	£140	£260
BE113f	Prefix NA- - (traced from NA01–NA18)............................	—	—	—
BE113g	Prefix NB- - and NC- -...	FV	£10	£20
BE113h	Prefix NC90	£15	£32	£60

BE114

BE114	Prefix DU55 to DU72 Error note missing signature............	£65	£120	£200

Experimental notes for Optical Character Recognition (OCR)
Prefix sequence: Letter/Letter/Number/Number

		VF	EF	UNC
BE115a	Prefix AN91 followed by serial number	£550	£850	£1200

BE115b

BE115b	Prefix BR91, CS91, DT91, EU91, HW91, JX91, KY91	£500	£800	£1100
BE115c	Prefix LZ91	£550	£850	£1200

(July 1987)
Blue and multicoloured. 145.5 x 78mm. With 1mm wide security thread. Printed by web offset
Signature: D .H. F. Somerset
Prefix sequence: Letter/Letter/Number/Number

BE116a	Prefix RA01 followed by serial number...............................	£15	£30	£65
BE116b	Prefix RA- - to RC- -..	FV	£10	£20
BE116c	Prefix RC90	£15	£28	£60

(March 1988)
Blue and multicoloured. 145.5 x 78mm.
Signature: G .M.Gill
Prefix sequence: Letter/Letter/Number/Number

BE117a	Prefix RD01 followed by serial number...............................	£15	£30	£65
BE117b	Prefix RD- -	£8	£15	£28
BE117c	Prefix RE- - to RL- -, SA- - to SE- -	FV	£10	£20

BE117d

BE117d	Prefix SE90 (*last prefix of Pictorial Series "D"£5 serial numbers below 998500 from circulation*)...	£35	£75	£140
BE117e	Prefix SE90 (*last prefix of Pictorial Series "D"£5*) (*serial numbers 998500 to 999999 from packs*)...	—	—	£90

SERIES "E" HISTORICAL ISSUE
(June 1990)
Turquoise and multicoloured. With windowed security thread. 135 x 70mm.
Reverse depicting George Stephenson
Signature: G .M. Gill

Prefix sequence: Letter/Number/Number

BE118a

		VF	EF	UNC
BE118a	Prefix A01 followed by serial number	£7	£16	£35
BE118b	Prefix A- -	FV	£10	£22
BE118c	Prefix B- - to L- -	FV	£8	£18
BE118d	Prefix N- -*(traced to N54 official last run)*...........................	£12	£28	£60
BE118e	Prefix R- - to T- - *(overlaps with Kentfield BE119b and BE119c below)*	£8	£20	£45
BE118f	Prefix U- -*(last series overlap traced to U17)*..........................	£85	£200	—

(November 1991)
Turquoise and multicoloured. 135 x 70mm. Printed on web presses.
Signature: G .E. A. Kentfield

Prefix sequence: Letter/Number/Number

BE119a	Prefix R01 followed by serial number	£8	£20	£45
BE119b	Prefix R- - *(overlaps with Gill BE118e above)*	FV	£12	£25
BE119c	Prefix S- - to U- - *(overlaps with Gill BE118e and BE118f above)*..	£7	£18	£35
BE119d	Prefix W- -..	£8	£20	£40
BE119e	Prefix W18 *(serial numbers below 998500 from circulation)* ...	£60	£130	—

BE119f

	VF	EF	UNC
BE119f Prefix W18 *(serial numbers 998500 to 999999 from packs)*	—	—	£90

(March 1993)

Turquoise and multicoloured. With darker £5 value tablet. 135 x 70mm.
Signature: G .E. A. Kentfield

Prefix sequence: Letter/Letter/Number/Number

		VF	EF	UNC
BE120a	Prefix AA01 followed by serial number	£6	£14	£30
BE120b	Prefix AA- -, AB- -	FV	£8	£16
BE120c	Prefix AB18 *(serial numbers below 998500 from circulation)* ..	£60	£130	—
BE120d	Prefix AB18 *(serial numbers 998500 to 999999 from uncut trios)*	—	—	£85

Printed by sheet fed offset litho

		VF	EF	UNC
BE121a	Prefix AC01 followed by serial number *(serial numbers 000001 to 001500 from uncut trios)*	—	—	£85

BE121b

		VF	EF	UNC
BE121b	Prefix AC01 followed by serial number *(serial numbers above 001500 from circulation)*	£40	£90	£165
BE121c	Prefix AC- - to AL- -, BA- - to BL- -, CA- - to CK- -	FV	£8	£14
BE121d	Prefix DA- -, DB- -	FV	£8	£16
BE121e	Prefix DC- - *(traced to DC90)*	FV	£10	£20
BE121f	Prefix DL99 *(special last run for collectors' packs)*	—	—	£45
BE122a	Prefix CL- -Column sort note *(traced to CL45)*......................	£8	£18	£35
BE122b	Prefix LL- -Replacement note *(traced to LL45 and overlaps with Lowther BE124b below)*	£25	£55	£100

(January 1999)
Turquoise and multicoloured.135 x 70mm.
Signature: Merlyn Lowther

Prefix sequence: Letter/Letter/Number/Number

		VF	EF	UNC
BE123a	Prefix EA01 followed by serial number..............................	£7	£15	£32
BE123b	Prefix EA- - to EJ- - (*traced to EJ45 last official run*)..............	FV	£6	£10
BE123c	Prefix EJ45 (*last official run*)..	£70	£125	£240

BE123d

BE123d	Prefix EJ90 (*special last run for collectors' packs and last prefix of Historical Series "E" £5*)...	—	—	£80
BE124a	Prefix CL- - Column sort note (*traced to CL45*)	FV	£12	£24

BE124b

BE124b	Prefix LL- -Replacement note (*traced to LL45 and overlaps with Kentfield BE122b above*)	£9	£22	£45

SERIES "E" NEW HISTORICAL ISSUE
(May 2002)
Turquoise and multicoloured.135 x 70mm. Withdrawn issue with faulty varnish coating and full halo silver hologram
Reverse depicting Elizabeth Fry
Signature: Merlyn Lowther

Prefix sequence: Letter/Letter/Number/Number

BE125a

		VF	EF	UNC
BE125a	Prefix HA01 followed by serial number	£6	£10	£22
BE125b	Prefix HA- -, HB- -, JA- -	FV	£6	£9
BE125c	Prefix JA90 (*last prefix of withdrawn issue*)	£20	£45	£80
BE126a	Prefix DL- - Column sort note (*traced to DL45 and overlaps with BE128a below*)	FV	£12	£25
BE126b	Prefix LL- - Replacement note (*traced from LL46-LL90 and overlaps with BE128c below*)	FV	£14	£28

(August 2002)
Turquoise and multicoloured.135 x 70mm. Reissue with improved varnish coating and cut halo hologram
Signature: Merlyn Lowther

Prefix sequence: Letter/Letter/Number/Number

BE127a	Prefix HC01 followed by serial number	£35	£60	—
BE127b	Prefix HC- - to HK- -	FV	FV	£8
BE127c	Prefix JB- - (*traced to JB90 and overlaps with Bailey BE129 below*)	FV	FV	£12

BE127d

		VF	EF	UNC
BE127d	Prefix XA- - to XE- -, XH- - to XK- - *(all traced from 01-45)*..	£35	£65	£110
BE128a	Prefix DL- - Column sort note *(traced to DL45 and overlaps with BE126a above)*	FV	£12	£25
BE128b	Prefix EL- - Column sort note *(traced to EL45 and overlaps with Bailey BE130a below)*	FV	£12	£25
BE128c	Prefix LL- - Replacement note *(traced from LL46-LL90 and overlaps with Lowther BE126b above and Bailey B130b below)*	FV	£14	£28

(January 2004)
Turquoise and multicoloured.135 x 70mm.
Signature: A. Bailey

Prefix sequence: Letter/Letter/Number/Number

BE129a

BE129a	Prefix JB46 followed by serial number	£18	£32	£60
BE129b	Prefix JB- - *(overlaps with Lowther BE127c above)*	FV	FV	£9
BE129c	Prefix JC- - to JK- -, KA- - KE- - KH- - to KL, ... LA- - LC*(continuing)*	FV	FV	£8
BE130a	Prefix EL- - Column sort note *(traced to EL45 and overlaps with Lowther BE128b above)*	FV	£8	£18
BE130b	Prefix LL- - Column sort note *(traced from LL46 to LL90 and overlaps with Lowther BE128c above)*	FV	£9	£20
BE131– BE149 *[Held in reserve]*				

TEN POUNDS
BLACK AND WHITE SERIES (continued)
(1925-29)

		F	VF	EF
BE150	*Signature: C. P. Mahon*			
	London	£385	£675	£1000

BE151

(1929-34)

		F	VF	EF
BE151	*Signature: B. G. Catterns*			
	London	£275	£475	£750

BE152

(1934-44)

		VF	EF	UNC
BE152	*Signature: K. O. Peppiatt*			
	London	£285	£475	£725

NB. There are deceptive German World War II forgeries of the White £10 note, almost all of these being forgeries of BE151 and BE152.

SERIES "C" PORTRAIT ISSUE
(February 1964)
Brown 150 x 93mm.
Signature: J .Q. Hollom

Prefix sequence: Letter/Number/Number

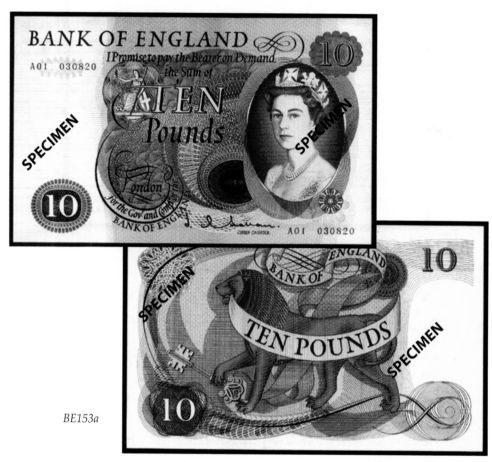

BE153a

		VF	EF	UNC
BE153a	Prefix A01 followed by serial number	£45	£80	£150
BE153b	Prefix A- -	£16	£32	£55
BE153c	Prefix A40	£50	£95	£175

(January 1967)
Brown 150 x 93mm.
Signature: J. S. Fforde

Prefix sequence: Letter/Number/Number

BE154a

		VF	EF	UNC
BE154a	Prefix A41 followed by serial number	£50	£95	£175
BE154b	Prefix A- - *(overlaps with Page BE155a, b below)*.....................	£16	£32	£55
BE154c	Prefix A95	£70	£135	£250

(1971 – date unknown)
Brown 150 x 93mm.
Signature: J .B. Page

Prefix sequence: Letter/Number/Number

BE155a	Prefix A91 followed by serial number	£650	£1200	£2000
BE155b	Prefix A- -*(overlaps with Fforde BE154b, c above)*	£500	£850	£1500
BE155c	Prefix B- -, C- -	£15	£28	£50
BE155d	Prefix C90 *(last prefix of Portrait Series "C" £10)*	£200	£375	—
BE156a	Prefix M01 Replacement note..	£70	£150	£285
BE156b	Prefix M- - Replacement note *(traced to M17)*	£25	£45	£80

BE157

It is thought that only six pairs are known.

		VF	EF	UNC
BE157	Pair of consecutively numbered notes with signatures of J. S. Fforde and J. B. Page (*traced in prefixes A91 to A95 only*)	—	£2350	£3500

SERIES "D" PICTORIAL ISSUE
(February 1975)
Brown and multicoloured. 151 x 85mm.
Reverse depicting Florence Nightingale
Signature: J .B. Page

Prefix sequence: Letter/Number/Number

BE158a

BE158a	Prefix A01 followed by serial number	£60	£100	£200

		VF	EF	UNC
BE158b	Prefix A- -	£14	£28	£50
BE158c	Prefix B- - to S- -......................................	FV	£22	£45
BE158d	Prefix T- -...	£32	£60	£110
BE158e	Prefix T20...	£225	£400	—
BE158f	Prefix U- - (*traced in U34, U35 and U39 with only 1 copy of each prefix known and overlaps with Somerset BE160b below*)........	£1250	£2500	—

BE158A

BE158A Pair of consecutively numbered notes with signatures of
J. B. Page and D. H. F. Somerset (*traced in prefix U35 only*)..... — Unique —

Note: This unique pair of notes made £7,880 in a Spink auction in June 2007.—Ed.

BE159a

BE159a	Prefix M01 Replacement note..............................	£90	£185	£350
BE159b	Prefix M- - Replacement note	£40	£85	£150
BE159c	Prefix M50 Replacement note	£65	£140	£275

(December 1980)

Brown and multicoloured. 151 x 85mm.
Reverse depicting Florence Nightingale
Signature: D. H. F. Somerset

Prefix sequence: Letter/Number/Number

		VF	EF	UNC
BE160a	Prefix U01 followed by serial number	£285	£550	£1000
BE160b	Prefix U- - *(overlaps with Page BE158f above)*	£20	£45	£85
BE160c	Prefix W- - to Y- -...	£18	£40	£75
BE160d	Prefix Z- -	£25	£50	£90
BE160e	Prefix Z80	£250	£450	—

Prefix sequence: Number/Number/Letter

BE161a

BE161a	Prefix 01A followed by serial number	£90	£165	£350
BE161b	Prefix - -A	£16	£35	£65
BE161c	Prefix - -B to - -K	£14	£28	£50
BE161d	Prefix - -L...	£35	£65	£125
BE161e	Prefix 40L...	£250	£450	—

(February 1984)

Brown and multicoloured. 151 x 85mm. With 0.5mm wide security thread. Reverse printed by
lithography. Small "L" on reverse
(see extract of note right)
Signature: D. H. F. Somerset

Prefix sequence: Letter/Letter/Number/Number

BE162, BE163, BE164 and BE165 all have a
small "L" for Litho at lower left on the reverse

BE162a	Prefix AN01 followed by serial number	£65	£125	£235
BE162b	Prefix AN- - to AZ- -, BN- - to BZ- -, CN- -	FV	£22	£40
BE162c	Prefix CR- -...	£18	£35	£65

BE162d

	VF	EF	UNC
BE162d Prefix CR90	£110	£200	£350

(July 1987)
Brown and multicoloured. 151 x 85mm. With 1mm wide windowed security thread.
Signature: D. H. F. Somerset

Prefix sequence: Letter/Letter/Number/Number

		VF	EF	UNC
BE163a	Prefix CS01 followed by serial number	£35	£75	£165
BE163b	Prefix CS- - to CZ- -	FV	£25	£45
BE163c	Prefix DN (*traced to DN30*)...	£22	£45	£80

(March 1988)
Brown and multicoloured. 151 x 85mm.
Signature: G. M. Gill

Prefix sequence: Letter/Letter/Number/Number

BE164a

		VF	EF	UNC
BE164a	Prefix DR01 followed by serial number	£28	£50	£90
BE164b	Prefix DR- - to DZ- -, EN- -, ER- - to EZ- -, HN- -,			
	HR- - to HZ- -, JN- -	FV	£18	£35
BE164c	Prefix JR..	£18	£40	£75
BE164d	Prefix JR60	£200	£375	—

(November 1991)
Brown and multicoloured. 151 x 85mm.
Signature: G. E. A. Kentfield

Prefix sequence: Letter/Letter/Number/Number

		VF	EF	UNC
BE165a	Prefix KN01 followed by serial number	£32	£60	£100
BE165b	Prefix KN- -, KR- -	£14	£28	£55

BE165c

BE165c	Prefix KR30 (*last prefix of Pictorial Series "D" £10 serial numbers from circulation below 998500 with the exception of 722501 to 723000*	£40	£75	£160
BE165d	Prefix KR30 (*serial numbers 722501 to 723000 and 998500 to 999999 from packs*)...	—	—	£120

SERIES "E" HISTORICAL ISSUE
(April 1992)
Orange and multicoloured. With windowed security thread. 142 x 75mm.
Reverse depicting Charles Dickens
Signature: G .E. A. Kentfield

Prefix sequence: Letter/Number/Number

BE166a

		VF	EF	UNC
BE166a	Prefix A01 followed by serial number	£14	£25	£45
BE166b	Prefix A- - to E- -, H- - to L- -, N- -, R- - to X- -	FV	£15	£28
BE166c	Prefix X40 (*last official run serial numbers from circulation*			
	below 998500)..	£35	£65	£125
BE166d	Prefix X40 (*serial numbers998500 to 999999 from packs*)........	—	—	£80
BE166e	Prefix Y- - (*extra run using unenhanced design traced from*			
	Y41 to Y96)...	£30	£55	£100
BE167a	Prefix M01 Replacement note	£120	£200	£350
BE167b	Prefix M- - Replacement note	£20	£45	£85
BE167c	Prefix M40 Replacement note	£65	£120	£200
BE167d	Prefix Z90 Experimental note..	£40	£70	£125

(October 1993)

Orange and multicoloured but with enhanced and additional value tablets. 142 x 75mm.
Signature: G .E. A. Kentfield

Prefix sequence: Letter/Letter/Number/Number

BE168a

		VF	EF	UNC
BE168a	Prefix AA00 followed by 000000 serial number (*Registration note issued in error*)..	£275	£500	£850
BE168b	Prefix DA01 followed by serial number	£100	£175	£325
BE168c	Prefix DA- - to DE- -, DH- - to DL- -, EA- - to EK- -, HA- - to HE- -, HH- - to HK- -, JA- - to JE- -, JH- - to JK- -, KA- - to KE- -, KH- - to KK- -…...	FV	£16	£30
BE168d	Prefix KK80 (*last official run*).......................................	£130	£250	—
BE168e	Prefix KK99 (*special last run for collectors' packs*)..................	—	—	£60
BE169a	Prefix DL- - Column sort note (*traced from DL81-DL96*).....	£18	£45	£80
BE169b	Prefix EL- - Column sort note (*traced from EL01-EL40*).......	FV	£35	£60
BE169c	Prefix LL- -Replacement note (*traced to LL40 and overlaps with Lowther BE171b below*)	£45	£85	£150

(January 1999)

Orange and multicoloured. 142 x 75mm.
Signature: Merlyn Lowther

Prefix sequence: Letter/Letter/Number/Number

BE170a	Prefix KL01 followed by serial number	£30	£55	£100
BE170b	Prefix KL- - and LA- -...	FV	£14	£25
BE170c	Prefix LA80 (*last prefix of Historical Series "E" £10 serial numbers below 999000 from circulation*)	£40	£75	£125

BE170d

		VF	EF	UNC
BE170d	Prefix LA80 (*serial numbers 999000 to 999999 from packs*)....	—	—	£40
BE171a	Prefix EL- - Column sort note (*traced to EL40*)	FV	£30	£55
BE171b	Prefix LL- -Replacement note (*traced to LL40 and overlaps with Kentfield BE169c above*)	£50	£90	£160

SERIES "E" NEW HISTORICAL ISSUE
(November 2000)

Orange and multicoloured.142 x 75mm.
Reverse depicting Charles Darwin
© 2000 wording incorrectly reads "The Governor and the Company of the Bank of England"
Signature: Merlyn Lowther

Prefix sequence: Letter/Letter/Number/Number

BE172a

BE172a	Prefix AA01 followed by serial number	FV	£18	£35

		VF	EF	UNC
BE172b	Prefix AA- - to AE- -, AH- - (*AD- - overlaps with BE174b below*)	FV	£14	£22
BE172c	Prefix AH80..	£100	£180	—
BE173a	Prefix EL- - Column sort note (*traced to EL40 and overlaps with BE175a below*)	FV	£18	£30
BE173b	Prefix LL- - Replacement note (*traced to LL40 and overlaps with BE175b below*)	£35	£60	£100

(2000–date unknown)

Orange and multicoloured.142 x 75mm.
© 2000 wording correctly reads "The Governor and Company of the Bank of England"
Signature: Merlyn Lowther

Prefix sequence: Letter/Letter/Number/Number

Copyright 2000 wording on front and back reads, "The Governor and the Company..."

Copyright 2000 wording on front and back reads, "The Governor and Company..."

		VF	EF	UNC
BE174a	Prefix AA01 (*special run for collectors' packs*)	—	—	£50
BE174b	Prefix AD- - (*traced to AD40 and overlaps with AD- - BE172b above*)	£20	£40	£85
BE174c	Prefix AJ01 (*first official run*)	£45	£80	£150
BE174d	Prefix AJ- -, AK- -, BA- - to BE- -, BH- - to BL- -, CA- - to CB-	FV	FV	£18
BE174e	Prefix CC41-CC79 (*overlaps with BE177a and b below*)	FV	FV	£25

BE174f

		VF	EF	UNC
BE174f	Prefix CC80 (*overlaps with BE177b below*)	£45	£85	—

	VF	EF	UNC
BE175a Prefix EL- - Column sort note *(traced from EL01-EL80 and overlaps with BE173a above and Bailey BE178a below)*	FV	£18	£32
BE175b Prefix LL- - Replacement note *(traced to LL40 and overlaps with BE173b above and Bailey BE178b below)*	FV	£20	£38

BE176

BE176 Prefix MH- -, MJ- -, MK- -, MM- - Experimental note	£100	£175	£325

(January 2004)

Orange and multicoloured.142 x 75mm.
Signature: A. Bailey

Prefix sequence: Letter/Letter/Number/Number

BE177a

	VF	EF	UNC
BE177a Prefix CC41	£45	£80	£140
BE177b Prefix CC- - to CE- -, CH- - to CK- -, DA- - to DE- -, DH- - to DK- -, EA- - to EE- -, EH- - to EK- -, HA to HE, HH- - *(continuing)*	FV	FV	£16
BE178a Prefix EL- - Column sort note *(traced from EL41-EL80 and overlaps with BE175a above)*......................................	FV	£14	£25
BE178b Prefix HL- - Column sort note *(traced from HL01-HL40)*.....	FV	£18	£35
BE178c Prefix LL- - Replacement note *(traced from LL01-LL40 and overlaps with BE175b above)*......................................	FV	£18	£35

BE179– BE199 [*Held in reserve*]

TWENTY POUNDS

BLACK AND WHITE SERIES (continued)
(1925-29)

		F	VF	EF
BE200	*Signature: C. P. Mahon*			
	London	£1100	£2000	£3500

(1929-34)

BE201

BE201	*Signature: B. G. Catterns*			
	London	£750	£1300	£2500

(1934-42)

BE202	*Signature: K. O. Peppiatt*			
	London	£500	£900	£1600

NB. There are deceptive German World War II forgeries of the White £20 note, almost all of these being forgeries of BE201 and BE202.

SERIES "D" PICTORIAL ISSUE
(July 1970)
Purple and multicoloured. 160 x 90mm.
Reverse depicting William Shakespeare
Signature: J.S. Fforde

Prefix sequence: Letter/Number/Number

BE203a

		VF	EF	UNC
BE203a	Prefix A01 followed by serial number	£140	£265	£465
BE203b	Prefix A- -	£110	£200	£350
BE203c	Prefix A05	£150	£285	£525

BE204

BE204	Prefix M01 Replacement note..................................	£145	£275	£500

(1970–date unknown)

Purple and multicoloured. 160 x 90mm.

Signature: J .B. Page

Prefix sequence: Letter/Number/Number

BE205a

		VF	EF	UNC
BE205a	Prefix A06 followed by serial number	£135	£260	£450
BE205b	Prefix A- -	£28	£50	£95
BE205c	Prefix B- -	—	—	—
BE205d	Prefix C- -	£25	£45	£85
BE205e	Prefix D- - *(traced to D80)*	£32	£60	£110

BE206a

BE206a	Prefix M01 Replacement note.................................	£150	£285	£525
BE206b	Prefix M- - Replacement note.................................	£70	£135	£250
BE206c	Prefix M04 Replacement note.................................	£160	£300	£550

(March 1981)

Purple and multicoloured. 160 x 90mm.

Signature: D .H. F. Somerset

Prefix sequence: Letter/Number/Number

BE207a	Prefix E01 followed by serial number	£260	£475	£800
BE207b	Prefix E- -	£70	£135	£265
BE207c	Prefix H- -	£32	£60	£110
BE207d	Prefix J- -...	£40	£70	£130
BE207e	Prefix J40...	£265	£500	—

(November 1984)

Purple and multicoloured with enhanced green and brown colouring and windowed security thread. Watermark is changed from H.M. Queen Elizabeth II to Shakespeare. 160 x 90mm.
Signature: D. H. F. Somerset

Prefix sequence: Number/Number/Letter

BE208a

		VF	EF	UNC
BE208a	Prefix 01A followed by serial number	£65	£120	£225
BE208b	Prefix - -A	£30	£55	£100
BE208c	Prefix - -B to - -J	£28	£50	£90
BE208d	Prefix - -K(*traced to 40K*)	£35	£65	£120

(March 1988)

Purple and multicoloured. 160 x 90mm.
Signature: G. M. Gill

Prefix sequence: Number/Number/Letter

		VF	EF	UNC
BE209a	Prefix 01L followed by serial number	£125	£225	—
BE209b	Prefix - -L	£35	£65	£120
BE209c	Prefix - -M to - -W	£32	£60	£110
BE209d	Prefix - -X...	£35	£65	£120

		VF	EF	UNC
BE209e	Prefix 20X (*last prefix of Pictorial Series "D" £20 serial numbers below 998500 from circulation*)	£125	£225	—

BE209f

BE209f	Prefix 20X (*serial numbers 998500 to 999999 from packs*)..........	—	—	£220

SERIES "E" HISTORICAL ISSUE
(June 1991)
Purple and multicoloured. With windowed security thread. 149 x 80mm.
Reverse depicting Michael Faraday
Signature: G. M. Gill

Prefix sequence: Letter/Number/Number

BE210a

BE210a	Prefix A01 followed by serial number	£28	£50	£90

		VF	EF	UNC
BE210b	Prefix A- - to D- -...	FV	£35	£65
BE210c	Prefix D70 (last official run)......................................	£95	£185	—

BE210d

		VF	EF	UNC
BE210d	Prefix E- -, H- -, J- -, L- -, R- -, S- -, U- - (*overlaps with Kentfield BE212a, b below*)	£35	£60	£110
BE210e	Prefix U19..	£120	£225	—
BE210f	Prefix Z13 Experimental note...................................	—	—	—
BE211	Prefix A- - to C- - Column sort note (*with control numbers above 70. Overlaps with Kentfield BE213a, b below*)................	£50	£95	£180

(November 1991)

Purple and multicoloured.149 x 80mm.
Signature: G .E. A. Kentfield

Prefix sequence: Letter/Number/Number

BE212a

		VF	EF	UNC
BE212a	Prefix E01 followed by serial number	£50	£90	£175
BE212b	Prefix E- -, H- - to L- -, N- -, R- - to U- -, W- - (*overlaps with Gill BE210d above*)..	FV	£45	£80
BE212c	Prefix W35 (*last official run with serial numbers below 998500 from circulation*)..	£70	£130	£250
BE212d	Prefix W35 (*with serial numbers 998500 to 999999 from packs*)	—	—	£170
BE213a	Prefix A- - Column sort note (*with control numbers above 70. Overlaps with Gill BE211 above*)...	£50	£95	£180
BE213b	Prefix B- - and C- - Column sort note (*with control numbers above 70. Overlaps with Gill BE211 above*)	£55	£100	£190

		VF	EF	UNC
BE214a	Prefix M- - Replacement note (*traced from M01 to M31*)	£85	£160	£280
BE214b	Prefix Z- - Experimental note (*traced to Z35*)........................	£65	£125	£240
BE214c	Prefix Z90 Experimental note	£85	£160	£280

(September 1993)

Purple and multicoloured. With enhanced and additional value tablets.149 x 80mm.
Signature: G .E. A. Kentfield

Prefix sequence: Letter/Number/Number

BE215a

BE215a	Prefix X01 followed by serial number...................................	£30	£55	£100
BE215b	Prefix X- - and Y- - (*traced to Y70*)..	FV	£35	£65
BE216	Prefix X- - and Y- - Column sort note (*with control numbers above 70*)	£60	£110	£190

(1994 – date unknown)

Purple and multicoloured. 149 x 80mm.
Signature: G .E. A. Kentfield

Prefix sequence: Letter/Letter/Number/Number

BE217a

BE217a	Prefix AA01 followed by serial number	£80	£150	£280
BE217b	Prefix AA- -	FV	£32	£60

		VF	EF	UNC
BE217c	Prefix AB- - to CJ- -	FV	£28	£50
BE217d	Prefix CJ80 (*last official run*)...................................	£175	£300	—
BE217e	Prefix CL99 (*special last run for collectors' packs*)	—	—	£70
BE218a	Prefix CL- - Column sort note (*traced to CL40*)	£35	£60	£125

BE218b

		VF	EF	UNC
BE218b	Prefix LL01 Replacement note	£65	£120	£225
BE218c	Prefix LL- - Replacement note (*traced to LL40*)	£40	£75	£140

(January 1999)
Purple and multicoloured. 149 x 80mm.
Signature: Merlyn Lowther

Prefix sequence: Letter/Letter/Number/Number

		VF	EF	UNC
BE219a	Prefix DA01 followed by serial number	£32	£60	£110
BE219b	Prefix DA- -	FV	£45	£80
BE219c	Prefix DA80 (*last prefix Historical Series "E" £20 with serial numbers below 999000 from circulation*)...	£90	£175	—

BE219d

		VF	EF	UNC
BE219d	Prefix DA80 (*serial numbers 999000 to 999999 from packs*)..	—	—	£120

SERIES "E" NEW HISTORICAL ISSUE
(June 1999)
Purple and multicoloured.149 x 80mm.
Reverse depicting Sir Edward Elgar
Signature: Merlyn Lowther

Prefix sequence: Letter/Letter/Number/Number

BE220a

		VF	EF	UNC
BE220a	Prefix AA01 followed by serial number	FV	£35	£60
BE220b	Prefix AA- -	FV	FV	£42
BE220c	Prefix AB- - to AE- -, AH- - to AK- -, BA- - to BE- -, BH- - to			
	BK- -, CA- - to CE- -, CH- -, CJ- -, DB- - to DD- -	FV	FV	£40
BE220d	Prefix DE- - (*overlaps with Bailey BE222a, b below*)................	FV	FV	£50

BE220e

BE220e	Prefix DE80 (*overlaps with Bailey BE222b below*).	£48	£90	£170
BE221a	Prefix AL- - Column sort note (*traced to AL40*)	FV	£28	£50
BE221b	Prefix BL- - Column sort note (*traced to BL40 and overlaps with*			
	Bailey BE223a below)...	FV	£28	£50
BE221c	Prefix LL- - Replacement note (*traced to LL40 and overlaps with*			
	Bailey BE223b below)...	FV	£45	£85

(January 2004)
Purple and multicoloured.149 x 80mm.
Signature: A. Bailey

Prefix sequence: Letter/Letter/Number/Number

BE222a

		VF	EF	UNC
BE222a	Prefix DE41 followed by serial number	£48	£90	£160
BE222b	Prefix DE- - (*overlaps with Lowther BE220d above*)	FV	FV	£40
BE222c	Prefix DH- - to DK- -, EA- - to EE- -, EH- - (*continuing*)......	FV	FV	£32
BE222d	Prefix EH40	£90	£175	—
BE223a	Prefix BL- - Column sort note (*traced from BL01-BL40 overlaps with Lowther BE221b above*)....................................	FV	£24	£40
BE223b	Prefix LL- - Replacement note (*traced from LL01-LL40 and overlaps with Lowther BE221c above*)......................................	FV	£28	£45

SERIES "F" THIRD HISTORICAL ISSUE
(March 2007)
Purple and multicoloured.149 x 80mm.
Reverse depicting Adam Smith, Scottish economist
Signature: A. Bailey

Prefix sequence: Letter/Letter/Number/Number

BE224a

		VF	EF	UNC
BE224a	Prefix AA01 followed by serial number	FV	£35	£60
BE224b	Prefix AA- - to AE - -, AH - - to AK, BA - - to BE - -,			
	BH - - to BK, CA - - to CE, CH - - to CK - -, DA - - to DE- -,			
	DH- - to DK- -, EA- - to EE *(continuing)*	FV	FV	£32
BE225a	Prefix AL - - Column sort note *(traced from AL01-AL40)*.....	FV	FV	£40

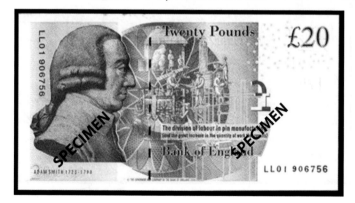

BE225b

		VF	EF	UNC
BE225b	Prefix LL01 Replacement note	FV	£90	£160
BE225c	Prefix LL - - Replacement note *(traced to LL40)*....................	FV	FV	£45
BE226-BE249	*[Held in reserve]*			

FIFTY POUNDS

BLACK AND WHITE SERIES (continued)

(1925-29)		F	VF	EF
BE250	*Signature: C. P. Mahon*			
	London	£850	£1500	£2750

(1929-34)

BE251

BE251	*Signature: B. G. Catterns*			
	London	£650	£1100	£1850

(1934-42)

BE252

BE252	*Signature: K. O. Peppiatt*			
	London	£400	£700	£1250

NB. There are deceptive German World War II forgeries of the White £50 note, almost all of these being forgeries of BE251 and BE252.

SERIES "D" PICTORIAL ISSUE
(March 1981)
Deep green and multicoloured. 169 x 95mm.
Reverse depicting Sir Christopher Wren
Signature: D. H. F. Somerset

Prefix sequence: Letter/Number/Number

BE253a

		VF	*EF*	*UNC*
BE253a	Prefix A01 followed by serial number	£60	£110	£190
BE253b	Prefix A- -, B- -	FV	£75	£130
BE253c	Prefix B90	£80	£150	£285

(July 1988)

Deep green and multicoloured with enhanced olive green colouring and windowed security thread.
169 x 95mm.
Signature: G. M. Gill

Prefix sequence: Letter/Number/Number

BE254a

		VF	EF	UNC
BE254a	Prefix C01 followed by serial number	£120	£200	£385
BE254b	Prefix C- -, D- -	FV	£95	£175
BE254c	Prefix D90 (*last official run*)	£80	£150	£285
BE254d	Prefix E- - (*overlaps with Kentfield BE256a, b below*)	£70	£125	£240

BE254e

BE254e	Prefix E30 (*overlaps with Kentfield BE256c below*)	£90	£165	£300
BE255	Prefix D- - Column sort note (*with control numbers above 90*)	£70	£130	£250

(November 1991)
Deep green and multicoloured. 169 x 95mm.
Signature: G. E. A. Kentfield

Prefix sequence: Letter/Number/Number

		VF	EF	UNC
BE256a	Prefix E01 followed by serial number	£65	£120	£225
BE256b	Prefix E- - (*overlaps with Gill BE254d, e above*).......................	FV	£80	£140
BE256c	Prefix E30 (*last prefix of Pictorial Series "D" £50 serial numbers from circulation below 998500 with the exception of 722501 to 723000*)	£125	£220	—

BE256d

BE256d	Prefix E30 (*last prefix of Pictorial Series "D" £50 (serial numbers 722501 to 723000 and 998500 to 999999 from packs*)	—	—	£200

SERIES "E" HISTORICAL ISSUE
(April 1994)
Red and multicoloured. 156 x 85mm.
Reverse depicting Sir John Houblon
Signature: G. E. A. Kentfield

Prefix sequence: Letter/Number/Number

BE257a

		VF	EF	UNC
BE257a	Prefix A01 followed by serial number	£60	£100	£160
BE257b	Prefix A- - to E- -, H- -	FV	£65	£110
BE257c	Prefix H70 (*last run from circulation*)	£130	£225	—
BE257d	Prefix H99 (*special last run for collectors' packs*)	—	—	£150
BE258a	Prefix A- -, B- -, H- - Column sort note (*with control numbers above 70*)...	FV	£85	£140
BE258b	Prefix L- - Column sort note (*traced to L35 and overlaps with Lowther BE 261 and Bailey BE263 below*)	FV	£85	£140

BE258c

BE258c	Prefix LL- - Replacement note (*traced to LL35*)....................	£70	£125	£240
BE259a	Prefix A99 Experimental note	FV	£90	£150
BE259b	Prefix M99 Experimental note	£120	£225	£400

(January 1999)
Red and multicoloured. 156 x 85mm.
Signature: Merlyn Lowther

Prefix sequence: Letter/Number/Number

BE260a

		VF	EF	UNC
BE260a	Prefix J01 followed by serial number	£60	£100	£160
BE260b	Prefix K- -	FV	FV	£100
BE260c	Prefix M- - *(overlaps with Bailey BE262b below)*	FV	FV	£100

BE260d

BE260d	Prefix M35	£65	£110	£185
BE261	Prefix L- - Column sort note *(traced from L01 to L70 and overlaps with Kentfield BE258b above and Bailey BE263 below)*	FV	£90	£150

(2006 Date unknown)
Red and multicoloured. 156 x 85mm.
Signature: Andrew Bailey

Prefix sequence: Letter/Number/Number

BE262a

		VF	EF	UNC
BE262a	Prefix M01 followed by serial number *(overlaps with Lowther BE260b above)*	FV	£90	£150
BE262b	Prefix M- - *(traced to M70 and overlaps with Lowther BE260c above)*	FV	FV	£90
BE263	Prefix L- - Column sort note *(traced from L01-L70 overlaps with Kentfield BE258b and Lowther BE261 above)*.....	FV	FV	£110

BE264– BE274 [*Held in reserve*]

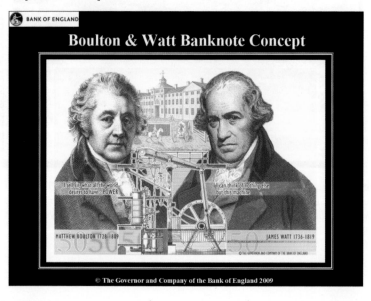

Back in May 2009 it was announced that two giants of the Industrial Age, James Watt and Matthew Boulton, were to appear on a new £50 note and the above concept design was released. Two years later and still no note has been forthcoming from the Bank of England. For updates on this and other stories check BANKNOTE NEWS every month or look on-line at www.tokenpublishing.com

ONE HUNDRED POUNDS

BLACK AND WHITE SERIES (continued)

	F	VF	EF

(1925-29)
BE275 *Signature: C. P. Mahon*

London	£1200	£2350	£4000

(1929-34)
BE276 *Signature: B. G. Catterns*

London	£800	£1500	£2700

(1934-42)
BE277a *Signature: K. O. Peppiatt*

London	£550	£950	£1700

BE277b

BE277b Liverpool	£525	£900	£1600

FIVE HUNDRED POUNDS

BLACK AND WHITE SERIES (continued)

	F	VF	EF
(1925–29)			
BE278 *Signature: C. P. Mahon*			
London	—	Rare	—
(1929–34)			
BE279 *Signature: B. G. Catterns*			
London	—	£22,000	—

(1934–42)

BE280

BE280 *Signature: K. O. Peppiatt*			
Liverpool	—	—	£8000

ONE THOUSAND POUNDS

BLACK AND WHITE SERIES (continued)

	F	VF	EF

(1925–29)

BE281   *Signature: C. P. Mahon*

London ....   —   Rare   —

(1929–34)

BE282   *Signature: B. G. Catterns*

London ....   —   —   £27,500

(1934–42)

BE283

BE283   *Signature: K. O. Peppiatt*

London ....   —   —   £25,000

TO ERR IS HUMAN;
TO COLLECT, DIVINE

THE mistakes made by others have always fascinated us, whether we are collectors or merely onlookers, and never is that fascination greater than when such mistakes are made by institutions renowned for their probity and quality. The Bank of England is a byword for strength, standing and accuracy and given the vast numbers of banknotes printed every day, errors in the production process are few and far between. However, notwithstanding the strictest of quality controls, real howlers do escape the eagle eyes of the checkers leading astonished collectors to exclaim, "How on earth did the Bank miss this one?". Many minor errors are actually much rarer than major ones, simply because the public are much less likely to spot them. But it is the really spectacular errors which attract the most attention, fuelling demand from all those keen on adding an extra dimension to their collections.

Paper money errors are inextricably linked with the production process and classification of them to some extent reflects differences in the printing method used by the issuer. Production of a banknote generally involves four distinct phases of treatment: (1) Paper, (2) Printing, (3) Numbering and (4) Cutting. However, at any stage during production the paper may be damaged, so for the purpose of error classification, folding and creasing must be added as a fifth category. Within each of these stages there are sub-categories and the classification for the purposes of this catalogue is therefore as follows:

1. PAPER
(a) Watermark (i) misplaced, (ii) exposed on surface, (iii) inverted (iv) missing.
(b) Security features (i) completely exposed, (ii) partly exposed, (iii) joined, (iv) missing.
(c) Join (i) white cotton tape, (ii) red or orange adhesive paper, (iii) yellow adhesive paper, (iv) brown adhesive paper.

2. PRINTING
(a) Uniface.
(b) Missing colour (i) underprint, (ii) main colour, (iii) dry print.
(c) Extra colour (i) streaks, (ii) solid lines, (iii) blobs and blots, (iv) excess of one or more colours, (v) wrong colour.
(d) Offset (i) front on back, (ii) back on front, (iii) misaligned.
(e) Part design missing (i) at edge of note, (ii) in body of note, (iii) as a result of foreign material.
(f) Print flaws (i) lines, (ii) spots, (iii) other.
(g) Missing signature.
(h) Misalignment (one side only as opposed to both sides cf 4(a) below)

3. NUMBERING
(a) No number. Sometimes a missing number is entered in pencil or ink.
(b) Only one number of two. Sometimes all or part of the number appears on the reverse.
(c) Shift. A major shift of a serial number to either the right or the left.
(d) Missing digits (i) single, (ii) multiple.
(e) Numeral misplaced (i) misaligned, (ii) parts of two numerals visible, (iii) inverted, (iv) on reverse (usually as a result of a fold).
(f) Different numbers (i) different prefix, (ii) one different serial numeral, (iii) two or more different serial numerals.
(g) Identical numbers on two or more notes.
(h) Slip and stick. Two or more identically numbered notes where the upper number differs from the lower one.

(j) Double number. A second different number is printed either directly over the first one or elsewhere on the note. (i) one serial number affected, (ii) both serial numbers affected.

(k) Dry print of number.

<hr>

4. CUTTING

(a) Design misplaced (i) vertically, (ii) horizontally (both sides cf 2(h) above).

(b) Rough edges.

<hr>

5. FOLDING

(a) Folds during the production process (i) extra paper, (ii) extra paper with marginal markings or colour bars, (iii) extra paper with part of adjoining note, (iv) without extra paper (v) extra paper with part of note missing.

(b) Creases within the sheet (i) single narrow, (ii) single wide or multiple.

Treasury note errors are only known in one or two categories and in such small quantities that it has been decided to exclude them from this publication. Series "A" and "B" errors are also rare, but there are enough available to collectors to warrant a limited listing and they are included for the first time in this edition. However it is only with the start of Series "C" and the introduction of reel-fed presses that almost every kind of error occurs. For ease of reference, the listings, commencing with the 10/- Britannia Series "A", are now all placed together rather than after each denomination. They use an "E" reference standing for "Error" combined with a numbering system based on the classification outlined above. So, for example, a 10/- error with no numbers is listed as E3a and a £1 error missing the underprint is listed as E2b(i). Since many errors vary in degree a distinction, where relevant, is also made between a major example and a minor example, the former being indicated by two asterisks and the latter by one. By far the widest variety of errors occur with the £1 Series C note and the listings for this denomination form the benchmark for all the other notes. No attempt has been made to list any errors for Series F Third Historical, because these are still being issued and more time is needed before they can be accurately evaluated.

It should be noted that the checkers at the printing works identify rejected notes by marking them with a solid orange phosphor band. This can be applied to an entire sheet, in which case the phosphor band will extend for the whole width of the note, or to individual notes, in which case the phosphor band will usually be slightly shorter. Phosphor bands on an error note add interest for collectors and may warrant a small premium. Very occasionally perfect notes are released with phosphor bands and these are very collectable. Errors on replacement and column sort notes are keenly collected and where these were actually used as such (as opposed to their general release as ordinary issued notes at the end of the Page era) dealers are likely to charge a premium.

Prices for Series "A" errors have been given for the three grades of Fine (F), Very Fine (VF) and Extremely Fine (EF) whereas pricing for the later issues is in Very Fine (VF), Extremely Fine (EF) and Uncirculated (Unc). Although condition is important for error notes, it is generally not so important as for perfect notes and the pricing between the grades reflects this. Nevertheless, higher grade untreated notes attract a considerable premium for issues prior to 1960 and here the price differential between the grades tends to be more marked. Three very important points, however, must be considered here: first, where a fold is the cause of an error, it should never be taken into account when grading it; secondly, erasure of pencilled or inked numbers on a note where serial numbers have been omitted is undesirable and reduces the grade; and thirdly, the prices given are for notes in their original untreated condition. In particular collectors should be aware that the vast majority of error notes in Series "A" have been pressed. Such notes should be graded in accordance with their condition prior to treatment and then reduced by one full grade.

It must be appreciated that error notes vary enormously in both type and extent and any attempt to price them cannot be an exact science. In particular, it should be noted that usually no attempt has been made to distinguish any of the error notes by signature, because with a few exceptions, this is not generally a factor in determining the value. Where it is definitely known to be, the signature of the Chief Cashier has been mentioned in the description. Occasionally where an error is found in many degrees of severity a price is given as "from" a stated value. If a variety is not listed, it may be appropriate to check it under a different denomination in the same series, because this will give some idea as to its relative scarcity. Notwithstanding these limitations, it is hoped that by listing a representative sample of errors for each denomination, collectors will be provided with some guidelines to assist them in that frequently tricky decision on what to pay for an error note.

In my role as contributing editor, I have been asked to clarify the difference between major and minor examples of errors as shown in the various listings. In view of the wide variety of errors, to some extent this must be a matter for subjective judgment and this is why many price listings for minor examples state a price "from" a certain amount. Furthermore there are numerous illustrations of both minor and major errors and these are clearly identified as such throughout the error section. Nevertheless I do accept that some dealers, particularly on eBay, are describing very minor errors as major ones and this can be misleading for new collectors. I have therefore decided to provide some guidance on this question by illustrating examples of minor and major offset errors as follows:-

1. Minor offset (impression)

2. Major offset (impression)

Offsets also exist in differing extents. An example of a partial offset is the Series "C" portrait 10/- illustrated as E2d(ii) in the listings and an example of a complete offset is the Series "C" portrait 10/- illustrated as E2d(i)**.

SERIES "A" BRITANNIA 10/- ERRORS

[A] Brown pre- and post-war issues

N.B. All brown Series "A" 10/- errors are very scarce and rare in original uncirculated condition

		F	VF	EF
E2d(i)*	Offset—front on back (minor)..from £40	£70	£125

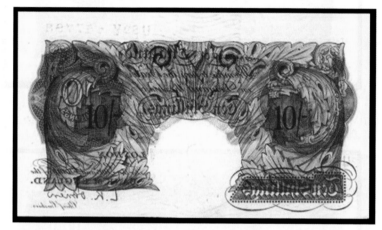

*E2d(i)****

E2d(i)**	Offset—front on back (major) £135	£250	£450

*E2d(iii)**

E2d(iii)*	Offset—misaligned (minor).. £50	£85	£140

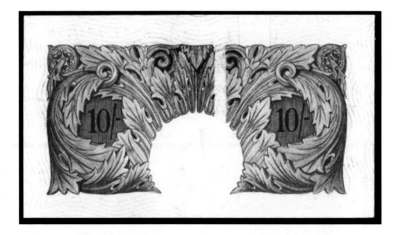

E2e(ii)*

	F	VF	EF
E2e(ii)* Part design missing (minor)..from £35	£60	£100

E2e(iii)

E2e(iii) Part design missing as a result of foreign material.............from £50   £85   £140

E2h

E2h Misalignment of obverse or reverse (minor) £85   £130   £250

		F	VF	EF
E3a	No number..	£225	£350	£500
E3b	Only one number of two..	£120	£180	£300
E3c	Shift of number..	£75	£120	£225
E3d(i)	Missing digits—single...	£30	£55	£85
E3d(ii)	Missing digits—multiple ....from £45		£85	£150
E3f(ii)	Different numbers—one different serial numeral..............	£90	£140	£225
E3f(iii)	Different numbers—two or more different serial numerals	£100	£175	£300

E5a(i)*

E5a(i)*	Folds with extra paper (minor).............................from £50		£90	£140
E5a(i)**	Folds with extra paper (major)	£120	£200	£300
E5a(iii)	Extra paper with part of adjoining note	£140	£240	£350

[B] Mauve wartime issues

N.B.1 All mauve Series "A" 10/- errors are very rare
N.B.2 There are numerous shade varieties of the wartime 10/- but these are not classified as errors

E2a	Uniface..	£400	£750	£1250
E2d(i)*	Offset—front on back (minor)..............................from £75		£120	£225

E3a

E3a	No number..	£275	£450	£750

	F	VF	EF
E3b Only one number of two..	£140	£250	£400

*E3b
and E3c
combined*

E3c Shift of number..	£90	£160	£300

E5a(i)*

E5a(i)* Folds with extra paper (minor)............................... from £80	£140	£250

SERIES "C" PORTRAIT 10/- ERRORS

N.B. All Series "C" 10/- errors are very scarce

E2b(i)*

		VF	EF	UNC
E2b(i)* Missing colour—Grey underprint only		£60	£100	£160

E2b(i)**

	VF	EF	UNC
E2b(i)** Missing colour—No underprint at all	£100	£185	£300
E2b(iii)* Missing colour—dry print (minor) on front or back ...... from £35	£60	£80

E2b(iii)**

	VF	EF	UNC
E2b(iii)** Missing colour—dry print (major) on front or back	£100	£175	£250

	VF	EF	UNC
E2d(i)* Offset—front on back (minor)..	£35	£60	£80

E2d(i)**

| **E2d(i)**** Offset—front on back (major) .... | £125 | £225 | £300 |

E2d(ii)

E2d(ii)	Offset (partial) ....from £50	£90	£150
E3a	No number... £125	£225	£300
E3b	Only one number of two.. £90	£140	£225
E3d(i)	Missing digits—single £25	£45	£70
E3d(ii)	Missing digits—multiple ....from £30	£65	£100

E3g

| **E3g** | Identical numbers on a pair of notes .... £350 | £500 | £750 |

		VF	EF	UNC
E5a(i)*	Folds with extra paper (minor)	from £50	£80	£125
E5a(i)**	Folds with extra paper (major)	£125	£200	£275

E5a(iii)

E5a(iii)	Extra paper with part of adjoining note £140	£240	£325

SERIES "A" BRITANNIA £1 ERRORS

[A] Green pre- and post-war issues

N.B. All green Series "A" £1 errors are very scarce and rare in original uncirculated condition.

		F	VF	EF
E2a	Uniface...	£400	£600	£900
E2d(i)*	Offset—front on back (minor)..	from £35	£60	£110

*E2d(i)***

E2d(i)**	Offset—front on back (major)...	£160	£275	£400
E2e(iii)	Part design missing as a result of foreign material........	£75	£120	£200

E3a

		F	VF	EF
E3a	No number	£160	£250	£400
E3b	Only one number of two	£110	£185	£300

E3c

		F	VF	EF
E3c	Shift of number	£60	£100	£200
E3d(i)	Missing digits—single	£25	£40	£65
E3d (ii)	Missing digits—multiple	£35	£65	£120

E3e(iii)

		F	VF	EF
E3e(iii)	Inverted numbers (both)	£350	£550	£800
E3e(iv)	Serial number on reverse as a result of folding	£125	£200	£325
E3f(ii)	Different numbers—one different serial numeral	£85	£120	£200
E3f(iii)	Different numbers—two or more different serial numerals	£100	£160	£275
E3g	Identical numbers on a pair of notes (*Mahon signature*)	—	£1000	£1500

E3g

		F	VF	EF
E3g	Identical numbers on a pair of notes (*post-war signatures*)	£450	£600	£800
E3j(i)	Double number–second different number on one serial number..	£85	£140	£250
E5a(i)*	Folds with extra paper (minor)	from £75	£120	£180
E5a(i)**	Folds with extra paper (major)	£140	£240	£350
E5a(ii)*	Folds with extra paper and marginal markings (minor)	from £85	£140	£250
E5a(v)	Folds with extra paper and part of note missing	£160	£275	£400

[B] Blue and pink wartime issues

N.B.1 All blue and pink Series "A" £1 errors are rare and very rare in original uncirculated condition
N.B.2 There are numerous shade varieties of the wartime £1 but these are not classified as errors.

E2a

E2a	Uniface...	£500	£750	£1250

E3a

		F	VF	EF
E3a	No number...	£200	£325	£500
E3b	Only one number of two...	£125	£200	£350

E5a(i)*

E5a(i)*	Folds with extra paper (minor)	from £85	£140	£225
E5a(i)**	Folds with extra paper (major)...	£185	£300	£450
E5a(ii)*	Folds with extra paper and marginal markings (minor)	from £90	£160	£275
E5a(v)	Folds with extra paper and part of note missing	£200	£325	£500

SERIES "C" PORTRAIT £1 ERRORS

		VF	EF	UNC
E1a(ii)	Inverted watermark	£100	£150	£200
E1b(i)	Securitythread—completely exposed	£28	£40	£60
E1b(iii)	Securitythread—joined	£14	£25	£40
E1b(iv)	Security thread—missing	£75	£100	£150

E1c(ii)

E1c(ii)	Paper join using red adhesive paper	£100	£150	£220

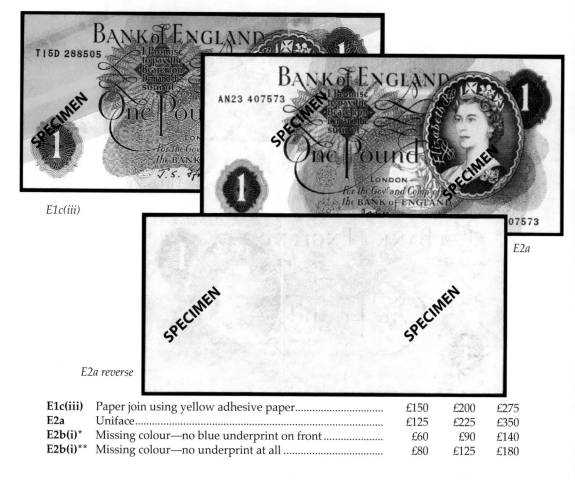

E1c(iii)

E2a

E2a reverse

E1c(iii)	Paper join using yellow adhesive paper	£150	£200	£275
E2a	Uniface	£125	£225	£350
E2b(i)*	Missing colour—no blue underprint on front	£60	£90	£140
E2b(i)**	Missing colour—no underprint at all	£80	£125	£180

161

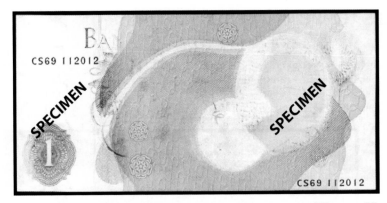

E2b(ii)

		VF	EF	UNC
E2b(ii)	Missing colour—no main green on front	£125	£250	£375
E2b(iii)**	Missing colour—dry print (major) main green on back	£100	£200	£275
E2c(i)	Extra colour—streak	£12	£20	£35
E2c(ii)	Extra colour—solid line	£15	£28	£45
E2c(iii)*	Extra colour—blobs & blots (minor)	£14	£25	£40

E2c(iii)**

		VF	EF	UNC
E2c(iii)**	Extra colour—blobs & blots (major)	£30	£60	£100
E2d(i)*	Offset—front on back (minor)	from £40	£75	£110
E2d(i)**	Offset—front on back (major)	£100	£200	£275
E2e(i)	Part design missing at edge	£30	£50	£80
E2e(ii)	Part design missing in body of note	£60	£90	£120
E2f	Print flaws	from £14	£25	£40
E3a	No number sometimes with number entered in pencil or ink	£75	£125	£175
E3b	Only one number of two	£50	£80	£125
E3d(i)	Missing digits—single	£14	£25	£40
E3d(ii)	Missing digits—multiple	from £20	£35	£65

E3e(i)   *E3e(ii)*   *E3e(i)*

		VF	EF	UNC
E3e(i)	Numeral misplaced—misaligned (major)	£25	£50	£75
E3e(ii)	Numeral misplaced—parts of two numerals visible	£18	£30	£55
E3f(i)	Different numbers—different prefix	£75	£125	£200
E3f(ii)	Different numbers—one different serial numeral	£18	£35	£60
E3f(iii)	Different numbers—two or more different serial numerals	£25	£50	£85
E3g	Identical number on two notes	£150	£250	£450

E3h

		VF	EF	UNC
E3h	Slip & stick pair	£65	£100	£180
E4a(i)*	Design misplaced—vertically, minor .... from £20	£35	£50
E4a(i)**	Design misplaced—vertically, major	£50	£85	£140
E4a(ii)*	Design misplaced—horizontally, minor .... from £25	£40	£60
E4a(ii)**	Design misplaced—horizontally, major	£60	£100	£175
E5a(i)	Folds with extra paper	£35	£75	£140
E5a(ii)	Folds with extra paper with marginal markings	£50	£100	£180
E5a(iii)	Folds with extra paper with part of adjoining note...........	£60	£120	£200
E5a(iv)	Folds without extra paper	£75	£150	£275

E5b(i)

E5b(i)	Crease within the sheet—single.............................	£25	£45	£75
E5b(ii)	Crease within the sheet—multiple .... from £45	£80	£130

SERIES "D" PICTORIAL £1 ERRORS

E2b(i)*   Missing colour—underprint, "bite out of orange" on back   £30   £55   £90

*E2b(i)***

E2b(i)**   Missing colour—almost all underprint, missing on back..   £45   £100   £180

*E2b(ii)***

	VF	EF	UNC
E2b(ii)** Missing colour—main green, front, Page signature	£125	£200	£300
N.B. the same error for Somerset is thought to be fraudulent.			
E2b(iii) Missing colour—dry print (major)— green and orange missing from back.. £250	—	—
E2c(ii)* Extra colour—solid line, front (minor) £12	£20	£30
E2d(i)* Offset—front on back (minor)..from £50	£80	£125
E2d(i)** Offset—front on back (major) £140	£240	£350
E2e(ii)* Part design missing in body of note—underprint by caduceus £200	—	
E2e(i)** Part design missing at edge, back (major)...................................... £90	£150	£225
E2f(i) Print flaw—front, line in tiara and another in garter sash.......... £12	£20	£30

Examples of E2f(ii)

E2f(ii)   Print flaw—front, white spot at right edge or back, spot on Newton's arm or spot on Newton's shoulder £12   £20   £30

		VF	EF	UNC
E2g*	Incorrect colour registration—front main green (over 1.5mm).. £60		£100	£150
E2g**	Incorrect colour registration—front main green (over 5mm)... £100		£150	£200
E3a	No number, sometimes with number entered in pencil or ink £100		£150	£225

E3c

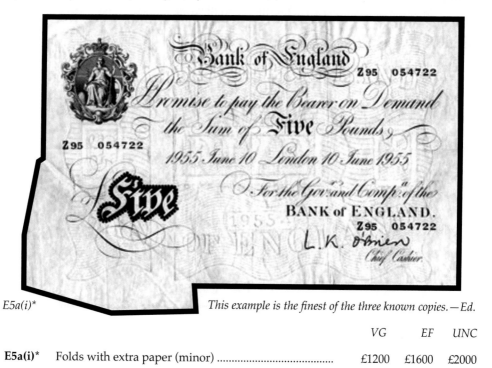

E3c	Shift of number—much too far to right or left	£50	£100	£160
E3d(i)	Missing digits—single..	£25	£45	£75
E3d (ii)	Missing digits—multiple ....from £40		£70	£125
E3e(i)	Numeral misplaced—misaligned, (major)............................	£25	£40	£75
E3e(ii)	Numeral misplaced—parts of two numerals visible..........	£35	£55	£90
E3j	Dry print of number	£70	£120	£175
E4a(ii)	Design misplaced horizontally with blue and white line at right..	£30	£50	£80
E4b	Rough edges (major)	£20	£35	£60
E5a(ii)	Fold with extra paper with marginal markings	£60	£110	£200
E5a(iv)	Fold without extra paper	£40	£75	£130
E5b(i)	Crease within the sheet (single)..	£40	£65	£100
E5b(ii)	Crease within the sheet (multiple) ....from £70		£120	£175

SERIES "A" BRITANNIA £5 ERRORS

N.B. *Series "A" £5 errors are of the utmost rarity and the rarest of all errors in the English series. Only one type of error (extra paper as a result of folding) has been seen and it is thought only three copies are known. Please report any examples to the Editor.*

E5a(i)*   *This example is the finest of the three known copies. —Ed.*

		VG	EF	UNC
E5a(i)*	Folds with extra paper (minor)	£1200	£1600	£2000

SERIES "B" HELMETED BRITANNIA £5 ERRORS

N.B. *Series "B" £5 errors are extremely rare and the only type thought to be known is the pair of notes with same serial numbers. Please report any other types of error to the editor.*

E3g

	VF	EF	UNC
E2b (iii)* Missing colours—dry print (minor) on back..................	£120	£200	—
E3g Identical number on two notes (BE97 and BE98 are known)	£500	£800	£1250

SERIES "C" PORTRAIT £5 ERRORS

N.B. All Series "C" £5 errors are rare

E2b(i)

Note: This example has added value as the error is on a replacement note.—Ed.

E2b(i) Missing colour—no mauve underprint on front.................	£100	£150	£275
E2d(i)* Offset—front on back (minor)...............................from £100	£180	£275

E2d(i)**

		VF	EF	UNC
E2d(i)**	Offset—front on back (major)	£275	£400	£600

E3a

		VF	EF	UNC
E3a	No number, sometimes with number entered in pencil or ink	£250	£350	£500
E3b	Only one number of two...	£150	£225	£350
E3d(i)	Missing digits—single..	£50	£85	£135
E3d(ii)	Missing digits—multiple ....from £75	£120	£185
E3j(i)	Double number—only one number affected	£175	£250	£350

E3j(ii)

		VF	EF	UNC
E3j(ii)	Double number—both numbers affected	£250	£350	£500
E5a(i)*	Folds with extra paper (minor)	from £50	£85	£160
E5a(i)**	Folds with extra paper (major)	£150	£275	£400

E5a(iii)

E5a(iii)	Folds with extra paper with part of adjoining note	from £150	£275	£400

SERIES "D" PICTORIAL £5 ERRORS

		VF	EF	UNC
E1b(i)	Security thread completely exposed	£40	£65	£100

E1b(ii)

E1b(ii)	Security thread partly exposed	£30	£50	£75
E1c(ii)	Paper join using red adhesive paper.....................................	£75	£120	£175
E1c(iv)	Paper join using brown adhesive paper..............................	£85	£140	£225
E2b(i)	Missing battle scene—no m/c underprint on back	£160	£275	£400

E2b(ii)

E2b(ii)	Missing Wellington—no main blue on back	£120	£200	£285
E2b(iii)*	Missing colours—dry print (minor) on front or back.........from £30	£50	£80

*E2b(iii)***

E2b(iii)**	Missing colours—dry print (major) on front or back	£75	£125	£175

169

		VF	EF	UNC
E2c(i)	Extra colour—streak	£25	£40	£70
E2c(ii)	Extra colour—solid line	£28	£50	£80
E2c(iii)*	Extra colour—blobs & blots (minor)	from £25	£45	£70
E2c(iii)**	Extra colour— blobs & blots (major)	£50	£90	£150
E2d(i)*	Offset—front on back (minor)	from £40	£60	£100
E2d(i)**	Offset—front on back (major)	£75	£140	£250
E2d(iii)	Offset—front on back, misaligned (major)	£80	£150	£280
E2g	Missing signature of D. H. F. Somerset			See BE114

E2h

E2h*	Misalignment of obverse or reverse (minor)	from £50	£85	£125
E2h**	Misalignment of obverse or reverse (major)	£160	£275	£400

E3a

		VF	EF	UNC
E3a	No number, sometimes with number entered in pencil or ink	£100	£185	£275
E3b	Only one number of two	£75	£110	£175
E3d(i)	Missing digits—single	£28	£45	£70
E3d(ii)	Missing digits—multiple	from £45	£75	£110
E3e(iii)	Inverted numbers (both)	£150	£275	£400
E3f(ii)	Different numbers— one different serial number	£30	£50	£75
E3f(iii)	Different numbers—two or more different serial numbers	from £50	£80	£125
E4a(i)*	Design misplaced—vertically (minor)	from £28	£45	£70
E4a(i)**	Design misplaced—vertically (major)	£100	£185	£285
E4a(ii)*	Design misplaced—horizontally (minor)	from £30	£50	£80
E4a(ii)**	Design misplaced—horizontally (major)	£135	£225	£350
E5a(i)*	Folds with extra paper (minor)	from £35	£50	£75
E5a(i)**	Folds with extra paper (major)	£80	£125	£200

VF   EF   UNC

E5a(ii)

E5a(ii) Folds with extra paper and colour bars................................. £120   £185   £275
E5a(iii) Folds with extra paper with part of adjoining note............from £90   £150   £240

E5a(iv)

E5a(iv) Folds without extra paper, showing part back on front and
blank area on back or vice versa.. £175   £275   £400
E5b(i) Crease within the sheet—single... £35   £60   £90
E5b(ii) Crease within the sheet—multiple.......................................from £60   £100   £150

SERIES "E" HISTORICAL £5 ERRORS

E2b(i)

		VF	EF	UNC
E2b(i)	Missing orange, yellow and olive-green in underprint on back £50		£80	£125
E2b(iii)*	Missing colours—dry print (minor) on front or back.........from	£20	£40	£60
E2b(iii)*	Missing colours—dry print (major) on front or back.	£85	£150	£225
E2d(i)*	Offset—front on back (minor).................................from	£40	£75	£120
E2d(i)*	Offset—front on back (major)	£120	£200	£275
E3f(ii)	Different numbers—one different serial number...............	£25	£45	£70
E3f(iii)	Different numbers—two or more different serial numbers from	£40	£65	£100
E4a(i)*	Design misplaced—vertically (minor)................................from	£25	£45	£70
E4a(i)*	Design misplaced—vertically (major)	£100	£180	£260
E4a(ii)*	Design misplaced—horizontally (minor) ....from	£30	£50	£75
E4a(ii)*	Design misplaced—horizontally (major)	£150	£240	£325
E5a(i)*	Folds with extra paper (minor).............................from	£35	£50	£75
E5a(i)*	Folds with extra paper (major)	£80	£130	£180
E5a(ii)	Folds with extra paper and colour bars.............................	£120	£200	£285

E5a(ii)

E5a(iii)

E5a(iii)	Folds with extra paper with part of adjoining note............from	£100	£175	£250

E5a(iv)

	VF	EF	UNC
E5a(iv) Folds without extra paper, showing part back on front and blank area on back or vice versa	£150	£240	£350

SERIES "E" NEW HISTORICAL £5 ERRORS

E2b(ii)

		VF	EF	UNC
E1b	Missing silver foil hologram on front	£70	£110	£175
E2b(ii)	Missing Queen and denomination on front	£120	£200	£325
E2b(iii)*	Missing colours—dry print (minor) on front or back	from £25	£45	£70
E2b(iii)**	Missing colours—dry print (major) on front or back	£75	£130	£200
E2d(i)*	Offset—front on back (minor)	from £35	£65	£100

E2d(i)**

		VF	EF	UNC
E2d(i) **	Offset—front on back (major)..	£100	£175	£250
E3a	No number, sometimes with number entered in pencil or ink	£125	£200	£280
E3c*	Shift of number (minor)	from £25	£45	£65

E3c**

E3c **	Shift of number (major)..	£70	£120	£175

E3f(i)

E3f(i)	Different numbers—different prefix..................................	£60	£100	£150

		VF	EF	UNC
E3f(ii)	Different numbers—one different serial number	£25	£45	£65
E3f(iii)	Different numbers—two or more different serial numbers	from £40	£65	£100

E4a(i)*

		VF	EF	UNC
E4a(i)*	Design misplaced—vertically (minor)	from £25	£40	£60
E4a(i)**	Design misplaced—vertically (major)	£100	£175	£250
E4a(ii)*	Design misplaced—horizontally (minor)	from £28	£45	£70
E4a(ii)**	Design misplaced—horizontally (major)	£125	£220	£300
E5a(i)*	Folds with extra paper (minor)	from £25	£40	£65
E5a(i)**	Folds with extra paper (major)	£75	£125	£175
E5a(ii)	Folds with extra paper and colour bars	£110	£185	£275
E5a(iii)	Folds with extra paper with part of adjoining note	from £100	£175	£250

SERIES "C" PORTRAIT £10 ERRORS

N.B. All Series "C" £10 errors are very rare

		VF	EF	UNC
E2b(i)	Missing colours—No underprint and multicolours on back...	£350	£550	£850
E2d(i)*	Offset—front on back (minor) .... from £120	£220	£300

E2d(i)**

		VF	EF	UNC
E2d(i)**	Offset—front on back (major)	£400	£650	£1000

		VF	EF	UNC
E2d(ii)*	Offset—back on front (minor)..	from £120	£200	£300

E2d(ii)**

E2d(ii)**	Offset—back on front (major)	£500	£800	£1200
E3d(i)	Missing digits—single	£75	£110	£150
E3d(ii)	Missing digits—multiple ....from	£120	£185	£275

E5a(i)*

E5a(i)*	Folds with extra paper (minor) ....from £90	£140	£200
E5a(i)**	Folds with extra paper (major) ....from £200	£325	£500
E5a(iii)	Folds with extra paper with part of adjoining note..........from £250	£375	£550

SERIES "D" PICTORIAL £10 ERRORS

		VF	EF	UNC
E1a(i)	Watermark misplaced	£60	£100	£160

E1a(i)

E1a(ii)

		VF	EF	UNC
E1a(ii)	Watermark exposed on surface—too dark on back	£90	£175	£250
E1b(i)	Security thread completely exposed	£60	£85	£125
E1b(ii)	Security thread partly exposed	£45	£70	£100
E1c(ii)	Paper join using red adhesive paper	£120	£200	£280

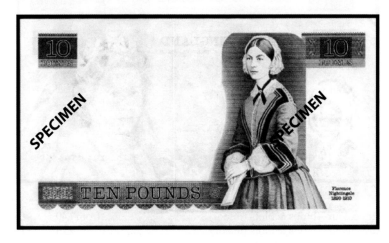

E2b(i)

		VF	EF	UNC
E2b(i)	Missing hospital scene— no m/c underprint on back	£140	£240	£325

177

E2b(ii)

		VF	EF	UNC
E2b(ii)	Missing Nightingale—no main brown on back	£120	£200	£280
E2b(iii)*	Missing colours—dry print (minor) on front or back......... from £45		£70	£100
E2b(iii)*	Missing colours—dry print (major) on front or back.	£90	£170	£240
E2c(i)	Extra colour—streak...	£35	£60	£85
E2c(ii)	Extra colour—solid line	£35	£60	£85

*E2c(iii)**

		VF	EF	UNC
E2c(iii)*	Extra colour—blobs & blots (minor)................................... from £40		£65	£90
E2c(iii)*	Extra colour—blobs & blots (major)....................................	£75	£140	£200
E2d(i)*	Offset—front on back (minor).. from £40		£60	£100

E2d(i)**

		VF	EF	UNC
E2d(i)**	Offset—front on back (major)	£130	£220	£300

E2g

		VF	EF	UNC
E2g	Missing signature of J. B. Page...............................	£250	£400	£600
E3d(i)	Missing digits—single	£45	£70	£90
E3d(ii)	Missing digits—multiple ....from £60		£100	£140
E3f(ii)	Different numbers—one different serial number	£40	£65	£100
E3f(iii)	Different numbers—two or more different serial numbers..from £60		£100	£140

E3j(i)

		VF	EF	UNC
E3j(i)	Double number—second (different) number over first serial number	£125	£220	£300
E4a(i)*	Design misplaced—vertically (minor)	from £45	£70	£90
E4a(i)**	Design misplaced—vertically (major)	£180	£300	£450
E4a(ii)*	Design misplaced—horizontally (minor)	from £45	£75	£100
E4a(ii)**	Designmisplaced—horizontally (major)	£200	£375	£500
E5a(i)*	Folds with extra paper (minor)	from £40	£65	£100
E5a(i)**	Folds with extra paper (major)	£100	£180	£250
E5a(ii)	Folds with extra paper and colour bars	£130	£240	£325
E5a(iii)	Folds with extra paper with part of adjoining note	from £110	£200	£275
E5b(i)	Crease within the sheet—single	£40	£65	£100
E5b(ii)	Crease within the sheet—multiple	from £70	£110	£170

SERIES "E" HISTORICAL £10 ERRORS

		VF	EF	UNC
E1b(i)	Security thread—completely exposed	£40	£75	£100
E1b(ii)	Security thread—partly exposed	£35	£60	£80

E1b(iv)

E1b(iv)	Security thread—completely missing	£100	£180	£250

E2b(i)

E2b(i)	Missing colour—no green underprint on back	£50	£85	£120
E2b(iii)*	Missing colours—dry print (minor) on front or back	from £28	£45	£75
E2b(iii)**	Missing colours—dry print (major) on front or back.	£75	£120	£175

E2c(iv)

		VF	EF	UNC
E2c(iv)	Excess brown (major) with Dickens blotted out on back...	£140	£225	£300
E2c(v)	Wrong colour—all brown including Dickens in green on back	£140	£225	£300
E2d(i)*	Offset—front on back (minor)..from £45		£65	£90

E2d(i)**

E2d(i)**	Offset—front on back (major)	£90	£150	£200
E3a	No number, sometimes with number entered in pencil or ink	£100	£185	£250
E3f(ii)	Different numbers—one different serial number...............	£35	£60	£85
E3f(iii)	Different numbers—two or more different serial numbers	from £50	£90	£120
E4a(i)*	Design misplaced—vertically (minor)................................from £35		£60	£80

E4a(i)**

		VF	EF	UNC
E4a(i)**	Design misplaced—vertically (major)	£100	£175	£250
E4a(ii)*	Design misplaced—horizontally (minor)	from £40	£65	£90
E4a(ii)**	Designmisplaced—horizontally (major)	£150	£240	£325
E5a(i)*	Folds with extra paper (minor)	from £35	£60	£80
E5a(i)**	Folds with extra paper (major)	£75	£120	£175
E5a(ii)	Folds with extra paper and colour bars	£90	£160	£240
E5a(iii)*	Folds with extra paper with part of adjoining note (minor)	from £60	£100	£150
E5a(iii)**	Folds with extra paper with two Queens or two Britannias (over 30% of adjoining note, major)	£275	£475	£650

SERIES "E" NEW HISTORICAL £10 ERRORS

		VF	EF	UNC
E1b(iv)	Missing silver foil hologram on front	£60	£100	£150

E2b(ii)

		VF	EF	UNC
E2b(ii)	Missing Queen and denomination on front......................	£175	£260	£375
E2b(iii)*	Missing colours —dry print (minor) on front or back...	from £35	£50	£75
E2b(iii)**	Missing colours—dry print (major) on front or back	£75	£120	£175

E2c(iii)*

		VF	EF	UNC
E2c(iii)*	Extra colour—blobs & blots (minor)	from £28	£45	£65
E2c(iii)**	Extra colour—blobs & blots (major)	£75	£120	£175
E2d(i)*	Offset—front on back (minor)	from £40	£60	£80
E2d(i)**	Offset—front on back (major)...	£90	£150	£200
E3a	No number, sometimes with number entered in pencil or ink	£100	£185	£250
E3f(ii)	Different numbers—one different serial number...........	£40	£60	£85
E3f(iii)	Different numbers—two or more different serial numbers.	from £50	£85	£125
E4a(i)*	Design misplaced—vertically (minor)............................	from £30	£50	£75
E4a(i)**	Design misplaced—vertically (major)	£90	£150	£225

E4a(ii)*

		VF	EF	UNC
E4a(ii)*	Design misplaced—horizontally (minor)	from £35	£55	£85
E4a(ii)**	Design misplaced—horizontally (major)	£140	£225	£300
E5a(i)*	Folds with extra paper (minor)	from £40	£60	£75
E5a(i)**	Folds with extra paper (major)	£70	£120	£160

E5a(ii)

E5a(ii)	Folds with extra paper and colour bars	£100	£160	£240
E5a(iii)*	Folds with extra paper with part of adjoining note(minor)	from £60	£100	£150

SERIES "D" PICTORIAL £20 ERRORS

N.B. *Errors on the first issues of the £20 note are much scarcer than those on the later notes with modified colours and are likely to attract a premium.*

E2b(i)

		VF	EF	UNC
E2b(i)	Missing St George & dragon and underprint on front and Romeo & Juliet and underprint on back	£180	£300	£450

E2b(ii)

		VF	EF	UNC
E2b(ii)	Missing Shakespeare—no main purple on back	£140	£220	£300
E2c(iii)*	Extra colour—blobs & blots (minor) .... from £50	£85	£120
E2c(iii)**	Extra colour—blobs & blots (major)	£100	£160	£250

E2c(iv)

		VF	EF	UNC
E2c(iv)	Extra colour—excess purple on front (major)......................	£100	£160	£250
E2d(i)*	Offset—front on back (minor)..	from £40	£60	£85
E2d(i)**	Offset—front on back (major)	from £90	£150	£240
E2d(ii)*	Offset—back on front (minor)..	from £45	£70	£100

E2d(ii)

E2d(ii)**	Offset—back on front (major)	£140	£220	£300
E3a	No number..	£180	£300	£450
E3d(i)	Missing digits—single..	£50	£80	£120
E3d(ii)	Missing digits—multiple ....from £60		£125	£200
E3f(ii)	Different numbers—one different serial number...............	£50	£80	£110
E3f(iii)	Different numbers—two or more different serial numbersfrom £75		£120	£175
E4a(i)*	Design misplaced—vertically (minor)...............................from £50		£80	£110
E4a(i)**	Design misplaced—vertically (major)	£150	£250	£350
E4a(ii)*	Design misplaced—horizontally (minor)...........................from £50		£85	£125
E4a(ii)**	Design misplaced—horizontally (major)	£160	£275	£400
E5a(i)*	Folds with extra paper (minor)...from £60		£90	£125
E5a(i)**	Folds with extra paper (major)	£100	£180	£275
E5a(ii)	Folds with extra paper and colour bars.............................	£150	£250	£350
E5a(iii)	Folds with extra paper with part of adjoining note..........from £120		£225	£300
E5a(v)	Extra paper with part of note missing			
	(see example at top of page 151 above)	£175	£300	£400
E5b(i)	Crease within the sheet—single narrow..............................	£60	£90	£125

E5b(ii)

	VF	EF	UNC
E5b(ii) Crease within the sheet—single wide or multiple..............from £100	£180	£275

SERIES "E" HISTORICAL £20 ERRORS

		VF	EF	UNC
E1a(i)	Watermark misplaced	£75	£120	£175
E1b(i)	Securitythread—completely exposed	£60	£90	£125
E1b(ii)	Securitythread—partly exposed	£50	£70	£90

E2b(ii)

	VF	EF	UNC
E2b(ii) Missing portrait of Queen—no main black on front	£85	£140	£200
E2b(iii)* Missing colours—dry print (minor) on front or back.........from £40	£65	£90
E2b(iii)**Missing colours—dry print (major) on front or back.	£85	£140	£200

E2c(iv)

		VF	EF	UNC
E2c(iv)	Excess purple and violet (major) on front............................	£75	£125	£175
E2d(i)*	Offset—front on back (minor).. from £50		£75	£100
E2d(i)**	Offset—front on back (major)	£100	£175	£240
E3b	Only one number of two..	£75	£125	£175

E3e(iii)

E3e(iii)	Inverted serial number..	£120	£185	£250
E3f(ii)	Different numbers— one different serial number..............	£50	£75	£100
E3f(iii)	Different numbers—two or more different serial numbers.. from £65		£110	£140
E3j(ii)	Double number—second different number on both serial numbers	£125	£200	£285
E4a(i)*	Design misplaced—vertically (minor)................................ from £35		£60	£85
E4a(i)**	Design misplaced—vertically (major)	£100	£175	£225
E4a(ii)*	Design misplaced— horizontally (minor)........................... from £40		£65	£90
E4a(ii)**	Design misplaced—horizontally (major)	£125	£200	£275
E5a(i)*	Folds with extra paper (minor).. from £35		£60	£85
E5a(i)**	Folds with extra paper (major)	£80	£125	£180

E5a(ii)

	VF	EF	UNC
E5a(ii) Folds with extra paper and colour bars................................	£120	£185	£250
E5a(iii)* Folds with extra paper with part of adjoining note (minor)...from £40		£100	£140

*E5a(iii)***

E5a(iii)* Folds with extra paper with two Queens or two Britannias
(over 30% of adjoining note, major).....................................£240   £400   £600

SERIES "E" NEW HISTORICAL £20 ERRORS

		VF	EF	UNC
E1b(iv)	Missing silver foil hologram on front	£75	£120	£185

E2b(ii)

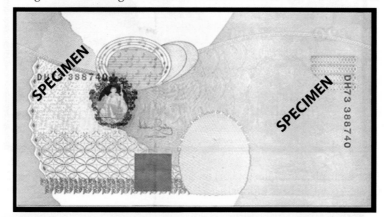

E2b(ii)	Missing Queen and denomination on front...................	£160	£240	£350

E2b(iii)*

Note: This example has added value as error is on a column sort note. Ed.

E2b(iii)*	Missing colours - dry print (minor) on front or back.....	from £40	£65	£90

E2b(iii)**

E2b(iii)**	Missing colours - dry print (major) on front or back.....	£85	£140	£200

E2c(iv)

		VF	EF	UNC
E2c(iv)	Excess purple and violet (major) on front	£75	£120	£185
E2d(i)*	Offset—front on back (minor)	from £60	£95	£125

*E2d(i)***

E2d(i)*	Offset—front on back (major)	£100	£175	£240
E3b	Only one number of two	£75	£120	£185

E3f(i)

E3f(i)	Different prefixes	£120	£185	£250
E3f(ii)	Different numbers—one different serial number	£45	£75	£100
E3f(iii)	Different numbers—two or more different serial numbers..	from £65	£110	£140

		VF	EF	UNC
E3j(ii)	Double number— second different number on both serial numbers	£125	£200	£285
E4a(i)*	Design misplaced—vertically (minor)	from £40	£65	£90
E4a(i)**	Design misplaced—vertically (major)	£100	£175	£225
E4a(ii)*	Design misplaced—horizontally (minor)	from £40	£65	£90
E4a(ii)**	Design misplaced—horizontally (major)	£125	£200	£275
E5a(i)*	Folds with extra paper (minor)	from £40	£65	£90
E5a(i)**	Folds with extra paper (major)	£80	£125	£180

E5a(ii)

E5a(iii)

E5a(ii)	Folds with extra paper and colour bars	£120	£185	£250
E5a(iii)	Folds with extra paper with part of adjoining note (major)	from £100	£175	£225

SERIES "D" PICTORIAL £50 ERRORS

N.B. *All Series "D" £50 errors are very scarce*

E2b(i)

	VF	EF	UNC
E2b(i) Missing phoenix and underprint on front and St. Paul's Cathedral and underprint on back..	£300	£500	£650

E2b(ii)

	VF	EF	UNC
E2b(ii) Missing Wren, plan of Cathedral and view of old London— no main green and brown on back..	£200	£375	£500
E2c(iii)* Extra colour—blobs & blots (minor)......................................from £90	£130	£160

E2c(iii)**

		VF	EF	UNC
E2c(iii)**	Extra colour—blobs & blots (major)	£140	£275	£375

E2d(i)*

		VF	EF	UNC
E2d(i)*	Offset—front on back (minor)	from £100	£150	£225
E2d(i)**	Offset—front on back (major)	£175	£325	£450

E3a

		VF	EF	UNC
E3a	No number	£200	£350	£550
E3g	Identical numbers on a pair of notes	£500	£800	£1000

E3j(ii)

		VF	EF	UNC
E3j(ii)	Double number with both serial numbers affected.........	£250	£450	£600
E4a(i)*	Design misplaced—vertically (minor).............................. from	£100	£180	£225
E4a(ii)*	Design misplaced—horizontally (minor)......................... from	£120	£190	£250
E5a(i)*	Folds with extra paper (minor)... from	£100	£180	£225
E5a(i)**	Folds with extra paper (major)	£185	£325	£450

E5a(ii)

E5a(ii)	Folds with extra paper and colour bars...............................	£250	£450	£600
E5a (iii)	Folds with extra paper with part of adjoining note (major)	£225	£375	£500
E5a (v)	Extra paper with part of note missing	£225	£375	£500

SERIES "E" HISTORICAL £50 ERRORS

N.B. *All Series "E" £50 errors are very scarce*

		VF	EF	UNC
E1b(iv)	Missing silver rose on front	£125	£225	£300
E2b(iii)*	Missing colours—dry print (minor) on front or back	from £75	£100	£125

E2b(iii)**

		VF	EF	UNC
E2b(iii)**	Missing colours—dry print (major) on front or back	from £100	£160	£225
E4a(i)*	Design misplaced—vertically (minor)	from £80	£120	£160
E4a(ii)*	Design misplaced—horizontally (minor)	from £90	£130	£175
E5a(i)*	Folds with extra paper (minor)	from £100	£180	£225
E5a(i)**	Folds with extra paper (major)	£175	£300	£400

E5a(ii)

E5a(ii)	Folds with extra paper and colour bars	£250	£450	£600
E5a (iii)	Folds with extra paper with part of adjoining note (major)	£225	£375	£500
E5a (v)	Extra paper with part of note missing	£225	£375	£500

A selection of spectacular error notes from the Laurence Pope collection

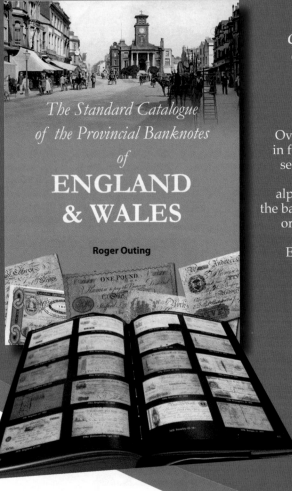

ISLE OF MAN

The Isle of Man has a very long history of paper money with the first banknote issues appearing during the latter part of the 18th century. Over the next 150 years there were numerous mergers and acquisitions as the fortunes of the different banks rose and fell. By the early part of the 20th century the banknote issues were in the hands of five Commercial Banks—The Isle of Man Bank Limited, Westminster Bank Limited, Martins Bank Limited, Lloyds Bank Limited and Barclays Bank Limited.

In 1961 the Isle of Man Government Notes Act was passed and the note issuing licences of all of the commercial banks were revoked. The first Government note issues, comprising denominations of 10 shillings, one pound and five pounds were put into circulation during July of this same year.

ISLE OF MAN BANK LIMITED

The Isle of Man Banking Company was established in Douglas in 1865 and subsequently set up branches in the other main towns in the Island. The name was changed to Isle of Man Bank Limited in 1925, and in 1961 the bank merged with the National Provincial Bank. Since 1969 the Isle of Man Bank has been part of the National Westminster Group.

ONE POUND NOTES

Size 168 mm x 120 mm approximately

Obverse—black with "ONE" in brown at the centre. Vignette of Douglas bay and harbour at the top
Reverse—blue. Triune and Isle of Man motto at the centre

	F	VF
IM1 Signatories: Handsigned by Manager and Assistant Manager Prefix P dated 9.6.1915 to prefix O/1 dated 1.3.1926		Rare

Size 158 mm x 90 mm approximately

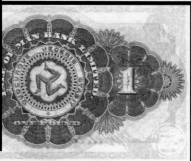

Obverse—black with "ONE" in pink geometric design at the centre. Vignette of Douglas bay and harbour at the top
Reverse—green panel. Triune and Isle of Man motto at the centre

	F	VF

IM2   *Signatories: Handsigned by Manager and Assistant Manager*
Prefix O/1 dated 1.5.1926 to prefix L/2 dated 1.3.1926 .... Rare

Size 150 mm x 84 mm approximately

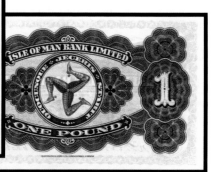

Obverse—blue on a pale green underprint with brown geometric design at the centre. Vignette of Douglas bay and harbour at the top
Reverse—blue on a pale green underprint. Triune and Isle of Man motto at the centre

IM3a   *Signatories: J. R. Quayle (Manager) and J. N. Ronan (Assistant Manager)*
Prefix N/2 dated 1.10.1934 to prefix W/2 dated 5.5.1937 .... Rare

IM3b   *Signatories: J. N. Ronan (Manager) and C. M. Watterson (Assistant Manager), or*
J. N. Ronan (Manager) and Edw. Corteen (per pro Assistant Manager)
Prefix X/2 dated 4.2.1938 to prefix L/3 dated 16.12.1942 .... £120   £220

IM3c   *Signatories: J. N. Ronan (Manager) and W. E. Quirk (Assistant Manager)*
Prefix L/3 dated 16.12.1942 to prefix P/3 dated 7.1.1948 .... £120   £220

IM3d   *Signatories: J. N. Ronan (Manager) and R. H. Kelly (Assistant Manager)*
Prefix P/3 dated 7.1.1948 to prefix B/4 dated 29.11.1954............ £100   £180

IM3e   *Signatories: J. N. Ronan (Manager) and W. E. Quirk (Assistant Manager), or*
J. N. Ronan (Manager) and J. E. Cashin (Assistant Manager)
Prefix B/4 dated 29.11.1954 .... Rare

IM3f   *Signatories: J. E. Cashin (Manager) and W. E. Quirk (Assistant Manager)*
Prefix C/4 dated 5.1.1956 to prefix O/4 dated 24.10.1960 .... £100   £180

FIVE POUND NOTES

Size 176 mm x 92 mm approximately

Obverse—blue on a pale green and pink underprint. Vignette of Douglas bay and harbour at the centre.
Reverse—blue on a pale green underprint. Triune and Isle of Man motto at the centre

		F	VF
IM4	*Signatories: Handsigned by Manager and Assistant Manager*		
	No prefix letters; dated 1.11.1927	£250	£450

Obverse—brown on a pale pink and green underprint. Vignette of Douglas bay and harbour at the centre
Reverse—brown on a pale pink underprint. Triune and Isle of Man motto at the centre

IM5	*Signatories: Handsigned by Manager and Assistant Manager*		
	No prefix letters; dated 1.12.1936 to 7.4.1960................................	£300	£560

WESTMINSTER BANK LIMITED

ONE POUND NOTES

In 1918 the London County & Westminster Bank merged with Parr's Bank Limited to form the London County Westminster & Parr's Bank Limited. A few years later in 1923, the decision was taken to shorten the name to Westminster Bank Limited.

Size 176 mm x 92 mm approximately

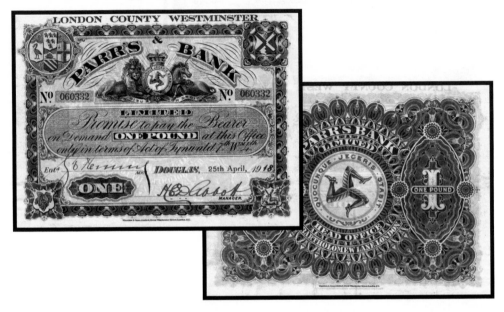

Overprint on banknote stock of Parr's Bank Limited
Obverse—black on a pale blue underprint. Triune flanked by a lion and unicorn at the top.
Overprinted in the top margin; "LONDON COUNTY WESTMINSTER"
Reverse –blue panel with the Isle of Man triune and motto at the centre

IM7 *Signatories: Handsigned by Manager and Accountant*
No prefix letters; dated 28.3.1918 to 22.11.1918............................   Rare

From 1919 to 1921 there were issues of £1 notes with a similar design to the earlier Parr's Bank notes but with the new title of London County Westminster & Parr's Bank Limited. Only 5,000 notes were printed and none are known to have survived. Following the adoption of the new Bank name in 1923, these notes were issued overprinted "WESTMINSTER BANK LIMITED" in the top margin.

Overprint on banknote stock of London County Westminster & Parr's Bank Limited
Obverse—black on a pale blue/grey underprint. Triune flanked by a lion and unicorn at the top
Overprinted in the top margin: "WESTMINSTER BANK LIMITED/FORMERLY"
Reverse—blue panel with the Isle of Man triune and motto at the centre

IM9   Signatories: Handsigned by Manager and Assistant Manager.
No prefix letters; dated 4.7.1923 to 4.4.1927.................................... Rare

Size 176 mm x 92 mm approximate

Obverse—black on a pale yellow underprint. Triune flanked by a lion and unicorn at the top
Reverse —blue panel with the Isle of Man triune and motto at the centre

		F	VF
IM10a	*Signatories: F. Proud (Manager) and A. O. Christian (Assistant Manager)* No prefix letters; dated 9.1.1929 to 14.11.1933...............................		Rare
IM10b	*Signatories: A. O. Christian (Manager) and R. E. Callin (Chief Clerk)* No prefix letters; dated 22.1.1935 to 4.2.1943...............................		from £180
IM10c	*Signatories: R. E. Callin (Manager) and W. G. Flinn (Chief Clerk)* No prefix letters; dated 11.2.1944 to 18.3.1949............................		Rare
IM10d	*Signatories: R. E. Callin (Manager) and G. D. Radcliffe (Chief Clerk)* No prefix letters; dated 7.11.1950 to 23.11.1955	£130	£250
IM10e	*Signatories: P. F. Barlow (Manager) and G. D. Radcliffe (Chief Clerk)* No prefix letters; dated 4.4.1956 to 3.3.1959.................................	*VF* £180	*EF* £330
IM10e	*Signatories: P. F. Barlow (Manager) and T. D. Russell (Chief Clerk)* No prefix letters; dated 8.12.1959 to 10.3.1961.............................	£180	£330

MARTINS BANK LIMITED

ONE POUND NOTES

Martins Bank Limited acquired a foothold in the Isle of Man following a merger with the Lancashire & Yorkshire Bank Limited in 1928. This latter bank had already absorbed the Mercantile Bank of Lancashire Limited which previously had purchased the Manx Bank in 1900. Thus the Lancashire and Yorkshire Bank Limited had been issuing banknotes in the Isle of Man since 1920. The initial banknotes of Martins Bank Limited were overprints on existing stock of Lancashire & Yorkshire Bank.

Size 165 mm x 85 mm approximately

Overprint on notes of The Lancashire & Yorkshire Bank Limited
Obverse—black. Bank's Coat of Arms to the left and the Tower of Refuge to the right. Overprinted at the top: "MARTINS BANK LIMITED" in black, and "WITH WHICH IS INCORPORATED" in red.
Reverse—black. Isle of Man Triune at the centre with vignettes of Castle Rushen and the Laxey Wheel to the left and right

IM12   *Signatories: Handsigned by the Manager and Assistant Manager*
        No prefix letters; dated 9.10.1928 and 3.11.1928...........................   Rare

Size 150 mm x 84 mm approximately

Obverse—*dark grey. Bank's Coat of Arms depicting a grasshopper and Liver bird to the left, and the Tower of Refuge to the right*
Reverse—*black. Isle of Man Triune at the centre with vignettes of Castle Rushen and the Albert Tower to the left and right*

		F	VF
IM13a	*Signatories: R. H. Milner* (Manager) *and E. S. Oldham* (Assistant Manager) No prefix letters, dated 2.4.1929 no notes are known to have survived		
IM13b	*Signatories: A. F. Shawyer* (General Manager) *and E. S. Oldham* (District Manager) No prefix letters, dated 1.12.1931 and 31.12.1932.......................		Rare
IM13c	*Signatory: J. M. Furniss* (General Manager) No prefix letters, dated 1.8.1934 and 1.10.1938............................	£200	£350
IM13d	*Signatory: Jas. McKendrick* (Chief General Manager) No prefix letters, dated 1.3.1946...	£200	£350
IM13e	*Signatory: C. J. Verity* (Chief General Manager) No prefix letters, dated 1.6.1950 and 1.5.1953	£100	£180
IM13f	*Signatory: M. Conacher* (Chief General Manager) No prefix letters, dated 1.2.1957	VF £130	EF £250

LLOYDS BANK LIMITED

Lloyds Bank Limited opened its first branch in the Isle of Man in Douglas in 1896 and acquired a licence to issue banknotes to a limit of £15,000 in about 1918. The first notes were issued in 1919, but the first known to have survived are dated 1921.

ONE POUND NOTES

Size 156 mm x 114 mm approximately

Obverse—black on a green and pale pink underprint. Black horse in panel towards top centre. Vignette of Viking ship at bottom centre
Reverse—blue. Isle of Man Triune and motto at centre

	F	VF
IM15 *Signatories: handsigned by the Manager and Accountant* Prefix A dated 23.4.1919 to prefix B dated 21.1.1927..................		Rare

Size 150 mm x 84 mm approximately

Obverse—black on a pale green and pink underprint. Black horse in panel with vignette of Viking ship at bottom centre
Reverse—blue on a pink sunburst underprint. Isle of Man Triune and motto at centre

		F	VF
IM16a	*Signatories: H. Towler* (Manager) *and R. A. Hodder* (Accountant) Prefix C dated 1.8.1929 to 14.2.1934		Rare
IM16b	*Signatories: H. Towler* (Manager) *and J. Greenwood* (Accountant) Prefix C dated 28.1.1935 to prefix D dated 12.3.1941 ....from £350		—
IM16c	*Signatories: J. Greenwood* (Manager) *and C. R. Collister* (Accountant) Prefix D dated 20.11.1942 to 6.3.1946...		Rare
IM16d	*Signatories: J. Greenwood* (Manager) *and R. C. Sale (Accountant)* Prefix D dated 25.2.1948 and 27.4.1949		Rare
IM16e	*Signatories: J. Greenwood* (Manager) *and C. R. Collister* (Accountant) Prefix D dated 27.2.1951 to 25.2.1957...	£380	—
IM16e	*Signatories: D. Berry* (Manager) *and C. R. Collister (Accountant)* Prefix D dated 28.2.1958 to 14.3.1961...	£280	£420

BARCLAYS BANK LIMITED

Barclays Bank Limited established a presence in the Isle of Man when it opened a branch in Douglas in 1922. The one Pound notes which it issued from 1924 onwards were all of the same size and design.

ONE POUND NOTES

Size 150 mm x 84 mm approximately

Obverse—brown on a yellow and green underprint
Reverse—brown. Vignette of Douglas bay and harbour

		F	VF
IM18a	*Signatories: E. E. Swan* (Manager) *and J. E. Callister* (Accountant) No prefix letters; dated from 7.6.1924 to 7.4.1926		Rare
IM18b	*Signatories: E. E. Swan* (Manager) *and M. Pullman* (Accountant) No prefix letters; dated from 28.8.1926 to 19.4.1929		Rare
IM18c	*Signatories: E. E. Swan* (Manager) *and A. Tranter* (Accountant) No prefix letters; dated from 10.12.1929 to 7.4.1937		Rare
IM18d	*Signatories: T. H. Hall* (Manager) *and A. Tranter* (Accountant) No prefix letters; dated from 17.12.1937 to 20.3.1950		from £450
IM18e	*Signatories: T. H. Hall* (Manager) *and J. A. Butterworth* (Accountant) No prefix letters; dated from 13.11.1950 to 4.12.1953.................	£300	£550
IM18f	*Signatories: T. H. Hall* (Manager) *and J. A. Butterworth* (Chief Clerk) No prefix letters; dated from 10.4.1954 to 25.3.1958	£300	£550
IM18e	*Signatories: J. A. Butterworth* (Manager) *and A. Smith* (Chief Clerk) No prefix letters; dated from 25.3.1958 to 30.3.1960		Rare

ISLE OF MAN GOVERNMENT ISSUES

TEN SHILLING NOTES

Size 140 mm x 67 mm approximately

First issued in 1961.
Obverse—mainly red. Portrait of Queen Elizabeth II to the right; Triune and motto at the centre
Reverse—red. Picture of a Viking ship under sail

		EF	UNC
IM21a	*Signatory: R. H. Garvey* (Lieutenant Governor)		
	No prefix letter (000001 to 1000000) and		
	Prefix A (000001 to 250000)	£35	£60
IM21b	*Signatory: P. G. H. Stallard* (Lieutenant Governor)		
	Prefix A (250001 to 517000)	£35	£60

FIFTY PENCE NOTES

Size 140 mm x 67 mm approximately

First issued in 1969
Obverse—mainly blue. Portrait of Queen Elizabeth II to the right; Triune and motto at the centre
Reverse—blue. Picture of a Viking ship under sail

IM22	*Signatory: P. G. H. Stallard* (Lieutenant Governor)		
	No prefix letter (000001 to 679000)	£25	£40

Size 127 mm x 61 mm approximately

First issued in 1972
Obverse—mainly blue. Portrait of Queen Elizabeth II to the right; Triune and motto at the centre
Reverse—blue. Picture of a Viking ship under sail

		EF	UNC
IM23a	*Signatory: P. G. H. Stallard* (Lieutenant Governor)		
	Prefix A (200001 to 800000)	£28	£45
IM23b	*Signatory: John Paul* (Lieutenant Governor)—*large signature*		
	Prefix A (800001 to 1000000) and		
	Prefix B (000001 to 370000)..	£18	£30
IM23c	*Signatory: John Paul* (Lieutenant Governor)—*small signature*		
	Prefix B (370001 to 1000000) and		
	Prefix C (000001 to 200000)	£14	£25

First issued in 1979. Similar to previous issue but for change of title of signatory
Obverse—mainly blue. Portrait of Queen Elizabeth II to the right; Triune and motto at the centre
Reverse—blue. Picture of a Viking ship under sail

IM24	*Signatory: W. Dawson* (Treasurer of the Isle of Man)		
	Prefix C (200001 to 750000)	£8	£15

ONE POUND NOTES

Size 151 mm x 72 mm approximately

First issued in 1961
Obverse—mainly violet. Portrait of Queen Elizabeth II to the right; Triune and motto at the centre
Reverse—violet. View of Tynwald Hill and St John's church

		EF	UNC
IM31a	*Signatory: R. H. Garvey (Lieutenant Governor)* No prefix letter (000001 to 1000000), Prefix A and prefix B (000001 to 200000).......................................	£50	£80
IM31b	*Signatory: P. G. H. Stallard (Lieutenant Governor)* Prefix B (200001 to 1000000) and prefix C (000001 to 745000)....	£50	£80

Size 135 mm x 67 mm approximately

First issued in 1972
Obverse—mainly violet. Portrait of Queen Elizabeth II to the right; Triune and motto at the centre
Reverse—violet. View of Tynwald Hill and St John's church

IM32a	*Signatory: P. G. H. Stallard (Lieutenant Governor)* Prefix C (850001 to 1000000) and Prefix D (000001 to 970000)	£60	£100
IM32b	*Signatory: John Paul (Lieutenant Governor)—large signature* Prefix D (970001 to 1000000) .... Prefix E	£25	Rare £45
IM32c	*Signatory: John Paul (Lieutenant Governor)—small signature* Prefix F, G and H (000001 to 440000)...	£20	£35

First issued in 1979. Similar to previous issue but for change of title of signatory
Obverse—mainly violet. Portrait of Queen Elizabeth II to the right; Triune and motto at the centre
Reverse—violet. View of Tynwald Hill and St John's church

		EF	UNC
IM33a	*Signatory: W. Dawson (Treasurer of the Isle of Man)* Prefix H (440001 to 1000000) to prefix K..................................... (issued before the Tyvek notes—ref. IM34)	£10	£16
IM33b	*Signatory: W. Dawson (Treasurer of the Isle of Man)* Prefix P (500001 to 1000000) to prefix R (000001 to 500000)....... (issued circa 1988 after the Tyvek notes—ref. IM34)	£10	£16

First issued in 1983.
Obverse—green on a light multicoloured underprint. Portrait of Queen Elizabeth II to the right;
Triune and motto at the centre
Reverse—green. View of Tynwald Hill and St John's church

IM34	*Signatory: W. Dawson (Treasurer of the Isle of Man)* Prefix M, N and P (000001 to 500000)..	£22	£40

Size 128 mm x 65 mm approximately

First issued in 1990
Obverse—mainly violet. Portrait of Queen Elizabeth II to the right; Triune and motto at the centre
Reverse—violet. View of Tynwald Hill and St John's church

		EF	UNC
IM35a	*Signatory: W. Dawson* (Chief Financial Officer)		
	Prefix R (500001 to 1000000), S and T	£10	£18
	Prefix Z—replacement note...	£120	£200
IM35b	*Signatory: J. A. Cashen* (Chief Financial Officer)		
	Prefix U to prefix Y	£2	£5
	Prefix Z—replacement note...	£15	£25
IM35c	*Signatory: P. M Shimmin* (Chief Financial Officer)		
	Prefix AA...	—	£3

FIVE POUND NOTES

Size 139 mm x 84 mm approximately

First issued in 1961
Obverse—blue and green on a multicoloured underprint. Portrait of Queen Elizabeth II to the right;
Triune and motto at the centre
Reverse—dark grey. View of Castle Rushen, 1775

		VF	EF
IM41a	*Signatory: R. H. Garvey* (Lieutenant Governor)		
	No prefix letter (000001 to 250000), ...	£220	£450
IM41b	*Signatory: P. G. H. Stallard* (Lieutenant Governor)		
	No prefix letter (250001 to 500000)	£220	£450

Size 147 mm x 78 mm approximately

First issued in 1972
Obverse—blue and maroon on a multicoloured underprint. Portrait of Queen Elizabeth II to the right;
Triune and motto at the centre
Reverse—dark grey. View of Castle Rushen, 1775

		EF	UNC
IM42a	*Signatory: P. G. H. Stallard* (Lieutenant Governor)		
	No prefix letter (500001 to 950000)	£200	£300
IM42b	*Signatory: John Paul* (Lieutenant Governor)		
	No prefix letter (950001 to 1000000)	£250	—
	Prefix A and B (000001 to 600000)	£100	£170

First issued in 1979. Similar to previous issue but for change of title of signatory
Obverse—blue and maroon on a multicoloured underprint. Portrait of Queen Elizabeth II to the right;
Triune and motto at the centre
Reverse—dark grey. View of Castle Rushen, 1775

IM43a	*Signatory: W. Dawson* (Treasurer of the Isle of Man)		
	Prefix B (600001 to 1000000), C and D (000001 to 100000 approx.)	£60	£110
	Prefix letters are in Serif script		
IM43b	*Signatory: W. Dawson* (Treasurer of the Isle of Man)		
	Prefix D (100000 approximately to 1000000)	£75	£130
	Prefix letters are in Sans Serif script		

Size 135 mm x 69 mm approximately.

First issued in 1991
Obverse—blue and maroon on a multicoloured underprint. Portrait of Queen Elizabeth II to the right; Triune and motto at the centre
Reverse—dark grey on a multicoloured underprint. View of Castle Rushen, 1775

		EF	UNC
IM44a	*Signatory: W. Dawson* (Chief Financial Officer)		
	Prefix E and	£35	£60
	Prefix F (000001 to 100000)	£100	Rare
	Prefix Z—replacement note		Rare
IM44b	*Signatory: J. A. Cashen* (Chief Financial Officer)		
	Prefix F (100001 to prefix K and ongoing)	—	£15
	Prefix Z—replacement note	£20	£35

TEN POUND NOTES

Size 151 mm x 85 mm approximately

First issued in 1972
Obverse—brown and green on a multicoloured underprint. Portrait of Queen Elizabeth II to the right; Triune and motto at the centre
Reverse—shades of brown. View of Peel Castle, circa 1830

IM51a	*Signatory: P. G. H. Stallard* (Lieutenant Governor)		
	No prefix letter (000001 to 050000)		Rare
IM51b	*Signatory: John Paul* (Lieutenant Governor)		
	No prefix letter (050001 to 360000)	£180	£300

Size 150 mm x 85 mm approximately

First issued in 1979. Similar to previous issue but for change of title of signatory.
Obverse—brown and green on a multicoloured underprint. Portrait of Queen Elizabeth II to the right;
Triune and motto at the centre
Reverse—shades of brown. View of Peel Castle, circa 1830

		EF	UNC
IM52	*Signatory: W. Dawson* (Treasurer of the Isle of Man)		
	No prefix letter (360001 to 1000000) and prefix A......................	£140	£250
	Prefix B (00001 to 010000)	—	Rare

Size 142 mm x 75 mm approximately

First issued in 1991
Obverse—brown and green on a multicoloured underprint. Portrait of Queen Elizabeth II to the right;
Triune and motto at the centre. The clause under the title at the top of the note reads: "promise to pay
the bearer on demand at any office of Isle of Man Bank Limited"
Reverse—shades of brown. View of Peel Castle, circa 1830

IM53	*Signatory: J. A. Cashen* (Chief Financial Officer)		
	Prefix C to prefix G (500000)...	£25	£45
	Prefix Z—replacement note...	£75	£120

First issued in 2002
Obverse—brown and green on a multicoloured underprint. Portrait of Queen Elizabeth II to the right; Triune and motto at the centre. The clause under the title at the top of the note reads: "promise to pay the bearer on demand at any office of Isle of Man Bank"
Reverse—shades of brown. View of Peel Castle, circa 1830

		EF	UNC
IM54a	*Signatory: J. A. Cashen* (Chief Financial Officer)		
	Prefix G 50001 to prefix M..	—	£30
	Prefix Z—replacement note..	£35	£55
IM54b	*Signatory: P. M. Shimmin* (Chief Financial Officer)		
	Prefix N and ongoing...	—	£20
	Prefix Z—replacement note..	£25	£45

TWENTY POUND NOTES

Size 160 mm x 90 mm approximately

First issued 1979. Commemorating the millennium year of the Isle of Man
Obverse—red and brown on a multicoloured underprint. Portrait of Queen Elizabeth II to the right; Triune and motto at the centre. Clause below Queen's portrait reads: "ISSUED DURING MILLENNIUM YEAR 1979"
Reverse—red, yellow and multicoloured. View of the Laxey Wheel, 1854

IM61	*Signatory: W. Dawson* (Treasurer of the Isle of Man)		
	No prefix letter (000001 to 005000).	£220	£350

First issued 1979. Similar to above but without commemorative clause
Obverse—red and brown on a multicoloured underprint. Portrait of Queen Elizabeth II to the right; Triune and motto at the centre
Reverse—red, yellow and multicoloured. View of the Laxey Wheel, 1854

		EF	UNC
IM62	*Signatory: W. Dawson* (Treasurer of the Isle of Man)		
	No prefix letter (005001 to 150000)...	£220	£350

Size 150 mm x 80 mm approximately

First issued 1991
Obverse—red and brown on a multicoloured underprint. Portrait of Queen Elizabeth II to the right; Triune and motto at the centre. The clause under the title at the top of the note reads: "promise to pay the bearer on demand at any office of Isle of Man Bank Limited"
Reverse—lilac and orange brown. View of the Laxey Wheel, 1854

IM63a	*Signatory: W. Dawson* (Chief Financial Officer)		
	No prefix letter (150001 to 450000)...	£150	£250
IM63b	*Signatory: J. A. Cashen* (Chief Financial Officer)		
	No prefix letter (450001 to 1000000) and prefix B to prefix D	£45	£70
	Prefix Z—replacement note	£80	£120

First issued 2002
Obverse—red and brown on a multicoloured underprint. Portrait of Queen Elizabeth II to the right; Triune and motto at the centre. The clause under the title at the top of the note reads: "promise to pay the bearer on demand at any office of Isle of Man Bank"
Reverse—lilac and orange brown. View of the Laxey Wheel, 1854

		EF	UNC
IM64a	*Signatory: J. A. Cashen* (Chief Financial Officer)		
	Prefix E to G (ongoing)	—	£40
	Prefix Z—replacement note	£50	£80
IM64b	*Signatory: P. M Shimmin* (Chief Financial Officer)		
	Prefix G (ongoing)	—	£38

FIFTY POUND NOTES

Size 170 mm x 95 mm approximately

First issued 1983
Obverse—blue and green on a multicoloured underprint. Portrait of Queen Elizabeth II to the right; Triune and motto at the centre
Reverse—blue green and multicoloured. View of Douglas Bay 1841

IM71	*Signatory: W. Dawson* (Treasurer of the Isle of Man)		
	No prefix letter (000001 to 250000)	—	£110

Krause Standard Catalogs ®

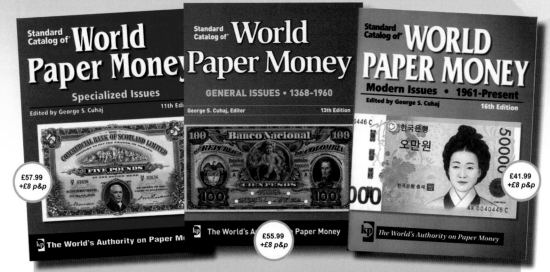
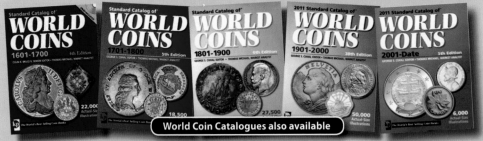

GUERNSEY

SOME EXAMPLES OF BANKNOTES IN CIRCULATION IN GUERNSEY PRIOR TO WWII

Guernsey banknotes issued before the outbreak of WWII are all scarce; quantities issued were small and relatively few have survived. Many note types are true rarities with just a handful being known in private collections. For this reason no attempt has been made to fully catalogue, or ascribe values to these issues, but a number of notes are illustrated below.

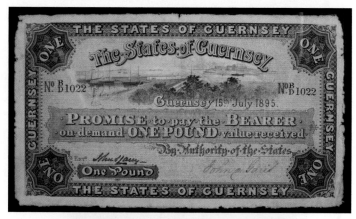

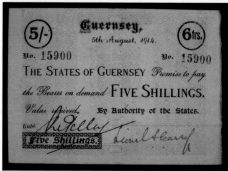

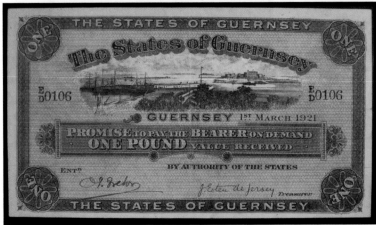

Size 140 mm x 85 mm approximately

Obverse—pale blue with 10/- in red/orange at the centre
Reverse—red panel with the Guernsey seal at the centre

	F	VF

GU21 **Ten Shillings**—*Signatory: H. E. Marquand* (Treasurer)
Prefix B/R (circa 1932) to prefix G/H dated 9.3.1940 .... from £450   £950

Size 150 mm x 87 mm approximately

Obverse—black with £1 in a red panel at the centre
Reverse—blue panel with the Guernsey seal at the centre

GU22 **One Pound**—*Signatory: H. E. Marquand* (Treasurer)
Prefix K/G (circa 1933) to prefix S/L dated 9.3.1940 .... from £600   £1,200

GUERNSEY WORLD WAR II ISSUES

Following the occupation of the Channel Island by Germany during WWII there was an acute shortage of coinage in the Island and permission was given by the Germans for the printing and distribution of small denomination banknotes, subject to the withdrawal from circulation of an equivalent amount of Guernsey and Bank of England notes. These Bank of England notes were overstamped "Withdrawn from Circulation September 18th, 1941." and "Withdrawn from Circulation November 10th, 1941." Some 5,000 Bank of England £1 notes and a similar amount of Guernsey 10 shilling and £1 notes (there is some doubt about the exact figure) were withdrawn to balance the introduction of notes of 6 pence, 1 shilling, 1 shilling and 3 pence, 2 shillings and 6 pence, and 5 shillings.

During the occupation, notes of 10 shillings, 1 pound and 5 pounds (references GU29 to GU31 below) were also printed covertly on the island and issued immediately following the liberation on Wednesday, May 9, 1945. They were used to redeem the small denomination occupation notes and were quickly superceded by the post War issue dated 1.8.1945.

_Bank of England notes (above) were withdrawn from circulation in Guernsey prior to the issue of the small denomination notes below. For full information and values on these notes, see catalogue references BE48 to BE50 in the Bank of England section.

Size 90 mm x 60 mm approximately

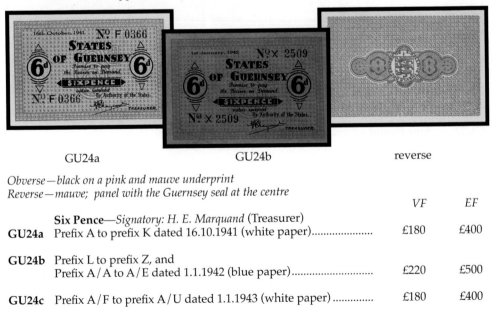

GU24a	GU24b	reverse

Obverse—black on a pink and mauve underprint
Reverse—mauve; panel with the Guernsey seal at the centre

	VF	EF
Six Pence—*Signatory: H. E. Marquand* (Treasurer)		
GU24a Prefix A to prefix K dated 16.10.1941 (white paper)......................	£180	£400
GU24b Prefix L to prefix Z, and Prefix A/A to A/E dated 1.1.1942 (blue paper)............................	£220	£500
GU24c Prefix A/F to prefix A/U dated 1.1.1943 (white paper)	£180	£400

Size 90 mm x 60 mm approximately

Obverse—1 Shilling overprint in red/brown on a note for 1 Shilling and 3 Pence
Printed on white or blue paper; black on a yellow and brown underprint
Reverse—brown; panel with the Guernsey seal at the centre

		VF	EF
One Shilling—*Signatory: H. E. Marquand* (Treasurer)			
GU25a	Prefix G to prefix M dated 18.7.1942 (blue paper)......................	£550	£850
GU25b	Prefix N to prefix Z dated 1.1.1943 (white paper)	£220	£400

Size 90 mm x 60 mm approximately

GU26a   GU26b   reverse

Obverse—Printed on white or blue paper; black on a yellow and brown underprint
Reverse—brown; panel with the Guernsey seal at the centre

		VF	EF
One Shilling and Three Pence—*Signatory: H. E. Marquand* (Treasurer)			
GU26a	Prefix A to prefix F dated 16.10.1941 (white paper)..................	£250	£450
GU26b	Prefix G dated 18.7.1942 (blue paper – only 500 notes printed)		Rare

Size 90 mm x 60 mm approximately

GU27a   GU27c   reverse

Obverse—Printed on white or blue paper; blue, with "2/6" in brown at the centre
Reverse—blue; panel with the Guernsey seal at the centre

		VF	EF
Two Shillings and Six Pence—*Signatory: H. E. Marquand* (Treasurer)			
GU27a	Prefix A / A to prefix A / E dated 25.3.1941 (white paper)	£250	£450
GU27b	Prefix A / F to prefix A / K dated 17.5.1941 (white paper)	£250	£450
GU27c	Prefix A / L to prefix B / A dated 1.1.1942 (blue paper)	£250	£450
GU27d	Prefix B / B to prefix B / J dated 1.1.1943 (white paper)................	£250	£450

Size 100 mm x 65 mm approximately

Obverse—Black with "5/-" in red at the centre
Reverse—red; panel with the Guernsey seal at the centre

		VF	EF
Five Shillings—*Signatory: H. E. Marquand* (Treasurer)			
GU28a	Prefix A/F to prefix A/H dated 25.3.1941	£320	£550
GU28b	Prefix A/H to prefix A/K dated 1.1.1942......................................	£320	£550
GU28c	Prefix A/L to prefix A/T dated 1.1.1943	£320	£550

Notes issued immediately following the liberation of Guernsey on May 9, 1945

Size 135 mm x 80 mm approximately

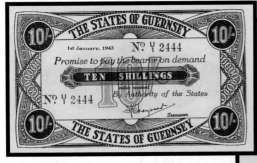 

Obverse—Blue with "10/-" in red at the centre
Reverse—red; panel with the Guernsey seal at the centre

Ten Shillings—*Signatory: H. E. Marquand* (Treasurer)			
GU29	Prefix A/1 to prefix W/1 dated 1.1.1943	£650	£1200

Size 150 mm x 87 mm approximately

Obverse—Printed on white or blue paper; black, with "£1" in red at the centre
Reverse—blue; panel with the Guernsey seal at the centre

		VF	EF
	One Pound—*Signatory: H. E. Marquand* (Treasurer)		
GU30a	Prefix A/1 to prefix Z/1, and Prefix A/2 to prefix N/2 dated 1.1.1943 (white paper)	£800	£1350
GU30b	Prefix O/2 to prefix S/2 dated 1.1.1945 (blue paper)		Rare

Size 165 mm x 95 mm approximately

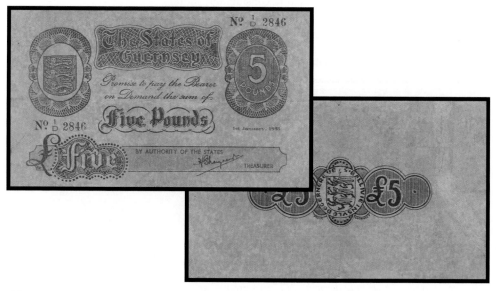

Obverse—Printed on blue paper; green with red date and serial numbers
Reverse—green; panel with the Guernsey seal at the centre

Five Pounds—*Signatory: H. E. Marquand* (Treasurer)

GU31	Prefix 1/A to prefix 1/H dated 1.1.1945	Rare
	(only 53 notes are outstanding)	

GUERNSEY POST WAR ISSUES

TEN SHILLING NOTES

Size 140 mm x 87 mm approximately

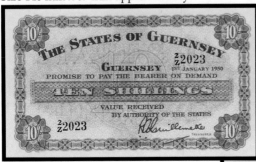

Obverse—Lilac on a light green underprint.
Reverse—purple; panel with the Guernsey seal at the centre

		VF	EF
GU32a	*Signatory: H. E. Marquand* (Treasurer)		
	Prefix 1/A to prefix 2/Z dated 1.8.1945.	£200	£350
GU32b	*Signatory: L. A. Guillemette* (Treasurer)		
	Prefix 2/Z dated 1.1.1950 to prefix 24/G dated 1.7.1966	from £40	£65
	(Some dates are scarce and worth considerably more)		

ONE POUND NOTES

Size 155 mm x 87 mm approximately

Obverse—purple on a green underprint. "£1" in a green panel at centre.
Reverse—green; panel with the Guernsey seal at the centre

GU33a	*Signatory: H. E. Marquand* (Treasurer)		
	Prefix 1/A dated 1.8.1945 to prefix 5/X dated 1.4.1948	£200	£400
GU33b	*Signatory: L. A. Guillemette* (Treasurer)		
	Prefix 5/Y dated 1.1.1950 to prefix 49/W dated 1.7.1966	from £75	£180
	(Some dates are scarce and worth considerably more)		

Size 135 mm x 75 mm approximately

First issued 1969
Obverse—olive on a pink and yellow underprint. Guernsey seal at the centre
Reverse—olive; illustration of Castle Cornet

		EF	UNC
GU34a	*Signatory: L. A. Guillemette (Treasurer)*		
	Prefix A and B to prefix C 100000	£40	£65
	Prefix C (to C 100000 only)	£70	£120
GU34b	*Signatory: C. H. Hodder (Treasurer)*		
	Prefix C 100001 to prefix G 630000	£18	£30
GU34c	*Signatory: W. C. Bull (Treasurer)*		
	Prefix G 630001 to prefix H 860000	£22	£35

Size 135 mm x 67 mm approximately

First issued 1980
Obverse—green on a multicoloured underprint. Guernsey seal at bottom left; picture of the old market square circa 1830 in underprint at the centre
Reverse—green; portrait of Daniel de Lisle Brock to the right with illustration of Royal Court, St. Peter Port 1840, in the background

GU35a	*Signatory: W. C. Bull (States Treasurer)*		
	Prefix A to prefix G	£6	£10
	Prefix Z—replacement note.	£20	£30
GU35b	*Signatory: M. J. Brown (States Treasurer)*		
	Prefix H only	£9	£15
	Prefix Z—replacement note.		Rare

Size 129 mm x 65 mm approximately

Similar to previous issue, but reduced size. First issued 1991
Obverse—green on a multicoloured underprint. Guernsey seal at bottom left; picture of the old market square circa 1830 in underprint at the centre.
Reverse—green; portrait of Daniel de Lisle Brock to the right with illustration of Royal Court, St. Peter Port 1840, in the background.

		EF	UNC
GU36a	*Signatory: M. J. Brown (States Treasurer)*		
	Prefix J to prefix L	£5	£8
	Prefix Z—replacement note.	£10	£20
GU36b	*Signatory: D. P. Trestain (States Treasurer)*		
	Prefix M to prefix S..	£2	£5
	Prefix Z—replacement note.	£6	£10
GU36c	*Signatory: D. M. Clark (States Treasurer)*		
	Prefix T and W (ongoing)..	—	£3
	Prefix Z—replacement note.	£6	£10

FIVE POUND NOTES

Size 155 mm x 90 mm approximately

Obverse—green on a multicoloured underprint
Reverse—light green; Guernsey seal at the centre

		F	VF
GU41	*Signatory: L. A. Guillemette (Treasurer)*		
	Prefix 1/J dated 1.12.1956 to prefix 4/C dated 1.7.1966	£350	£550

Size 145 mm x 85 mm approximately

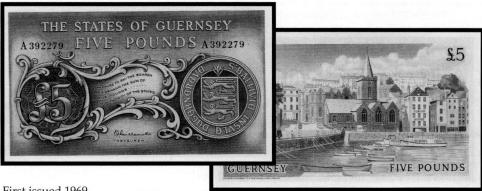

First issued 1969
Obverse—purple on a light brown underprint. Guernsey seal to the lower right
Reverse—mainly purple; town sea front and harbour scene

		EF	UNC
GU42a	*Signatory: L. A. Guillemette (Treasurer)*		
	Prefix A (to 400000)	£100	£170
GU42b	*Signatory: C. H. Hodder (Treasurer)*		
	Prefix A and prefix B (to 850000).......................................	£65	£110
GU42c	*Signatory: W. C. Bull (Treasurer)*		
	Prefix B (from B850001) and C	£65	£110

Size 145 mm x 78 mm approximately

First issued 1980
Obverse—brown and multicoloured. Guernsey seal at bottom left; Fort Grey in underprint at the centre
Reverse—mainly brown; portrait of Thomas de la Rue with illustrations of Fountain Street, St. Peter Port 1977, and an envelope making machine, 1851

GU43	*Signatory: W. C. Bull (States Treasurer)*		
	Prefix A to prefix F...	£20	£30
	Prefix Z—replacement note.	£45	£70

Size 135 mm x 70 mm approximately

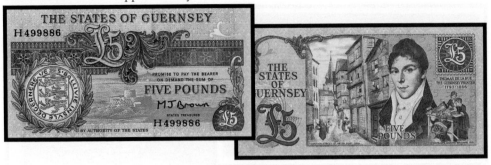

Similar to earlier issue but reduced size. First issued 1991
Obverse—brown and multicoloured. Guernsey seal at bottom left; Fort Grey in underprint at the centre
Reverse—mainly brown; portrait of Thomas de la Rue with illustrations of Fountain Street, St. Peter Port 1977, and an envelope making machine, 1851

		EF	UNC
GU44a	*Signatory: M. J. Brown (States Treasurer)*		
	Prefix G and prefix H (to 500000)	£18	£30
	Prefix Z—replacement note.	£35	£55
GU44b	*Signatory: D. P. Trestain (States Treasurer)*		
	Prefix H 500001 and prefix J..	£14	£25
	Prefix Z—replacement note.	£25	£45

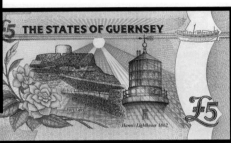

First issued 1996.
Obverse—brown and multicoloured. Portrait of Queen Elizabeth II to the right; Guernsey seal at bottom centre.
Reverse—multicoloured, illustrations of Fort Grey and Hanois Lighthouse, 1862

GU45a	*Signatory: D. P. Trestain (States Treasurer)*		
	Prefix A and prefix B	—	£20
	Prefix Z—replacement note.	£20	£35
GU45b	*Signatory: D. M. Clark (States Treasurer)*		
	Prefix C to serial number C600000 with micro-printed security thread —		£16
	Prefix Z—replacement note.	—	£35
	Change to windowed security thread		
GU45c	*Signatory: D. M. Clark (States Treasurer)*		
	Prefix C from serial number C600001	—	£10
	Prefix Z—replacement note.	—	£35

Similar to previous issue. Issued in 2000 to commemorate the Millennium
Obverse—multicoloured. Portrait of Queen Elizabeth II to the right; Guernsey seal at bottom centre
Commemorative overprint to the left
Reverse—multicoloured, illustrations of Fort Grey and Hanois Lighthouse, 1862

		EF	UNC
GU46	Signatory: D. P. Trestain (States Treasurer)		
	Prefix M only.	£10	£18

TEN POUND NOTES

Size 150 mm x 90 mm approximately

First issued 1975
Obverse—blue and multicoloured; Britannia at left centre holding a spear and the Guernsey seal
Reverse—blue; an illustration of the Battle of Queenston Heights 1812, with a portrait of Major General Sir Isaac Brock KB, to the right

GU51	Signatory: C. H. Hodder (States Treasurer)		
	Prefix A (to 571400)	£220	£330

Size 150 mm x 85 mm approximately

First issued 1980.
Obverse — blue on a multicoloured underprint. Guernsey seal at bottom left; Castle Cornet in underprint at the centre
Reverse — blue; an illustration of the Battle of Queenston Heights 1812, with a portrait of Major General Sir Isaac Brock KB, to the right

		EF	UNC
GU52a	*Signatory: W. C. Bull* (States Treasurer)		
	Prefix A and prefix B	£40	£60
	Prefix Z—replacement note.	£65	£100
GU52b	*Signatory: M. J. Brown* (States Treasurer)		
	Prefix C and prefix D...	£35	£55
	Prefix Z— replacement note.	£65	£100

Size 143 mm x 75 mm approximately

Similar to above but smaller size. First issued 1990
Obverse — blue on a multicoloured underprint. Guernsey seal at bottom left; Castle Cornet in underprint at the centre.
Reverse — blue; an illustration of the Battle of Queenston Heights 1812, with a portrait of Major General Sir Isaac Brock KB, to the right

GU53	*Signatory: M. J. Brown* (States Treasurer)		
	Prefix E and prefix F.	£28	£45
	Prefix Z—replacement note.	£45	£80

First issued 1995

Obverse—blue and multicoloured. Portrait of Queen Elizabeth II to the right; Picture of Elizabeth College to the left of Guernsey seal, lower centre
Reverse—blue and multicoloured; illustrations of Saumarez Park, Le Trepied Dolman and Les Niaux Waterwheel

		EF	UNC
GU54a	*Signatory: D. P. Trestain* (States Treasurer)		
	Prefix A to prefix C....................................	£18	£30
	Prefix Z—replacement note.............................	£25	£45
GU54b	*Signatory: D. M. Clark* (States Treasurer)		
	Prefix D to serial number D91000 with micro printed security thread	£18	£30
	Prefix Z—replacement note.............................	£22	£40
	Change to windowed security thread		
GU54c	*Signatory: D. M. Clark* (States Treasurer)		
	Prefix D from serial number D 910001 and Prefix E (ongoing) .	—	£18
	Prefix Z—replacement note	£22	£35

TWENTY POUND NOTES

Size 160 mm x 90 mm approximately

First issued 1980
Obverse—red on a multicoloured underprint. Guernsey seal at bottom left; Saumarez Park, 1815 in underprint at the centre
Reverse—red on a multicoloured underprint; an illustration of British ships in Gibraltar Bay 1801 with a portrait of Admiral Lord de Saumarez to the right

		EF	UNC
GU61a	*Signatory: W. C. Bull* (States Treasurer)		
	Prefix A (to 500000)	£80	£130
	Prefix Z—replacement note...	£150	—

GU61b *Signatory: M. J. Brown* (States Treasurer)
Prefix A (500001–813000).. £75 £120
Prefix Z—replacement note. .... £150 —

Size 150 mm x 80 mm approximately

Similar to above but smaller size. First issued 1990
Obverse—red on a multicoloured underprint. Guernsey seal at bottom left; Saumarez Park, 1815 in underprint at the centre
Reverse—red on a multicoloured underprint; an illustration of British ships in Gibraltar Bay 1801 with a portrait of Admiral Lord de Saumarez to the right

	EF	*UNC*
GU62a *Signatory: M. J. Brown* (States Treasurer)		
Prefix B (to 500000)..	£60	£110
Prefix Z— replacement note.	£80	£150
GU62b *Signatory: D. P. Trestain* (States Treasurer)		
Prefix B (500001 upwards).	£55	£90
Prefix Z—replacement note.	£75	£120

First issued 1995
Obverse—red and multicoloured. Portrait of Queen Elizabeth II to the right; Picture of St. James Concert Hall to the left of Guernsey seal, lower centre
Reverse—red and multicoloured; illustrations of St. Sampson's Church with Sailing dinghies in the foreground and Vale Castle in the background

	EF	*UNC*
GU63a *Signatory: D. P. Trestain* (States Treasurer)		
Prefix A and prefix B..	£30	£50
Prefix Z—replacement note.	£45	£70
GU63b *Signatory: D. M. Clark* (States Treasurer)		
Prefix C (ends at C900000)	—	£45
Prefix Z— replacement note.	£45	£70

First issued 2009

Obverse —red and multicoloured. Portrait of Queen Elizabeth II to the right; Picture of St. James Concert Hall to the left of Guernsey seal, lower centre. Silver foil flower head to the left of the Queen's portrait.

Reverse—red and multicoloured; illustrations of St. Sampson's Church with Sailing dinghies in the foreground and Vale Castle in the background.

		EF	UNC
GU64	*Signatory: Bethan Haines* (Chief Accountant)		
	Prefix C (starts at C900001)...	—	£38
	Prefix Z—replacement note...	£35	£50

FIFTY POUND NOTES

Size 155 mm x 85 mm approximately

First issued 1994

Obverse—brown and multicoloured. Portrait of Queen Elizabeth II to the right; Picture of The Royal Court House to the left of Guernsey seal, lower centre

Reverse—multicoloured; illustrations of St. Andrew's Church, La Gran'mere, the Letter of Marque and the Pointe de la Moye

GU71a	*Signatory: D. P. Trestain* (States Treasurer)		
	Prefix A	—	£120
	Prefix Z—replacement note	probably exists	

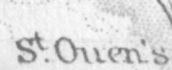

JERSEY

Prior to the Jersey States banknote issues of 1963, Bank of England notes were used in Jersey. During the German occupation of the Channel Islands during WWII, permission was given for the printing and circulation of banknotes from six Pence to one Pound (reference JE1 to JE6 below). This was to alleviate a shortage of cash, particularly coinage, in the island.

JERSEY WORLD WAR II ISSUES

Size 110 mm x 70 mm approximately

Obverse—black on a red/brown underprint which has "six pence" in large script. Jersey Shield to the left
Reverse—red/brown with "six pence" in large script, exactly as the underprint on the obverse

		VF	EF
JE1	**Six Pence**—*Signatory: H. F. Ereaut* (Treasurer of the States of Jersey)		
	Prefix JN only, issued from April 1942 to February 1945...............	£45	£75

Size 110 mm x 70 mm approximately

Obverse—brown on a blue underprint of a silhouette of two old people chatting. Jersey Shield to the left
Reverse—brown; silhouette of two old people chatting—same as obverse underprint

JE2	**One Shilling**—*Signatory: H. F. Ereaut* (Treasurer of the States of Jersey)		
	Prefix JN only, issued in April 1942 and June 1942.........................	£55	£85

Size 108 mm x 70 mm approximately.

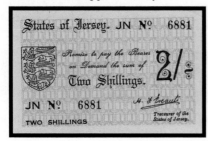 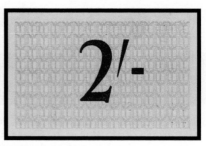

Obverse—blue on a salmon pink underprint; Jersey Shield to the left
Reverse—large "2/-" in blue on a salmon pink underprint

	VF	EF
JE3 **Two Shillings**—*Signatory: H. F. Ereaut* (Treasurer of the States of Jersey) Prefix JN only, issued in June 1941	£95	£200

Size 108 mm x 70 mm approximately

Obverse—blue on a light brown and blue underprint depicting a cart and two horses in silhouette. Jersey Shield to the left
Reverse—blue; silhouette of a cart and horses, same as obverse underprint

JE4 **Two Shillings**—*Signatory: H. F. Ereaut* (Treasurer of the States of Jersey) Prefix JN only, issued in April 1942	£65	£110

Size 130 mm x 85 mm approximately

Obverse—green on a pale green and brown underprint. Jersey Shield to the left
Reverse—green; picture of a milkmaid with three cows

JE5 **Ten Shillings**—*Signatory: H. F. Ereaut* (Treasurer of the States of Jersey) Prefix JN only, issued in April 1942 and June 1942	£180	£350

Size 130 mm x 85 mm approximately

Obverse—mauve on a pale mauve and green underprint. Jersey Shield to the left
Obverse—picture of a cart and horses on the sea shore

		VF	EF
JE6	**One Pound**—*Signatory: H. F. Ereaut* (Treasurer of the States of Jersey) Prefix JN only, issued in April 1942 and June 1942..........................	£220	£400

JERSEY STATES ISSUES FROM 1963

TEN SHILLING NOTES

Size 140 mm x 70 mm approximately

First issued 1963
Obverse—brown on a multicoloured underprint. Portrait of Queen Elizabeth II to the right
Reverse—brown on a pale blue underprint. Illustration of St. Ouen's Manor

		EF	UNC
JE10	*Signatory: F. N. Padgham* (Treasurer of the States) Prefix A, B and C first issued 1963	£22	£35

ONE POUND NOTES

Size 154 mm x 77 mm approximately

First issued 1963
Obverse—green on a multicoloured underprint. Portrait of Queen Elizabeth II to the right
Reverse—green. Illustration of Mont Orgueil Castle

		EF	UNC
JE11a *Signatory: F. N. Padgham (Treasurer of the States)*			
Prefix A to prefix E, first issued 1963		£45	£65
JE11b *Signatory: J. Clennett (Treasurer of the States)*			
Prefix F to prefix K, first issued 1972		£40	£60
Prefix Z—replacement note			Rare

Size 135 mm x 67 mm approximately

First issued 1976
Obverse—blue on a pink and blue underprint. Portrait of Queen Elizabeth II to the right
Reverse—mainly blue. Picture of the death of Major Peirson at the Battle of Jersey

		EF	UNC
JE12a *Signatory: J. Clennett (Treasurer of the States)*			
Prefix AB to prefix LB, first issued 1976		£7	£12
Prefix ZB—replacement note.		£17	£25
JE12b *Signatory: L. May (Treasurer of the States)*			
Prefix MB to prefix TB, first issued 1985		£6	£10
Prefix ZB—replacement note.		£15	£22

Size 128 mm x 66 mm approximately

First issued 1989
Obverse — green on a multicoloured underprint. Portrait of Queen Elizabeth II to the right
"£1" at top right in outline print
Reverse — mainly green. Illustration of St. Helier Parish Church

	EF	UNC
JE13 *Signatory: L. May* (Treasurer of the States)		
Prefix AC to prefix GC, first issued 1989..	£5	£9
Prefix CZ—replacement note..	£18	£30

First issued 1993.
Obverse — green on a multicoloured underprint. Portrait of Queen Elizabeth II to the right. "£1" at
top right in solid print
Reverse — mainly green. Illustration of St. Helier Parish Church

JE14a *Signatory: G. Baird* (Treasurer of the States)		
Prefix GC to prefix RC, first issued 1993	£2	£5
Prefix CZ—replacement note..	£10	£20
JE14b *Signatory: I. Black* (Treasurer of the States)		
Prefix SC to prefix AEC..	—	£3
Prefix CZ—replacement note..	£8	£15

Issued to commemorate the 50th Anniversary of the liberation of Jersey, 9th May 1995
Obverse—green on a multicoloured underprint. Similar to regular issue notes , with a
commemorative overprint to the left
Reverse—mauve, green and yellow with a reproduction of the front and back of the
German occupation £1 note, ref. JE6

	EF	UNC
JE15 *Signatory: G. Baird (Treasurer of the States)*		
Prefix LJ only, issued in 1995...	£4	£8

Issued to commemorate the 800th anniversary of the States of Jersey, 1204–2004
Obverse—green on a multicoloured underprint. Similar to regular issue notes with
"Jersey 1204–2004" overprint to the left.
Reverse—green, brown and multicoloured. Illustration of Mont Orgueil Castle.

JE16 *Signatory: I. Black (Treasurer of the States)*		
Prefix J8C, issued in 2004..	£3	£6

First issued May 2010
Obverse—mainly shades of green; illustration of Liberation Square at the centre and a portrait of
Queen Elizabeth II to the right.
Reverse—shades of green; illustrations of Le Hocq Tower to the left and La Hougue Bie at the centre

JE17 *Signatory: I. Black (Treasurer of the States)*		
Prefix AD and ongoing	—	£2
Prefix DZ—replacement note..		£8

FIVE POUND NOTES

Size 140 mm x 91 mm approximately

First issued 1963
Obverse—red on a multicoloured underprint. Portrait of Queen Elizabeth II to the right
Reverse—red. Illustration of St. Aubin's Fort

		EF	UNC
JE21a *Signatory: F. N. Padgham* (Treasurer of the States)			
Prefix A only, first issued 1963		£150	£220
JE21b *Signatory: J. Clennett* (Treasurer of the States)			
Prefix B and prefix C, first issued 1972.		£40	£65
Prefix Z—replacement note.		£80	£180

Size 145 mm x 78 mm approximately

First issued 1976
Obverse—brown on a multicoloured underprint. Portrait of Queen Elizabeth II to the right
Reverse—brown and mauve. Beach scene with old ships and Elizabeth Castle in the background

JE22a *Signatory: J. Clennett* (Treasurer of the States)			
Prefix AB and prefix GB, first issued 1976		£25	£40
Prefix ZB—replacement note.		£40	£65
JE22b *Signatory: L. May* (Treasurer of the States)			
Prefix GB to prefix KB, first issued 1983		£20	£35
Prefix ZB—replacement note.		£35	£55

Size 135 mm x 70 mm approximately

First issued 1989
*Obverse—maroon on a multicoloured underprint. Portrait of Queen Elizabeth II to the right. "£5" at
top right in outline print*
Reverse—mainly purple. Illustration of La Corbiere lighthouse

	EF	UNC
JE23 *Signatory: L. May (Treasurer of the States)*		
Prefix AC and prefix BC	£12	£18
Prefix CZ—replacement note	£20	£30

First issued 1993
*Obverse—maroon on a multicoloured underprint. Portrait of Queen Elizabeth II to the right. "£5" at
top right in solid print*
Reverse—mainly purple. Illustration of La Corbiere lighthouse

JE24a *Signatory: G. Baird (Treasurer of the States)*		
Prefix CC to prefix JC	£10	£15
Prefix CZ—replacement note	£20	£35
JE24b *Signatory: I. Black (Treasurer of the States)*		
Prefix KC	—	£12
Prefix CZ—replacement note	£25	£45

First issued May 2010

Obverse—mainly shades of blue; illustration of Le Rât Cottage at the centre and portrait of Queen Elizabeth II to the right

Reverse—mainly shades of blue; illustrations of the Archirondel Tower to the left and Les Augrès Manor at the centre

		EF	UNC
JE25	*Signatory: I. Black* (Treasurer of the States)		
	Prefix AD and ongoing	—	£9
	Prefix DZ—replacement note...	—	£25

TEN POUND NOTES

Size 151 mm x 86 mm approximately

First issued 1963

Obverse—purple on a multicoloured underprint. Portrait of Queen Elizabeth II to the right

Reverse—purple. Illustration of St. Ouen's Manor

JE31	*Signatory: J. Clennett* (Treasurer of the States)		
	Prefix A only, first issued 1972	£60	£100
	Prefix Z—replacement note..	£100	£180

Size 150 mm x 85 mm approximately

First issued 1976
Obverse—green on a multicoloured underprint. Portrait of Queen Elizabeth II to the right
Reverse—mainly green. Picture of Victoria College

		EF	UNC
JE32a *Signatory: J. Clennett (Treasurer of the States)*			
Prefix AB and prefix DB, first issued 1976		£45	£75
Prefix ZB—replacement note.		£65	£100
JE32b *Signatory: L. May (Treasurer of the States)*			
Prefix DB to prefix GB, first issued 1983		£40	£65
Prefix ZB—replacement note.		£60	£90

Size 143 mm x 75 mm approximately

First issued 1989
Obverse—orange and brown on a multicoloured underprint. Portrait of Queen Elizabeth II to the right
"£10" at top right in outline print
Reverse—mainly red/brown. Picture of the death of Major Peirson at the Battle of Jersey

JE33 *Signatory: L. May (Treasurer of the States)*			
Prefix AC to prefix CC, first issued 1989		£15	£25
Prefix CZ—replacement note		£30	£45

First issued 1993
*Obverse—orange and brown on a multicoloured underprint. Portrait of Queen Elizabeth II to the right.
"£10" at top right in solid print*
Reverse—mainly red/brown. Picture of the death of Major Peirson at the Battle of Jersey

		EF	UNC
JE34a	*Signatory: G. Baird* (Treasurer of the States)		
	Prefix DC to prefix MC, first issued 1993	—	£22
	Prefix CZ—replacement note..	£25	£40
JE34b	*Signatory: I. Black* (Treasurer of the States)		
	Prefix NC to prefix TC..	—	£18
	Prefix CZ—replacement note..	£25	£40

First issued May 2010
*Obverse—mainly shades of brown; illustration of The Hermitage at the centre and a portrait of Queen
Elizabeth II to the right*
*Reverse—shades of brown; illustrations of the Seymour Tower to the left and the Glass Church at the
centre*

JE35	*Signatory: I. Black* (Treasurer of the States)		
	Prefix AD and ongoing	—	£18
	Prefix DZ—replacement note..	—	£40

TWENTY POUND NOTES

Size 160 mm x 90 mm approximately

First issued 1976
Obverse—Orange and red on a multicoloured underprint. Portrait of Queen Elizabeth II to the right
Reverse—mainly red. Picture of Gorey Castle

		EF	UNC
JE41a	*Signatory: J. Clennett* (Treasurer of the States)		
	Prefix AB only	£70	£110
	Prefix ZB—replacement note.	£100	£180
JE41b	*Signatory: L. May* (Treasurer of the States)		
	Prefix AB and prefix AC, first issued 1983	£65	£100
	Prefix ZB—replacement note.	£100	£180

Size 150 mm x 80 mm approximately

First issued 1989
Obverse—mainly blue on a multicoloured underprint. Portrait of Queen Elizabeth II to the right
"£20" at top right in outline print
Reverse—blue on a multicoloured underprint. Illustration of St. Ouen's Manor

JE42	*Signatory: L. May* (Treasurer of the States)		
	Prefix AC and prefix BC..	£50	£70
	Prefix CZ—replacement note..	£65	£100

First issued 1993

Obverse—mainly blue on a multicoloured underprint. Portrait of Queen Elizabeth II to the right "£20" at top right in solid print

Reverse – blue on a multicoloured underprint. Illustration of St. Ouen's Manor

		EF	UNC
JE43a	*Signatory: G. Baird (Treasurer of the States)*		
	Prefix BC to prefix JC..	—	£45
	Prefix CZ—replacement note..	£40	£65
JE43b	*Signatory: I. Black (Treasurer of the States)*		
	Prefix KC to prefix MC and ongoing	—	£40
	Prefix CZ—replacement note..	£35	£55

First issued May 2010

Obverse—mainly shades of mauve and purple; illustration of The States Building at the centre and a portrait of Queen Elizabeth II to the right

Reverse—shades of mauve and purple; illustrations of La Rocco Tower to the left and the States Chamber at the centre

JE44	*Signatory: I. Black (Treasurer of the States)*		
	Prefix AD and ongoing	—	£36
	Prefix DZ—replacement note...	—	£65

FIFTY POUND NOTES

Size 155 mm x 85 mm approximately

First issued 1989
*Obverse dark grey on a multicoloured underprint. Portrait of Queen Elizabeth II to the right
"£50" at top right in outline print*
Reverse — mainly dark grey. Picture of Government House with the Jersey flag to the left

	EF	UNC
JE51 Signatory: L. May (Treasurer of the States)		
Prefix AC only, first issued 1989	£100	£170
Prefix CZ—replacement note..		Rare

First issued 1993
*Obverse — dark grey on a multicoloured underprint. Portrait of Queen Elizabeth II to the right
"£50" at top right in solid print*
Reverse — mainly dark grey. Picture of Government House with the Jersey flag to the left

JE52a Signatory: G. Baird (Treasurer of the States)		
Prefix AC only	—	£120
Prefix CZ—replacement note..	£110	£180
JE52b Signatory: I. Black (Treasurer of the States)		
Prefix AC and BC (to BC 200000)	—	£100
Prefix CZ—replacement note..	£100	£150

First issued May 2010
Obverse—mainly shades of red; illustration of Mont Orgueil at the centre and a portrait of Queen Elizabeth II to the right
Reverse—shades of red; illustrations of the Ouaisne Tower to the left and Les Écréhous at the centre

	EF	UNC
JE53 *Signatory: I. Black* (Treasurer of the States)		
Prefix AD and ongoing	—	£90
Prefix DZ—replacement note...		£125

IRELAND

Ireland was a relative latecomer to banking, the first notes of the Bank of Ireland being introduced in 1783. Thereafter the history of banking paralleled that of Scotland, with a number of private banks in the early 19th century which, as a result of mergers and amalgamations, resulted in half a dozen major banks still producing distinctive notes at the turn of the century.

The situation was complicated by the political developments which led to the establishment of the Irish Free State and the province of Northern Ireland in 1921. The Belfast Banking Company, whose notes circulated through the whole of Ireland, confined its activities to Northern Ireland from 1922 onwards. On the other hand, the Bank of Ireland, which was traditionally based in Dublin, was obliged to produce separate issues from 1929 onwards for Northern Ireland and the Irish Free State, while both the Provincial Bank of Ireland and the Ulster Bank likewise had distinctive issues for the Free State and Northern Ireland in the same period.

In the Irish Free State, the government established a Currency Commission in 1927 under whose auspices notes, inscribed in English and Irish, were issued from 1928 onwards, notable on account of the portrait of Hazel, Lady Lavery in the guise of an Irish colleen. The inscriptions in these notes were altered in 1938 from Irish Free State (Saorstát Éireann) to Ireland (Eire), following the constitutional changes of that year. In addition the Currency Commission produced distinctive notes, showing a farmer ploughing, with the names of one or other of the eight "shareholder" banks inscribed at the foot: the Bank of Ireland, the Hibernian Bank, the Munster & Leinster Bank, the National Bank, the Northern Bank, the Provincial Bank, the Royal Bank and the Ulster Bank. These notes were replaced from 1943 onwards by the notes of the Central Bank of Ireland, which at first retained the Lady Lavery portrait, but since 1976 have used historic scenes and personalities.

Distinctive notes for circulation in Northern Ireland have been produced by the Bank of Ireland, the Belfast Banking Company and the National, Northern, Provincial and Ulster banks and it is interesting to note that the Bank of Ireland even produced a commemorative £20 in 1983 to celebrate its bicentenary. Generally speaking, the notes of Northern Ireland have always been much more varied in their designs and subject matter. Bank amalgamations led to the formation of the Allied Irish Banks Limited whose notes, similar to the last issue of the Provincial Bank, were introduced in January 1982.

REPUBLIC OF IRELAND

CURRENCY COMMISSION
(Consolidated banknotes) (1929–41)

Designs for the notes issued by the eight Banks under the auspices of the
Currency Commission are virtually identical except for the values, titles and
signatures. Notes representative of the design, are illustrated below. (In keeping
with the current regulations for the reproduction of banknote illustrations, the
serial numbers have been obscured.)

ONE POUND
Size: 151 x 84mm

Obverse—Green on orange and mauve underprint; "Ploughman"
Reverse—The Customs House, Dublin

FIVE POUNDS
Size 165 x 92mm

Obverse—Brown on green and mauve underprint; "Ploughman"
Reverse—St Patrick's Bridge, Cork city

TEN POUNDS
Size 189 x 107mm

Obverse—Blue on green and mauve underprint; "Ploughman"
Reverse—Currency Commission Building, Foster Place, Dublin

TWENTY POUNDS
Size 203 x 114mm

Obverse—Red on yellow and mauve underprint; "Ploughman"
Reverse—Ruined Monastery on the Rock of Cashel, Co. Tipperary

FIFTY POUNDS
Size 203 x 114mm

Obverse—Mauve on yellow underprint; "Ploughman"
Reverse—View of Croagh Patrick Mountain, Co. Mayo

ONE HUNDRED POUNDS
Size 203 x 114mm

Obverse—Brown on mauve and yellow underprint; "Ploughman"
Reverse—View of Killiney Bay, Co. Dublin

NB. £20, £50 and £100 notes exist only as Bank of Ireland Specimens. No issued notes remain. We illustrate them here but have not included them in the listings that follow.

The catalogue numbering used in this section is as the standard work on the subject: *Irish Banknotes—Irish Paper Money from 1928* by Mártan Mac Devitt.

THE BANK OF IRELAND

	VF	*EF*

ONE POUND

E001 *Signatures: Joseph Brennan and J. A. Gargan*		
1929–38. Prefix 01BA–89BA	£300	£550
E002 *Signatures:: Joseph Brennan and H. J. Johnston*		
1939–40. Prefix 89BA–09BB	£300	£550

FIVE POUNDS

E003 *Signatures: Joseph Brennan and J. A. Gargan*		
1929–31. Prefix 01BK–02BK	£1000	£1800
E004 *Signatures: Joseph Brennan and H. J. Johnston*		
1939. 02BK–03BK	£1000	£1800

TEN POUNDS

E005 *Signatures: Joseph Brennan and J. A. Gargan*		
1929. Prefix 01BT	£3000	£5000

HIBERNIAN BANK LTD.

ONE POUND

E009	*Signatures: Joseph Brennan and H. J. Campbell*		
	1929–39. Prefix 01HA–22HA..	£500	£800
E010	*Joseph Brennan and A. K. Hodges*		
	1939–40. Prefix 23HA–25HA..	£500	£800

FIVE POUNDS

E011	*Signatures: Joseph Brennan and H. J. Campbell*		
	1929–May 1939. Prefix 01HK–03HK.................................	£1500	£2500

TEN POUNDS

E013	*Signatures: Joseph Brennan and H. J. Campbell*		
	1929–31. Prefix 01HT...	£3000	£5000

MUNSTER & LEINSTER BANK LTD.

ONE POUND

E016	*Signatures: Joseph Brennan and J. L. Gubbins*		
	1929–35. Prefix 01MA–25MA	£300	£600
E017	*Signatures: Joseph Brennan and A. E. Hosford*		
	1936–40. Prefix 26MA–50MA	£300	£600

FIVE POUNDS

E018	*Signatures: Joseph Brennan and J. L. Gubbins*		
	1929–33. Prefix 01MK–03MK	£1000	£1700
E019	*Signatures: Joseph Brennan and A. E. Hosford*		
	1938–39. Prefix 03MK–04MK	£1000	£1700

TEN POUNDS

E020	*Signatures: Joseph Brennan and J. L. Gubbins*		
	1929–31. Prefix 01MT..	£2000	£3000
E021	*Signatures: Joseph Brennan and A. E. Hosford*		
	1938–39. Prefix 01MT..	£2200	£3500

NATIONAL BANK LTD.

ONE POUND

E025 *Signatures: Joseph Brennan and H. A. Russell*
1929–39. Prefix 01NA–44NA.. £300   £550

FIVE POUNDS

E026 *Signatures: Joseph Brennan and H. A. Russell*
1929–1939. Prefix 01NK–04NK £750   £1500

TEN POUNDS

E027 *Signatures: Joseph Brennan and J. L. Gubbins*
1929–39. Prefix 01NT £2000   £3000

NORTHERN BANK LTD.

ONE POUND

E028 *Signatures: Joseph Brennan and S. W. Knox*
1929. Prefix 01OA–02OA £3500   £4500
E029 *Signatures: Joseph Brennan and H. H. Stewart*
1931–33. Prefix 03EA–04EA.................................... £3000   £4000

FIVE POUNDS

E031 *Signatures: Joseph Brennan and S. W. Knox*
1929. Prefix 01OK... £5000   £6500
E032 *Signatures: Joseph Brennan and H. H. Stewart*
1931–33. Prefix 01EK £4000   £5000

TEN POUNDS

E034 *Signatures: Joseph Brennan and S. W. Knox*
1929. Prefix 01OT .... Rare   Rare

PROVINCIAL BANK OF IRELAND LTD.

ONE POUND

E036　*Signatures: Joseph Brennan and Hume Robertson*
　　　1929. Prefix 01PA–06PA .... £700　　£900
E037　*Signatures: Joseph Brennan and F. S. Forde*
　　　1931–36. Prefix 07PA–13PA .... £400　　£750
E038　*Signatures: Joseph Brennan and G. A. Kennedy*
　　　1937–40. Prefix 13PA–23PA .... £400　　£750

FIVE POUNDS

E039　*Signatures: Joseph Brennan and Hume Robertson*
　　　1929. Prefix 01PK .... £1500　　£2500
E040　*Signatures: Joseph Brennan and F. S. Forde*
　　　1931. Prefix 01PK–02PK .... £900　　£2000
E041　*Signatures: Joseph Brennan and G. A. Kennedy*
　　　1939. Prefix 02PK .... £1500　　£2500

TEN POUNDS

E042　*Signatures: Joseph Brennan and Hume Robertson*
　　　1929. Prefix 01PT .... £3000　　£5000
E043　*Signatures: Joseph Brennan and F. S. Forde*
　　　1931. Prefix 01PT .... £2500　　£3500
E044　*Signatures: Joseph Brennan and G. A. Kennedy*
　　　1939. Prefix 01PT .... Rare　　Rare

ROYAL BANK OF IRELAND LTD.

ONE POUND

E046　*Signatures: Joseph Brennan and G. A. Stanley*
　　　1929. Prefix 01RA–08RA .... £700　　£1200
E047　*Signatures: Joseph Brennan and D. R. Mack*
　　　1931–39. Prefix 09RA–26RA .... £600　　£1000
E048　*Signatures: Joseph Brennan and J. Wilson*
　　　1939. Prefix 26RA–28RA .... £600　　£1000

FIVE POUNDS

E049　*Signatures: Joseph Brennan and G. A. Stanley*
　　　1929. Prefix 01RK .... £3000　　£4000
E050　*Signatures: Joseph Brennan and D. R. Mack*
　　　1931. Prefix 01RK .... £3000　　£4000

TEN POUNDS

E052　*Signatures: Joseph Brennan and G. A. Stanley*
　　　1929. Prefix 01RT .... £5000　　£9000

ULSTER BANK LTD.

ONE POUND

E056 *Signatures: Joseph Brennan and C. W. Patton*
1929–39. Prefix 01UA–08UA... £800   £1500
E057 *Signatures: Joseph Brennan and C. W. Lester*
1939–40. Prefix 08UA–12UA... £800
£1500

FIVE POUNDS

E058 *Signatures: Joseph Brennan and C. W. Patton*
1929–33. Prefix 01UK.. £2000   £3000
E059 *Signatures: Joseph Brennan and C. W. Lester*
1938–39. Prefix 01UK–02UK.. £2000
£3000

TEN POUNDS

E060 *Signatures: Joseph Brennan and C. W. Patton*
1929–39. Prefix 01UT... £5000   £7000
E061 *Signatures: Joseph Brennan and C. W. Lester*
1938–39. Prefix 01UT... £5000
£7000

For example illustrations of the "Ploughman" notes see pages 258–260.

SERIES A
"LADY LAVERY" NOTES (1928–77)

Designs for the notes issued under the auspices of the Currency Commission Irish Free State, the Currency Commission of Ireland and the Central Bank of Ireland are virtually identical except for the values, titles and signatures. Notes representative of the design, are illustrated below. (In keeping with the current regulations for the reproduction of banknote illustrations, the serial numbers have been obscured.)

TEN SHILLINGS
Size: 138 x 78mm

Orange on green and mauve underprint.

ONE POUND
Size: 151 x 84mm

Green on pink and yellow underprint.

FIVE POUNDS
Size: 166 x 92mm

Brown on yellow and mauve underprint.

TEN POUNDS
Size: 189 x 107mm

Blue on green and mauve underprint.

TWENTY POUNDS
Size: 203 x 114mm

Red on orange and mauve underprint.

FIFTY POUNDS
Size: 203 x 114mm

Mauve on yellow underprint.

ONE HUNDRED POUNDS
Size: 203 x 114mm

Black on yellow and mauve underprint.

CURRENCY COMMISSION IRISH FREE STATE

		VF	EF
TEN SHILLINGS			
	Signatures: Joseph Brennan and J. J. McElligott		
E065	Fractional prefix—Letter over Number (1928)	£800	£1400
E066	Straight prefix—Number/Number/Letter (1929–37)	£300	£800
ONE POUND			
	Signatures: Joseph Brennan and J. J. McElligott		
E075	Fractional prefix—Letter over Number (1928)	£400	£800
E076	Straight prefix—Number/Number/Letter (1930–37)	£200	£450
FIVE POUNDS			
	Signatures: Joseph Brennan and J. J. McElligott		
E088	Fractional prefix—Letter over Number (1928)	£800	£1400
E089	Straight prefix—Number/Number/Letter (1932–37)	£250	£500

Series A, "Lady Lavery". Currency Commission Irish Free State (continued)   VF   EF

TEN POUNDS

Signatures: Joseph Brennan and J. J. McElligott

		VF	EF
E100	Fractional prefix—Letter over Number (1928)	£1000	£2000
E101	Straight prefix—Number/Number/Letter (1932–33)	£450	£1500

TWENTY POUNDS

Signatures: Joseph Brennan and J. J. McElligott

		VF	EF
E113	Fractional prefix—Letter over Number (1928)	£2000	£3700

FIFTY POUNDS

Signatures: Joseph Brennan and J. J. McElligott

		VF	EF
E121	Fractional prefix—Letter over Number (1928)	£4000	£9000

ONE HUNDRED POUNDS

Signatures: Joseph Brennan and J. J. McElligott

		VF	EF
E128	Fractional prefix—Letter over Number (1928)	£4000	£9000
E129	Straight prefix—Number/Number/Letter (1937)	£2000	£4500

CURRENCY COMMISSION IRELAND

TEN SHILLINGS

		VF	EF
E067	*Signatures: Joseph Brennan and J. J. McElligott. With title of Secretary of the Department of Finance as "Rúnaidhe na Roinne Airgedais" (1938–39)*	£200	£250
E068	*Signatures: Joseph Brennan and J. J. McElligott. With Emergency Tracer Overprint codes H, K, J in circles (1940–41)*	£150	£190

ONE POUND

		VF	EF
E077	*Signatures: Joseph Brennan and J. J. McElligott. "Rúnaidhe na Roinne Airgedais" (1939)*	£140	£180
E078	*Signatures: Joseph Brennan and J. J. McElligott. With ETO codes T, B, P, V in circles (1941–42)*	£120	£150

FIVE POUNDS

		VF	EF
E090	*Signatures: Joseph Brennan and J. J. McElligott "Rúnaidhe na Roinne Airgedais" (1938–39)*	£160	£280
E091	*Signatures: Joseph Brennan and J. J. McElligott. With ETO codes A, C, D in circles (1940–42)*	£180	£280

TEN POUNDS

		VF	EF
E102	Signatures: Joseph Brennan and J. J. McElligott. "Rúnaidhe na Roinne Airgedais"(1938–40)	£200	£350
E103	Signatures: Joseph Brennan and J. J. McElligott. With ETO codes E, F in circles (1941–42)	£250	£400

CENTRAL BANK OF IRELAND

TEN SHILLINGS

		VF	EF
E069	Signatures: Joseph Brennan and J. J. McElligott. With ETO codes L, M, R, E in circles (1943–44)	£150	£190
E070	Signatures: Joseph Brennan and J. J. McElligott. ETO codes discontinued (1945–50)	£35	£50
E071	Signatures: Joseph Brennan and J. J. McElligott. Serial nos. extended (1951–52)	£20	£35
E072	Signatures: J. J. McElligott and O. J. Redmond (1955)	£80	£160
E073	Signatures: J. J. McElligott and T. K. Whitaker (1957–59)	£20	£30
E074	Signatures: M. Ó Muimhneacháin and T. K. Whitaker (1962–68)	£15	£20

ONE POUND

		VF	EF
E079	Signatures: Joseph Brennan and J. J. McElligott. With ETO codes G, Y, E, F in circles (1943–44)	£130	£160
E080	Signatures: Joseph Brennan and J. J. McElligott. ETO codes discontinued (1945–50)	£20	£40
E081	Signatures: Joseph Brennan and J. J. McElligott. Serial nos. extended (1951–52)	£10	£25
E082	Signatures: J. J. McElligott and O. J. Redmond (1954–55)	£10	£25
E083	Signatures: J. J. McElligott and T. K. Whitaker (1957–60)	£8	£13
E084	Signatures: M. Ó Muimhneacháin and T. K. Whitaker (1962–68)	£8	£13
E085	Signatures: T. K. Whitaker and C. H. Murray (1969–70)	£8	£13
E086	Signatures: T. K. Whitaker and C. H. Murray. Metallic security thread introduced (1971–75). Replacement prefixes S (1974), 00A (1975)	FV	£10
E087	Signatures: C. H. Murray and M. O. Murchú (1976). Replacement prefix 00A	FV	£5

FIVE POUNDS

		VF	EF
E092	Signatures: Joseph Brennan and J. J. McElligott. With ETO codes N, R, M in circles (1943–44)	£180	£280
E093	Signatures: Joseph Brennan and J. J. McElligott. ETO codes discontinued (1945–51)	£80	£110
E094	Signatures: Joseph Brennan and J. J. McElligott. Serial nos. extended (1952–53)	£40	£80
E095	Signatures: J. J. McElligott and O. J. Redmond (1954–55)	£50	£110
E096	Signatures: J. J. McElligott and T. K. Whitaker (1956–60)	£25	£70
E097	Signatures: M. Ó Muimhneacháin and T. K. Whitaker (1961–68)	£12	£35
E098	Signatures: T. K. Whitaker and C. H. Murray (1969–70)	£12	£35
E099	Signatures: T. K. Whitaker and C. H. Murray. Metallic security thread introduced (1971–75). Replacement prefixes R, 00K (1975 only)	£12	£25

TEN POUNDS

		VF	EF
E104	Signatures: Joseph Brennan and J. J. McElligott. With ETO codes S, W, B, G in circles (1943–44)	£250	£400
E105	Signatures: Joseph Brennan and J. J. McElligott. ETO codes discontinued (1945–52)	£50	£150
E106	Signatures: J. J. McElligott and O. J. Redmond (1954–55)	£90	£220
E107	Signatures: J. J. McElligott and T. K. Whitaker (1957–1960)	£40	£70
E108	Signatures: J. J. McElligott and T. K. Whitaker. Serial numbers extended (1960)	£40	£70
E109	Signatures: M. Ó Muimhneacháin and T. K. Whitaker (1962–1968)	£40	£70
E110	Signatures: T. K. Whitaker and C. H. Murray (1969–1970)	£35	£70
E111	Signatures: T. K. Whitaker and C. H. Murray. Metallic security thread introduced (1971–1975). Replacement prefix T (1975)	£35	£65
E112	Signatures: C. H. Murray and M. O. Murchú (1976). Replacement prefix T	£35	£65

TWENTY POUNDS

		VF	EF
E114	Signatures: Joseph Brennan and J. J. McElligott. With ETO code A in circle (1943–44)	£2500	£3000
E115	Signatures: Joseph Brennan and J. J. McElligott. ETO codes discontinued (1945–52)	£280	£550
E116	Signatures: J. J. McElligott and O. J. Redmond (1954–55)	£280	£550
E117	Signatures: J. J. McElligott and T. K. Whitaker (1957)	£280	£400
E118	Signatures: M. Ó Muimhneacháin and T. K. Whitaker (1961–65)	£50	£160
E119	Signatures: T. K. Whitaker and C. H. Murray (1969–75)	£50	£80
E120	Signatures: T. K. Whitaker and M. O. Murchú (1976) Replacement prefix V	£40	£80

FIFTY POUNDS

		VF	EF
E122	Signatures: Joseph Brennan and J. J. McElligott (1943–51)	£800	£1400
E123	Signatures: J. J. McElligott and O. J. Redmond (1954)	£800	£1400
E124	Signatures: J. J. McElligott and T. K. Whitaker (1957–60)	£750	£1200
E125	Signatures: M. Ó Muimhneacháin and T. K. Whitaker (1962–68)	£400	£500
E126	Signatures: T. K. Whitaker and C. H. Murray (1970–75)	£330	£420
E127	Signatures: C. H. Murray and M. O. Murchú (1977)	£280	£380

ONE HUNDRED POUNDS

		VF	EF
E130	Signatures: Joseph Brennan and J. J. McElligott (1943–49)	£900	£1400
E131	Signatures: J. J. McElligott and O. J. Redmond (1954)	£800	£1400
E132	Signatures: J. J. McElligott and T. K. Whitaker (1959)	£750	£1200
E133	Signatures: M. Ó Muimhneacháin and T. K. Whitaker (1963–68)	£350	£800
E134	Signatures: T. K. Whitaker and C. H. Murray (1970–75)	£350	£600
E135	Signatures: C. H. Murray and M. O. Murchú (1977)	£300	£500

For example illustrations of the "Lady Lavery" notes see pages 265–267.

For a concise and complete study of the notes of Ireland
visit the website
www.irishpapermoney.com

CENTRAL BANK OF IRELAND
SERIES B NOTES, 1976–93

ONE POUND

1976–93 ISSUE. Replacement prefixes BBB, DDD, GGG   *EF*   *UNC*
Green on multicoloured underprint. Obverse—Portrait of Queen Medb, legendary Queen of
Connaught. Next to portrait is an early Irish geometric design.
Reverse—Decorated excerpt from Lebor na hUidre.
Size 150 x 78mm

E136	*Signatures: C. H. Murray and M. O. Murchú (1977)*	£5	£12
E137	*Signatures: C. H. Murray and Tomás F. Ó Cofaigh (1978–81)*	£5	£12
E138	*Signatures: Tomás F. Ó Cofaigh and Maurice F. Doyle (1982–87)*	£5	£10
E139	*Signatures: Maurice F. Doyle and S. P. Cromien (1988–89)*	£5	£10

FIVE POUNDS

1976–93 ISSUE. Replacement prefixes AAA, FFF
Brown on multicoloured underprint. Obverse—Portrait of philosopher John Scots Eriugena
(c. 828–878).
Reverse—Extract from the Book of Kells.
Size 156 x 83mm

E140	*Signatures: T. K. Whitaker and C. H. Murray (1976)*	£18	£60
E141	*Signatures: C. H. Murray and M. O Murchú (1976–77)*	£10	£35
E142	*Signatures: C. H. Murray and Tomás F. Ó Cofaigh (1979–81)*	£10	£35
E143	*Signatures: Tomás F. Ó Cofaigh and Maurice F. Doyle (1983–87)*	£10	£25
E144	*Signatures: Maurice F. Doyle and S. P. Cromien (1988–93)*	£9	£25

Central Bank of Ireland. Series B (continued)   *EF*   *UNC*

TEN POUNDS

1976–93 ISSUE. Replacement prefixes CCC, HHH

Purple on multicoloured underprint. Obverse—Portrait of Jonathan Swift (1667–1745), Dean of St Patrick's Cathedral, Dublin.
Reverse—Famous map of Dublin by John Rocques, first published 1756.
Size 164 x 86mm

		EF	UNC
E145	*Signatures: C. H. Murray and Tomás F. Ó Cofaigh (1978–81)*.............	£30	£80
E146	*Signatures: Tomás F. Ó Cofaigh and Maurice F. Doyle (1983–87)*........	£25	£60
E147	*Signatures: Maurice F. Doyle and S. P. Cromien (1987–92)*.................	£25	£60

TWENTY POUNDS

1976–93 ISSUE. Replacement prefixes EEE, LLL

Blue on multicoloured underprint. Obverse—Portrait of poet and writer William Butler Yeats (1865–1939).
Reverse—Group of the Blasket Islands of the Kerry coast.
Size 172 x 90mm

		EF	UNC
E148	*Signatures: C. H. Murray and Tomás F. Ó Cofaigh (1980–81)*.............	£50	£90
E149	*Signatures: Tomás F. Ó Cofaigh and Maurice F. Doyle (1983–86)*	£40	£70
E150	*Signatures: Maurice F. Doyle and S. P. Cromien (1987–92)*.................	£40	£70

Central Bank of Ireland. Series B (continued)   EF   UNC

FIFTY POUNDS

1976–93 ISSUE. Replacement prefixes KKK

Brown on multicoloured underprint. Obverse—Portrait of harpist and composer Turlough Ó Carolan (1670–1738).
Reverse—Design based on the wood carving in the organ loft of St Michans Church, Dublin.
Size 180 x 94mm

		EF	UNC
E151	*Signatures: Tomás F. Ó Cofaigh and Maurice F. Doyle (1982)*..............	£90	£235
E152	*Signatures: Maurice F. Doyle and S. P. Cromien (1991)*	£90	£235

CENTRAL BANK OF IRELAND
SERIES C NOTES, 1992–2001

FIVE POUNDS

1992–2001 ISSUE. Replacement prefixes HHH, MMM
Brown and blue on multicoloured underprint. Obverse—Catherine Macauley (1778–1841), foundress of the Catholic Order of the Sisters of Mercy.
Reverse—A classroom scene.
Size 120 x 64mm

		EF	UNC
E153	*Signatures: Maurice F. Doyle and S. P. Cromien (1994)*	—	£25
E154	*Signatures: Muiris S. Ó Conaill and P. Mullarkey (Dec. 1994–97)*	—	£25
E155	*Signatures: Muiris S. Ó Conaill and P. Mullarkey (Dec. 1998–99)*	—	£15

TEN POUNDS

1992–2001 ISSUE. Replacement prefixes JJJ, NNN
Brown, blue and green on multicoloured underprint. Obverse—James Joyce (1882–1941).
Reverse— River mask sculpture from the Dublin Custom House.
Size 128 x 68mm

E156	*Signatures: Maurice F. Doyle and S. P. Cromien (1993–94)*	—	£35
E157	*Signatures: Muiris S. Ó Conaill and P. Mullarkey (1995–97)*	—	£35
E158	*Signatures: Muiris S. Ó Conaill and P. Mullarkey (Dec. 1997–99)*	—	£30

Central Bank of Ireland. Series C (continued)

TWENTY POUNDS

1992–2001 ISSUE. Replacement prefixes BBB, FFF, CCC, PPP
Mauve and brown on multicoloured underprint. Obverse—Daniel O'Connell (1775–1847).
Reverse—Four Courts Building, Dublin.
Size 136 x 72mm

		EF	UNC
E159	*Signatures: Maurice F. Doyle and S. P. Cromien (1992–94)*..................	—	£70
E160	*Signatures: Muiris S. Ó Conaill and P. Mullarkey (1995–97)*...............	—	£60
E161	*Signatures: Muiris S. Ó Conaill and P. Mullarkey. With prefix letters M–Z (O and Q not used) (1997–99)*	—	£45

FIFTY POUNDS

1992–2001 ISSUE. Replacement prefixes EEE
Blue and green on multicoloured underprint. Obverse—Douglas Hyde (1860–1949).
Reverse—An uillean piper.
Size 144 x 76mm

E162	*Signatures: Muiris S. Ó Conaill and P. Mullarkey (1995–96)*...............	—	£180
E164	*Signatures: Muiris S. Ó Conaill and P. Mullarkey. New design security thread introduced (1999)*...	—	£160
E165	*Signatures: Muiris S. Ó Conaill and John A. Hurley (2001)*.................	—	£180

Central Bank of Ireland. Series C (continued)

ONE HUNDRED POUNDS

1992–2001 ISSUE. Replacement prefixes KKK
Purple, red and blue on multicoloured underprint. Obverse— Charles Stewart Parnell (1846–1891).
Reverse—Parnell Monument, O'Connell Street, Dublin.
Size 152 x 80mm

	EF	UNC
E163 *Signatures: Muiris S. Ó Conaill and P. Mullarkey (1996)*......................	£150	£350

NORTHERN IRELAND
ALLIED IRISH BANKS LIMITED

Formed in 1966 as a result of a merger of the Provincial Bank of Ireland Ltd. with the Munster & Leinster Bank and The Royal Bank of Ireland. The Banknotes share a common design with the last issues of the Provincial Bank. In the early 1990's the Allied Irish Banks plc merged with the Trustee Savings Bank to form the First Trust Bank.

ONE POUND

Size 134 mm x 67 mm approximately

Obverse — green and brown on a multicoloured underprint. Portrait of a teenage boy to the right
Reverse — mainly green. Illustration of the Spanish galleass "The Girona" at the centre

		EF	UNC
NI.101	*Signatory: P. O'Keiffe* (Group Chief Executive)		
	Prefix PN dated 1.1.1982..	£20	£30
	Prefix ZY—replacement note..	£60	£100

FIVE POUNDS

Size 146 mm x 78 mm approximately

Obverse—blue and purple on a multicoloured underprint. Portrait of a young lady to the right
Reverse—mainly blue. Illustration of Dunluce Castle at the centre

NI.102   *Signatory: P. O'Keiffe* (Group Chief Executive)

	EF	UNC
Prefix QN dated 1.1.1982; 1.7.1983 and 1.12.1984	£40	£60
Prefix ZY—replacement note	£75	£125

TEN POUNDS

Size 150 mm x 84 mm approximately

Obverse—brown and purple on a multicoloured underprint. Portrait of a young man to the right
Reverse—mainly brown. Illustration of the sinking of the Spanish galleass The Girona at the centre

NI.103   *Signatory: P. O'Keiffe* (Group Chief Executive)

Prefix RN dated 1.1.1982; 1.7.1983 and 1.12.1984	£60	£95
Prefix ZY—replacement note	£100	£160

TWENTY POUNDS

Size 160 mm x 90 mm approximately

Obverse—mauve on a multicoloured underprint. Portrait of a mature lady to the right
Reverse—mauve on a multicoloured underprint. Illustration of rock chimney at Lacada Point at the centre

NI.104	*Signatory: P. O'Keiffe* (Group Chief Executive)	*EF*	*UNC*
	Prefix SN dated 1.1.1982; 1.7.1983 and 1.12.1984	£100	£180
	Prefix ZY—replacement note...		probably exists

ONE HUNDRED POUNDS

Size 160 mm x 90 mm approximately

Obverse—black green and olive on a multicoloured underprint. Portrait of an older man to the right
Reverse—black on a mainly green underprint. Illustration of the Spanish Armada at the centre

NI.105	*Signatory: P. O'Keiffe* (Group Chief Executive)		
	Prefix TN dated 1.1.1982..	£450	£650
	Prefix ZY—replacement note...		probably exists

ALLIED IRISH BANKS P.L.C.

FIVE POUNDS

Size 146 mm x 78 mm approximately

Obverse—blue and purple on a multicoloured underprint. Portrait of a young lady to the right
Reverse—mainly blue. Illustration of Dunluce Castle at the centre

		EF	UNC
NI.106	*Signatory: G. B. Scanlon* (Group Chief Executive)		
	Prefix QN and UN dated 1.1.1987 and 1.1.1990.........................	£32	£50
	Prefix ZY—replacement note..	£75	£125

TEN POUNDS
Size 150 mm x 84 mm approximately

Obverse—brown and purple on a multicoloured underprint. Portrait of a young man to the right
Reverse—mainly brown. Illustration of the sinking of the Spanish galleon The Girona at the centre

	EF	UNC
NI.107 *Signatory: G. B. Scanlon* (Group Chief Executive)		
Prefix RN dated 1.1.1986 to prefix WN dated 18.5.1993	£45	£75
Prefix ZY—replacement note..	£100	£150

TWENTY POUNDS

Size 160 mm x 90 mm approximately

Obverse—red and maroon on a multicoloured underprint. Portrait of an older woman to the right
Reverse—maroon on a multicoloured underprint. Illustration of rock chimney at Lacada Point at the centre

NI.108 *Signatory: G. B. Scanlon* (Group Chief Executive)		
Prefix SN dated 1.1.1987, 1.4.1987 and 1.1.1990	£65	£90
Prefix ZY—replacement note..		probably exists

ONE HUNDRED POUNDS

Size 160 mm x 90 mm approximately

Obverse—black, green and olive on a multicoloured underprint. Portrait of an older man to the right
Reverse—black on a mainly green underprint. Illustration of the Spanish Armada at the centre

		EF	UNC
NI.109	*Signatory: G. B. Scanlon* (Group Chief Executive)		
	Prefix TN dated 1.12.1988...	£350	£480
	Prefix ZY—replacement note..		probably exists

BANK OF IRELAND

Established in Dublin by royal charter in 1783, the Bank of Ireland quickly became the dominant force in Irish banking despite having no branch offices. For many years no rival bank was permitted by law to have more than six partners or shareholders, which led to the setting up of a large number of small and inadequately capitalised banks throughout Ireland.

Around 1820 many of these banks failed, but still the Bank of Ireland refused to establish branches outside Dublin, leading to an amendment in the law to permit the establishment of joint stock banking companies in Ireland from 1824 onwards. This change persuaded the Bank of Ireland to immediately open branch offices in order to compete with its new rivals.

For a time the Bank of Ireland retained some privileges, in that prior to 1845 no note-issuing joint stock bank was permitted to carry on business anywhere within a 65 mile radius of Dublin. Even after it lost that advantage, the Bank of Ireland remained by far the largest Irish bank until recent years. It was the Government banker and acted in a similar capacity to the Bank of England, whilst at the same time offering a full range of clearing bank services through a widespread branch network. Until 1929 it had a dominant share of the Irish note issue.

The Bank of Ireland's position was further strengthened when it took over the Hibernian Bank in 1958, and seven years later acquired the Irish business of the National Bank. However, Allied Irish Banks has recently come to rival it in size and profitability.

ONE POUND

Size 150 mm x 83 mm approximately

Obverse—black and green on a blue underprint. Statues of Hibernia to the left and right
Reverse—blue and green; Hibernia seated in a round panel with sunburst effect

		F	VF
NI.201a	*Signatory: J. H. Craig* Prefix B/10 dated 6.5.1929 and prefix B/11 dated 8.5.1929.....	£80	£150
NI.201b	*Signatory: G. W. Frazer* Prefix B/12 dated 3.4.1933 and prefix B/13 dated 9.3.1936.....	£55	£95

Obverse—black and blue on a green underprint. Statues of Hibernia to the left and right
Reverse—Hibernia seated in a blue panel with green underprint

		VF	EF
NI.202a	*Signatory: G. W. Frazer*		
	Prefix B/13 dated 9.3.1936 to prefix B17 dated 1.11.1940.........	£70	£130
NI.202b	*Signatory: H. J. Adams*		
	Prefix B/18 dated 23.2.1942 to prefix B/21 dated 15.11.1943 ..	£40	£75

Size 150 mm x 70 mm approximately

First issued in 1967
Obverse—blue grey on a multicoloured underprint. Hibernia to the right
Reverse—blue grey; Bank of Ireland building surrounded by images representing industry in Northern Ireland

		EF	UNC
NI.203	*Signatory: W. E. Guthrie* (Agent)		
	Prefix A to prefix C	£35	£55

Size 135 mm x 66mm approximately

Design similar to previous issue. First issued in 1972. Value sign at top right and bottom left is shown as "1"
Obverse – blue grey on a multicoloured underprint. Hibernia to the right
Reverse – blue grey; Bank of Ireland building surrounded by images representing industry in Northern Ireland

NI.204a	*Signatory: H. H. M. Chestnutt* (Manager)		
	Prefix D and E	£25	£40
	Prefix Z—replacement note		Rare
NI.204b	*Signatory: A. S. J. O'Neill* (Manager)		
	Prefix E and F	£12	£20
	Prefix Z—replacement note	£65	—

"Sterling" added at centre and value sign at top right and bottom left is now shown as "£1". (From 1984)

NI.205	*Signatory: A. S. J. O'Neill* (Manager)	*EF*	*UNC*
	Prefix G and H..	£8	£13
	Prefix Z—replacement note	£10	£16

FIVE POUNDS

Size 178 mm x 97 mm approximately

Obverse—black and red on an orange/yellow underprint. Statues of Hibernia to the left and right
Reverse—red panel on an orange underprint. Hibernia seated at the centre

NI.211a	*Signatory: J. H. Craig*	*F*	*VF*
	Prefix S/10 dated 5.5.1929 and 15.5.1929	£95	£180
	Prefix S/11 dated 7.5.1929	£95	£180
NI.211b	*Signatory: G. W. Frazer*		
	Prefix S/12 dated 15.8.1935 to prefix S/15 dated 2.12.1940.....	£60	£110
NI.211c	*Signatory: H. J. Adams*	*VF*	*EF*
	Prefix S/16 dated 16.2.1942 to prefix S/23 dated 20.12.1943...	£70	£125
NI.211d	*Signatory: S. G. Skuce*		
	Prefix S/24 dated 1.9.1958 and prefix S/25 dated 1.10.1958 ...	£70	£150

Size 140 mm x 85 mm approximately

First issued in 1967
Obverse—blue grey on a brown/violet underprint. Hibernia to the right
Reverse—blue grey; Bank of Ireland building surrounded by images representing industry in Northern Ireland

		VF	EF
NI.212a	*Signatory: W. E. Guthrie* (Agent)		
	Prefix M	£140	£240
NI.212b	*Signatory: H. H. M. Chestnutt* (Agent)		
	Prefix M...	£140	£240

Size 146 mm x 77 mm approximately

Design similar to previous issue. First issued in 1972. Value sign at top right and bottom left is shown as "5".
Obverse—blue grey on a multicoloured underprint. Hibernia to the right
Reverse—blue grey; Bank of Ireland building surrounded by images representing industry in Northern Ireland

		EF	UNC
NI.213a	*Signatory: H. H. M. Chestnutt* (Manager)		
	Prefix N and prefix P..	£70	£110
	Prefix Z—replacement note	£300	—
NI.213b	*Signatory: A. S. J. O'Neill* (Manager)		
	Prefix Q and prefix R..	£60	£95
	Prefix Z—replacement note	£250	—

"Sterling" added at centre and value sign at top right and bottom left is now shown as "£5". (From 1984)

		EF	UNC
NI.214a	*Signatory: A. S. J. O'Neill* (Manager)		
	Prefix R and S...	£55	£100
	Prefix Z—replacement note	£200	—
NI.214b	*Signatory: D. J. Harrison* (Manager)		
	Prefix S to prefix V...	£35	£60
	Prefix Z—replacement note	£140	—

Size 136 mm x 70 mm approximately

Obverse—blue and violet on a multicoloured underprint. Hibernia to the left
Reverse—blue and multicoloured. Illustration of the Queen's University of Belfast

NI.215	*Signatory: D. J. Harrison* (Manager)		
	Prefix A dated 28.8.1990 to prefix U dated 1.7.1994..................	£16	£28
	Prefix Z—replacement note	£50	£75

Similar to previous issue with bolder colours
Obverse—blue and purple on a multicoloured underprint. Hibernia to the left
Reverse—blue and multicoloured. Illustration of the Queen's University of Belfast

			EF	UNC
NI.216a	*Signatory: G. McGinn (Chief Executive N.I.)*			
	Prefix U dated 1.7.1997 to prefix Y dated 4.8.1998, and			
	Prefix AA dated 4.8.1998 to prefix AY dated 5.9.2000..............		£12	£22
	Prefix Z—replacement note		£30	£50
NI.216b	*Signatory: M. S. Soden (Group Chief Executive)*			
	Prefix AY to prefix BP 300000 dated 1.3.2003............................		£10	£18
	Prefix Z—replacement note		£25	£40

Front similar to previous issue; new reverse design.
Obverse—blue and purple on a multicoloured underprint. Hibernia to the left
Reverse—blue and multicoloured. Illustration of the "Old Bushmills" Distillery

NI.217	*Signatory: D. McGowan (Chief Executive UK)*			
	Prefix BD to BK dated 20.4.2008 and ongoing..........................		—	£10
	Prefix ZZ—replacement note...		£18	£30

TEN POUNDS

Size 200 mm x 108 mm approximately

Obverse—black and blue on an green underprint. Statues of Hibernia to the left and right
Reverse—blue panel on a green underprint. Hibernia seated at the centre

		F	VF
NI.221a	*Signatory: J. H. Craig*		
	Prefix U/10 dated 4.5.1929 and 14.5.1929.	£160	£320

		VF	EF
NI.221b	*Signatory: H. J. Adams*		
	Prefix U/11 dated 26.1.1942 and prefix U/12 dated 19.1.1943	£125	£250

Size 150 mm x 93 mm approximately

First issued in 1967
Obverse—brown on a multicoloured underprint. Hibernia to the right
Reverse—brown and grey; Bank of Ireland building surrounded by images representing industry in
Northern Ireland

NI.222	*Signatory: W. E. Guthrie* (Agent)		
	Prefix T	£275	£500

Size 152 mm x 85 mm approximately

Design similar to previous issue. First issued in 1972. Value sign at top right and bottom left is shown as "10"
Obverse—brown on a multicoloured underprint. Hibernia to the right
Reverse—brown on a green underprint; Bank of Ireland building surrounded by images representing industry in Northern Ireland

		EF	UNC
NI.223a	*Signatory: H. H. M. Chestnutt* (Manager)		
	Prefix U..	£240	£350
	Prefix Z—replacement note		rare
NI.223b	*Signatory: A. S. J. O'Neill* (Manager)		
	Prefix U and prefix V...	£160	£250
	Prefix Z—replacement note	£250	—

"Sterling" added at centre and value sign at top right and bottom left is now shown as "£10". (From 1984)

NI.224a	*Signatory: A. S. J. O'Neill* (Manager)		
	Prefix V and prefix W (possibly to W900000)............................	£75	£120
	Prefix Z—replacement	£200	—
NI.224b	*Signatory: D. J. Harrison* (Manager)		
	Prefix W (possibly from W900001) X and Y, and	£60	£90
	Prefix AA to AF		
	Prefix Z—replacement note	£160	—

Size 142 mm x 75 mm approximately

Obverse—purple and maroon on a multicoloured underprint. Hibernia to the left
Reverse—maroon and multicoloured. Illustration of the Queen's University of Belfast

		EF	UNC
NI.225	*Signatory: D. J. Harrison* (Manager)		
	Prefix A dated 14.5.1991 to prefix P dated 28.5.1992..................	£35	£55
	Prefix Z—replacement note	£75	£125

Similar to previous design.
Obverse—blue and brown on a multicoloured underprint. Hibernia to the left
Reverse—maroon and multicoloured. Illustration of the Queen's University of Belfast

NI.226a	*Signatory: G. McGinn* (Chief Executive N. I.)		
	Prefix R dated 1.7.1995 to prefix BD dated 5.9.2000	£20	£30
	Prefix Z—replacement note.	£50	£80
NI.226b	*Signatory: D. McGowan* (Chief Executive N. I.)		
	Prefix BE to prefix BU dated 1.5.2005	£18	£25
	Prefix Z—replacement note.	£45	£65

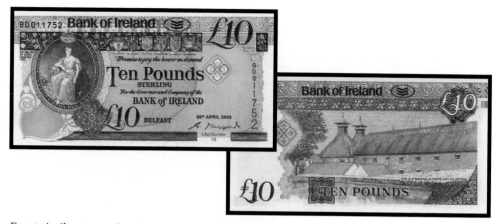

Front similar to previous issue; new reverse design.
Obverse—blue and brown on a multicoloured underprint. Hibernia to the left
Reverse—maroon and multicoloured. Illustration of the "Old Bushmills" Distillery

		EF	UNC
NI.227	*Signatory: S. Kirkpatrick* (Chief Executive N. I.)		
	Prefix BD dated 20.4.2008 and ongoing	—	£18
	Prefix ZZ—replacement note...		£45

TWENTY POUNDS

Size 200 mm x 108 mm approximately

Obverse—black on an orange/brown and pale green underprint. Statues of Hibernia to the left and right
Reverse—orange/brown panel on a pale green underprint. Hibernia seated at the centre

		F	VF
NI.231	*Signatory: J. H. Craig*		
	Prefix X/10 dated 9.5.1929 (print run of just 2,500 notes).	£700	£1500

Size 160 mm x 90 mm approximately

Issued in 1983 to commemorate the bicentenary anniversary of the Bank of Ireland 1783–1983
Obverse—green on a multicoloured underprint. Hibernia to the right
Reverse—mainly green; Bank of Ireland building surrounded by images representing industry in Northern Ireland

		VF	EF
NI.232	*Signatory: A. S. J. O'Neill* (Manager)		
	Prefix A...	£250	£450
	Prefix Z—replacement note	£400	—

Similar to the above note but without the commemorative text near the top. (From 1984)
Obverse—green on a multicoloured underprint. Hibernia to the right
Reverse—mainly green; Bank of Ireland building surrounded by images representing industry in Northern Ireland

		EF	UNC
NI.233a	*Signatory: A. S. J. O'Neill* (Manager)		
	Prefix A and prefix B	£140	£240
	Prefix Z—replacement note		Rare
NI.233b	*Signatory: D. J. Harrison* (Manager)		
	Prefix B to prefix F	£85	£140
	Prefix Z—replacement note	£160	£220

Size 150 mm x 80 mm approximately

Obverse—green and brown on a multicoloured underprint. Hibernia seated in a roundel to the left
Reverse—mainly green on a multicoloured underprint. Illustration of the Queen's University of Belfast

NI.234	Signatory: D. J. Harrison (Manager)	*EF*	*UNC*
	Prefix A dated 9.5.1991 to prefix K dated 28.5.1993.	£50	£80
	Prefix Z—replacement note	£120	£200

Similar to previous issue with some design and colour changes
Obverse—green, brown and purple on a multicoloured underprint. Hibernia seated in a roundel to the left
Reverse—mainly green on a multicoloured underprint. Illustration of the Queen's University of Belfast

NI.235	Signatory: G. McGinn (Chief Executive N. I.)		
	Prefix L dated 1.7.1995 to prefix V dated 1.7.1997	£40	£60
	Prefix Z—replacement note.	£85	£125

As previous issue but with enhanced security feature at top right on the front and changes to reverse design

Obverse—green, brown and purple on a multicoloured underprint. Hibernia seated in a roundel to the left
Reverse—mainly green on a multicoloured underprint. Illustration of the Queen's University of Belfast

		EF	UNC
NI.236a	*Signatory: G. McGinn (Chief Executive N. I.)*		
	Prefix W dated 1.1.1999 to prefix BC dated 5.9.2000	£35	£55
	Prefix Z—replacement note	£70	£110
NI.236b	*Signatory: D. McGowan (Chief Executive N. I.)*		
	Prefix BD dated 1.1.2003 to prefix CS dated 22.2.2007	—	£40
	Prefix Z—replacement note	£70	£100

Front similar to previous issue; new reverse design.

Obverse—green, brown and purple on a multicoloured underprint. Hibernia seated in a roundel to the left
Reverse—green and multicoloured. Illustration of "Old Bushmills" Distillery

NI.237	*Signatory: S. Kirkpatrick (Chief Executive N. I.)*		
	Prefix BD to BX dated 20.4.2008 and ongoing	—	£35
	Prefix ZZ—replacement note	—	£65

FIFTY POUNDS

Size 156 mm x 85 mm approximately

Obverse—green, brown and blue on a multicoloured underprint. Hibernia seated in a roundel to the left
Reverse—mainly brown on a multicoloured underprint. Illustration of the Queen's University of Belfast

		EF	UNC
NI.241a	*Signatory: G. McGinn (Chief Executive N. I.)*		
	Prefix A dated 1.7.1995...	£100	£130
	Prefix Z—replacement note.	£200	£300
NI.241b	*Signatory: R. Keenan (Chief Executive U.K.)*		
	Prefix A dated 5.4.2004 (starting from A 200001)	—	£95
	Prefix Z—replacement note.	£100	£230

ONE HUNDRED POUNDS

Size 160 mm x 90 mm approximately

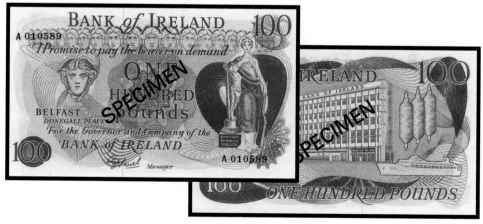

First issued in 1974. Value sign at top right and bottom left is shown as "100"
Obverse—red on a multicoloured underprint. Hibernia to the right
Reverse—mainly red; Bank of Ireland building surrounded by images representing industry in Northern Ireland

		VF	EF
NI.251a	*Signatory: H. H. M. Chestnutt (Manager)*		
	Prefix A..	£450	£750
NI.251b	*Signatory: A. S. J. O'Neill (Manager)*		
	Prefix A..	£350	£550

"Sterling" added at centre and value sign at top right and bottom left is now shown as "£100". (From 1984)

		EF	UNC
NI.252a	*Signatory: A. S. J. O'Neill* (Manager)		
	Prefix A...	£380	£500
NI.252b	*Signatory: D. J. Harrison* (Manager)		
	Prefix A...	£280	£400

Size 164 mm x 90 mm approximately

Obverse — red and brown on a multicoloured underprint. Hibernia seated in a roundel to the left
Reverse — mainly red on a multicoloured underprint. Illustration of the Queen's University of Belfast

NI.253	*Signatory: D. J. Harrison* (Manager)		
	Prefix A dated 28.8.1992..	£280	£400

Obverse—red, mauve, brown and blue on a multicoloured underprint. Hibernia seated in a roundel to the left
Reverse—mainly mauve on a multicoloured underprint. Illustration of the Queen's University of Belfast

		EF	UNC
NI.254a	*Signatory: G. McGinn* (Chief Executive N. I.)		
	Prefix A dated 1.7.1995	£200	£300
	Prefix Z—replacement note	£300	£450
NI.254b	*Signatory: G. McGowan* (Chief Executive N. I.)		
	Prefix A dated 1.3.2005	—	£190
	Prefix Z—replacement note	£250	£360

BELFAST BANKING COMPANY LIMITED

The Belfast Banking Company was formed in Belfast in 1827, taking over the business of two local private banking partnerships which dated back to 1808 and 1809. In 1917 it was acquired by the London City and Midland Bank, and six years later all of its branches in what was then the Irish Free State were sold off to the Royal Bank of Ireland. This made the Belfast Bank the only Irish note-issuing bank which had no branches outside Northern Ireland.

The Midland Bank made a successful takeover bid for the Northern Bank in 1965, and in July 1970 the Belfast Bank's separate existence ended when the Midland's two Irish subsidiaries were merged in the name of the Northern Bank Limited.

ONE POUND

Size 152 mm x 84 mm approximately

Obverse—black with a blue value panel at the centre
Reverse—blue panel with the name of the bank and value

		F	VF
NI.301a	*Handsigned, with black serial numbers*		
	Prefix A dated 2.1.1922 to prefix E/E dated 8.11.1928	£160	£250

		EF	UNC
NI.301b	*Handsigned, with blue serial numbers*		
	Prefix E/F dated 9.11.1939 to prefix F/G dated 10.8.1940........	£110	£150

FIVE POUNDS

Size 185 mm x 90 mm approximately

Obverse—black with the value in red at the centre
Reverse—red panel with the name of the bank and value

		F	VF
NI.302a	*Handsigned, with black serial numbers*	*F*	*VF*
	Prefix B/G dated 3.1.1923 to prefix B/U dated 7.9.1927	£180	£300
NI.302b	*Handsigned, with red serial numbers*	*VF*	*EF*
	Prefix B/U dated 8.3.1928 to prefix D/X dated 2.10.1942........	from £75	£150
NI.302c	*Handsigned, with red serial numbers*	*EF*	*UNC*
	Prefix D/X to prefix E/D dated 6.1.1966	£100	£150

TEN POUNDS

Size 213 mm x 108 mm approximately

Obverse—black with the value in green at the centre
Reverse—green panel with the name of the bank and value

		F	VF
NI.303a	*Handsigned, with black serial numbers*	*F*	*VF*
	Prefix X to prefix Y dated 3.1.1923...		Rare

NI.303b	*Handsigned, with green serial numbers*		*VF*	*EF*
	Prefix Y dated 9.1.1929 to prefix A/N dated 1.1.1943............... from		£150	£240

NI.303c	*Handsigned, with green serial numbers*		*EF*	*UNC*
	Prefix A/N dated 3.12.1963 to prefix A/O dated 5.6.1965.......		£120	£170

TWENTY POUNDS

Size 210 mm x 110 mm approximately

Obverse—black with the value in purple at the centre
Reverse—purple panel with the name of the bank and value

		F	*VF*
NI.304a	*Handsigned, with black serial numbers*		
	Prefix D dated 3.1.1923..	£380	£650
NI.304b	*Handsigned, with purple serial numbers*		
	Prefix D dated 9.11.1939 to prefix E dated 10.8.1940.................	£250	£450
NI.304c	*Handsigned, with black serial numbers*		
	Prefix E dated 3.2.1943 and 5.6.1965...	£300	£500

FIFTY POUNDS

Size 210 mm x 110 mm approximately

Obverse—black with the value in orange at the centre
Reverse—orange panel with the name of the bank and value

		F	VF
NI.305a	*Handsigned, with black serial numbers*		
	Prefix B dated 3.1.1923 and 3.5.1923...	£550	£950
NI.305b	*Handsigned, with orange serial numbers*		
	Prefix B dated 9.11.1939 and 10.8.1940.......................................	£380	£650

		VF	EF
NI.305c	*Handsigned, with black serial numbers*		
	Prefix B dated 3.2.1943 and 3.12.1963...	£600	£1100

ONE HUNDRED POUNDS

Size 210 mm x 110 mm approximately

Obverse—black with the value in red at the centre
Reverse—red panel with the name of the bank and value

		F	VF
NI.306a	*Handsigned, with black serial numbers*		
	Prefix A dated 3.1.1923 and 3.5.1923	£550	£900
NI.306b	*Handsigned, with red serial numbers*		
	Prefix A dated 9.11.1939	£550	£900
NI.306c	*Handsigned, with black serial numbers*		
	Prefix A dated 3.2.1943	£500	£900

		VF	EF
NI306d	*Handsigned, with red serial numbers*		
	Prefix A dated 3.12.1963	£700	£1250
NI306e	*Printed signature G. B. Smyth, red serial numbers*		
	Prefix B dated 8.5.1968..	£800	£1350

FIRST TRUST BANK

The First Trust Bank was established in the early 1990s as a result of a merger between Allied Irish Banks plc and the Trustee Savings Bank. The new bank did not issue any five Pound notes.

TEN POUNDS

Size 142 mm x 75 mm approximately

Obverse—brown and purple on a multicoloured underprint. Portrait of a young man to the right.
Reverse—brown and multicoloured. Illustration of the Spanish galleass "The Girona" at the centre

		EF	UNC
NI.411a	*Signatory: E. F. McElroy* (Group Managing Director)		
	Prefix AB to prefix HB dated 10.1.1994	£40	£65
	Prefix ZB—replacement note...		Rare
NI.411b	*Signatory: D. E. Harvey* (Managing Director)		
	Prefix JB to prefix NB dated 1.3.1996..	£50	£80
	Prefix ZB—replacement note...		Rare

Obverse—brown and purple on a multicoloured underprint. Portrait of a young man to the right.
Additional gold security feature at top right
Reverse—brown and multicoloured. Illustration of the Spanish galleass "The Girona" at the centre

		EF	UNC
NI.412	*Signatory: D. J. Licence* (Managing Director, First Trust Bank)		
	Prefix AA to prefix SA dated 1.1.1998, and ongoing	—	£25
	Prefix ZA—replacement note	£80	£120

TWENTY POUNDS

Size 150 mm x 80 mm approximately

Obverse—mauve and brown on a multicoloured underprint; portrait of a mature lady to the right
Reverse—mauve on a multicoloured underprint. Illustration of rock chimney at Lacada Point, Giant's
Causeway

		EF	UNC
NI.421a	*Signatory: E. F. McElroy* (Group Managing Director)		
	Prefix AC to prefix HC dated 10.1.1994......................................	£45	£85
	Prefix ZC—replacement note...		Rare
NI.421b	*Signatory: D. E. Harvey* (Managing Director)		
	Prefix JC to prefix NC dated 1.1.1996, and..................................	£95	£150
	Prefix PC to prefix RC dated 1.3.1996..	£95	£150
	Prefix ZC—replacement note...		Rare

Obverse—mauve and brown on a multicoloured underprint; portrait of a mature lady to the right. Additional gold security feature at top right
Reverse—mauve on a multicoloured underprint. Illustration of rock chimney at Lacada Point, Giant's Causeway

NI.422a *Signatory: D. J. Licence* (Managing Director, First Trust Bank)

	EF	*UNC*
Prefix AA to prefix KB 500000 dated 1.1.1998	£30	£50
Prefix ZA—replacement note	£100	£140

NI.422b *Signatory: T. McDade* (Managing Director, First Trust Bank)

	EF	*UNC*
Prefix KB 500001 to RB dated 1.5.2007 and ongoing................	—	£40
Prefix ZA—replacement note.	£100	£140

FIFTY POUNDS

Size 155 mm x 85 mm approximately

Obverse—blue and green on a multicoloured underprint. Portrait of a mature man to the right
Reverse—blue, green and multicoloured. Picture of two cherubs holding a commemorative medal of 1588 depicting the defeat of the Spanish Armada

NI.431 *Signatory: E. F. McElroy* (Group Managing Director)

Prefix AD dated 10.1.1994	£120	£200
Prefix ZD—replacement note.		Rare

Obverse—blue and green on a multicoloured underprint. Portrait of a mature man to the right. Additional silver security feature over value at top right
Reverse—blue, green and multicoloured. Picture of two cherubs holding a commemorative medal of 1588 depicting the defeat of the Spanish Armada

	EF	UNC
NI.432 *Signatory: D. J. Licence* (Managing Director, First Trust Bank)		
Prefix AA and BA dated 1.1.1998	—	£100
Prefix ZA—replacement note.		Rare

ONE HUNDRED POUNDS

Size 160 mm x 90 mm approximately

Obverse—green, brown and black on a multicoloured underprint. Portraits of a mature man and woman to the right
Reverse—green, brown and black on a multicoloured underprint. Illustration of the Spanish Armada at the centre

			EF	UNC
NI.441a	*Signatory: E. F. McElroy* (Group Managing Director)			
	Prefix AE dated 10.1.1994		£220	£350
	Prefix ZE—replacement note.			Rare
NI.441b	*Signatory: D. E. Harvey* (Managing Director)			
	Prefix AE dated 1.3.1996		£300	£500
	Prefix ZE—replacement note.			Rare

Obverse—green, brown and black on a multicoloured underprint. Portraits of a mature man and woman to the right. Additional silver security feature over value at top right
Reverse—green, brown and black on a multicoloured underprint. Illustration of the Spanish Armada at the centre

NI.442	*Signatory: D. J. Licence* (Managing Director, First Trust Bank)			
	Prefix AA dated 1.1.1998		—	£200
	Prefix ZA—replacement note.			Rare

NATIONAL BANK LIMITED

The Bank was founded in 1835 by Daniel O'Connell. Its Irish branches were acquired by the Bank of Ireland in December 1965, and for a short time thereafter it carried on business as the National Bank of Ireland Limited. A few years later its separate identity disappeared when it was merged into the Bank of Ireland.

Examples of early National Bank notes.

ONE POUND

Size 149 mm x 80 mm approximately

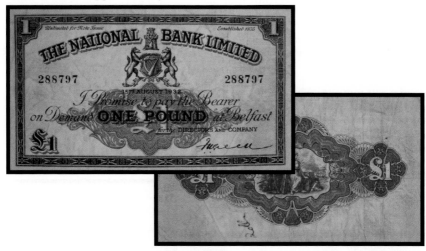

Obverse—black—green panel at centre with "£1"
Reverse—green—Hibernia with harp and wolfhound at the centre flanked by £1 value

		F	VF
NI.501	Signatory: F. H. Green		
	No prefix letters; dated 6.5.1929, 1.11.1931, 1.1.1932	£350	£800
	15.8.1932 and 1.8.1933.		

Size 152 mm x 84 mm approximately

Obverse—black on a green and yellow underprint. Hibernia with harp and wolfhound at the centre
Reverse—green and lilac. Bank's Coat of Arms flanked by £1 value panels

		VF	EF
NI.502	Signatory: F. H. Green		
	Prefix A dated 1.2.1937, 1.9.1937 and 2.10.1939	£100	£200

FIVE POUNDS

Size 149 mm x 80 mm approximately
Obverse—dark blue—brown panel at centre with "£5"
Reverse—brown—Hibernia with harp and wolfhound at centre flanked by £5 value

		F	VF
NI.503	*Signatory: F. H. Green* No prefix letters; dated 6.5.1929, 1.8.1933 and 1.10.1934		Rare

Size 155 mm x 91 mm approximately

Obverse—blue on a blue and tan underprint. Hibernia at lower left with harp and wolfhound
Reverse—black on a green and tan underprint. Bank's Coat of Arms at centre

		VF	EF
NI.504a	*Signatory: F. H. Green* Prefix A dated 1.2.1937; 1.9.1937 and 2.10.1939	£160	£320
NI.504b	*Signatory: J. J. O'Donnell* Prefix A dated 1.8.1942; 1.1.1949 and 2.5.1949	£150	£280
NI.504c	*Signatory: R. W. Maguire* Prefix A dated 1.5.1964 – specimens only		Rare

TEN POUNDS

Size 149 mm x 80 mm approximately

Obverse—green – red/brown panel at centre with "£10"
Reverse—brown – Hibernia with harp and wolfhound at centre flanked by £10 value

		F	VF
NI.505	*Signatory: F. H. Green* No prefix letters; dated 6.5.1929; 2.10.1931 and 1.8.1933		Rare

Size 152 mm x 84 mm approximately

Obverse—green on a pink and yellow underprint. Hibernia seated with harp and wolfhound at the centre
Reverse—brown on a green and yellow underprint. Bank's Coat of Arms at left centre flanked by £10 value panels

		VF	EF
NI.506a	*Signatory: F. H. Green* Prefix A dated 1.2.1937, 1.9.1937 and 2.10.1939	£220	£450
NI.506b	*Signatory: J. J. O'Donnell* Prefix A dated 1.8.1942 and 2.5.1949	£180	£350
NI.506c	*Signatory: R.H.R. Fry* Prefix A dated 1.7.1959	£180	£320

TWENTY POUNDS

Size 149 mm x 80 mm approximately

Obverse—brown—blue panel at centre with "£20"
Reverse—blue—Hibernia with harp and wolfhound at centre flanked by £20 value panels

		F	VF
NI.507	*Signatory: F. H. Green* No prefix letters; dated 6.5.1929		Rare

Size 160 mm x 90 mm approximately

Obverse—brown on a grey and yellow underprint. Hibernia at lower left with harp and wolfhound
Reverse—blue, green and yellow. Bank's Coat of Arms at the centre

		VF	EF
NI.508a	*Signatory: F. H. Green* Prefix A dated 1.2.1937 and 2.10.1939	£550	£1200
NI.508b	*Signatory: J. J. O'Donnell* Prefix A dated 1.8.1942 and 1.1.1949	£480	£850
NI.508c	*Signatory: R.H.R. Fry* Prefix A dated 1.7.1959	£500	£950

NORTHERN BANK LIMITED

The Northern Bank began life as a private partnership in Belfast in 1809, and became the joint stock Northern Banking Company in 1824, at which time it was the only joint stock banking company anywhere in the British Isles apart from Scotland.

Branches outside Belfast were established from 1835 onwards, and in 1888 the bank opened its first office in Dublin by acquiring the business of the private bankers Ball & Co. Five years earlier the Northern had adopted limited liability, thereby becoming the Northern Banking Company Limited, and in 1929 it shortened its name to Northern Bank Limited.

The Midland Bank (which already owned the Belfast Banking Company) acquired the share capital of the Northern Bank in 1965, and in 1970 merged its two Irish banks in the name of the Northern. In order to raise capital following a disastrous investment in the USA, the Midland sold the Northern Bank in 1987 to National Banks Australia Limited, who in turn sold it to Danske Bank, Copenhagen.

Some examples of early notes

ONE POUND

Size 151 mm x 84 mm approximately

Obverse—black with "ONE" in a blue panel at the centre; vignette with sailing ship above
Reverse—blue. "NBL" in round design at centre with value "1" at either side

		F	VF
NI.601a	*Signatory: S. W. Knox* (on prefix N-I/A and N-I/E)	–	–
NI.601b	*Signatory: H. H. Stewart* (on prefix N-I/B and N-I/F)	–	–
NI.601c	*Signatory: W. F. Scott* (on prefix N-I/C)	–	–
NI.601d	*Signatory: A. P. Tibbey* (on prefix N-I/D)	–	–

Red serial numbers
Prefix <u>N-I</u> dated 6.5.1929 to prefix <u>N-I</u> dated 1.8.1929.............. £55 £100
    A   F

		EF	UNC
NI.601e	*Signatory: F. W. White* Black serial numbers Prefix <u>N-I</u> dated 1.1.1940 .... H	£60	£90

Size 135 mm x 67 mm approximately

Obverse—green on a multicoloured background; illustrations of agriculture, shipbuilding and weaving
Reverse—green on a multicoloured background; Griffin emblem at the centre

		EF	UNC
NI.602a	*Signatory: W. S. Wilson*		
	Prefix C dated 1.7.1970..	£20	£35
NI.602b	*Signatory: H. M. Gabbey*		
	Prefix C dated 1.10.1971..	£20	£35
NI.602c	*Signatory: W. Ervin*		
	Prefix C dated 1.8.1978..	£14	£25

FIVE POUNDS

Size 150 mm x 86 mm approximately

Heading: Northern Bank Ltd. on earlier notes of the Northern Banking Company Limited
Obverse – black with "FIVE" in a blue panel at the centre. Vignette with sailing ship above
Reverse – blue; "NBC" in a round panel at the centre with "5" in small round panels at either side

		F	VF
NI.611	*Signatories: Handsigned*		
	Prefix B dated 1.9.1927 (but issued on or after 6th May 1929)		Rare

Heading: Northern Bank Limited
Obverse—black with "FIVE" in a blue panel at the centre. Vignette with sailing ship above
Reverse—blue; "NBL" in a round panel at the centre with "5" in small round panels at either side

		F	VF
NI.612a	Signatory: S.W.Knox		
	Prefix <u>N-I</u> dated 6.5.1929 .... A	£80	£180
NI.612b	Signatory: H. H. Stewart		
	Prefix <u>N-I</u> dated 6.5.1929 .... B	£80	£180

Size 170 mm x 95 mm approximately

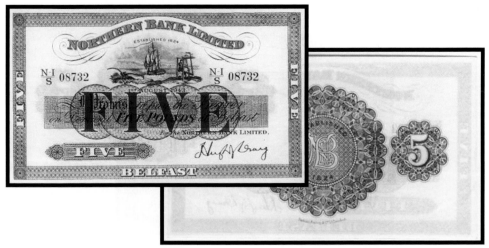

Obverse—black with "FIVE" in a green panel at the centre. Vignette with sailing ship above
Reverse—blue; "NBL" in a round panel at the centre with "5" in small round panels at either side

		VF	EF
NI.613a	Signatory: F. W. White (on prefix N-I/D, N-I/H, N-I/L, N-I/P)	–	–
NI.613b	Signatory: H. J. Craig (on prefix N-I/E, N-I/I, N-I/M, N-I/S)	–	–
NI.613c	Signatory: W. F. Scott (on prefix N-I/B, N-I/F, N-I/J, N-I/N, N-I/T)	–	–
NI.613d	Signatory: A. P. Tibbey (on prefix N-I/C, N-I/G, N-I/K, N-I/O)	–	–
NI.613e	Signatory: J. E. Forde (on prefix N-I/R)	–	–

		F	VF
	Prefix <u>N-I</u> dated 1.9.1937 to prefix <u>N-I</u> dated 1.11.1943 from .. B T	£75	£130

Size 150 mm x 86 mm approximately

Obverse—black with "FIVE" in a green panel at the centre. Vignette with sailing ship above
Reverse—blue; "NBL" in a round panel at the centre with "5" in small round panels at either side

		EF	UNC
NI.614	*Signatory: E. D. Hill*		
	Prefix <u>N-I</u> dated 1.10.1968	£80	£120
	U		

Size 150 mm x 84 mm approximately

Obverse—blue on a multicoloured background; illustrations of agriculture, shipbuilding and weaving
Reverse—blue on a multicoloured background; Griffin emblem at the centre

NI.615a	*Signatory: W. S. Wilson*		
	Prefix D dated 1.7.1970	£85	£150
NI.615b	*Signatory: H. M. Gabbey*		
	Prefix D dated 1.10.1971	£85	£150
NI.615c	*Signatory: J. B. Newland*		
	Prefix D dated 1.7.1974 and 1.1.1976...	£40	£70
NI.615d	*Signatory: W. Ervin*		
	Prefix D dated 1.4.1982	£35	£60
NI.615e	*Signatory: J. Roberts*		
	Prefix D dated 3.2.1986	£35	£60

Size 136 mm x 70 mm approximately

Obverse—blue on a multicoloured background; portrait of W.A.Trail 1844-1933
Reverse—blue on a multicoloured background; images of satellite dish and computer systems

		EF	UNC
NI.616	Signatory: S.H.Torrens (Chief Executive)		
	Prefix A dated 24.8.1988 to 24.8.1990	£18	£35
	Prefix Z—replacement note	£50	£85

Size 70 mm x 136 mm approximately

 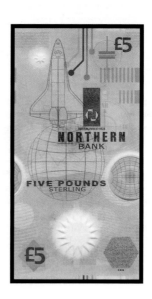

Polymer note—vertical format
Obverse—blue with a coloured globe to left and right of centre and a transparent star shape at the bottom
Reverse—blue with a line drawing of a globe and the space shuttle

		EF	UNC
NI.617	Signatory: D. Price (Chief Executive)		
	Prefix MM dated 8.10.1999	£10	£25
	Prefix Y2K dated 1.1.2000, issued in a presentation pack........	£12	£35
	Prefix N (replacement notes).	£85	£180

TEN POUNDS

Size 200 mm x 112 mm approximately

Heading: Northern Bank Ltd. on earlier notes of the Northern Banking Company Limited
Obverse—black with "TEN" in a blue panel at the centre. Vignette with sailing ship above. Listing of the various branches of the Bank printed across the lower centre
Reverse—blue; "NBC" in a round panel at the centre with "10" in small round panels at either side

		F	VF

NI.621 *Signatory: handsigned*
Prefix A dated 1.3.1920 (but issued on or after 6th May 1929)   –   Rare

Heading: Northern Bank Ltd. on earlier notes of the Northern Banking Company Limited
Obverse—black with "TEN" in a blue panel at the centre. Vignette with sailing ship above. Without the listing of the Bank's branches
Reverse—blue; "NBC" in a round panel at the centre with "10" in small round panels at either side

NI.622 *Signatory: handsigned*
Prefix B dated 10.10.1921 (but issued on or after 6th May 1929)   –   Rare

Size 168 mm x 95 mm approximately

Obverse—black with "TEN" in a red panel at the centre. Vignette with sailing ship above
Reverse—blue; "NBL" in a round panel at the centre with "10" in small round panels at either side

		F	VF
NI.623a	*Signatory: handsigned*		
	Prefix <u>N-I</u> dated 1.1.1930 to prefix <u>N-I</u> dated 1.1.1940 from.... A E	£70	£140

		VF	EF
NI.623b	*Signatory: W. F. Scott* (on prefix N-I/F, N-I/J)............................	–	–
NI.623c	*Signatory: A. P. Tibbey* (on prefix N-I/G, N-I/K)	–	–
NI.623d	*Signatory: F. W. White* (on prefix N-I/H, N-I/L)........................	–	–
NI.623e	*Signatory: H. J. Craig* (on prefix N-I/I, N-I/N)	–	–
NI.623f	*Signatory: J. E. Forde* (on prefix N-I/M)	–	–
	Prefix <u>N-I</u> dated 1.8.1940 to prefix <u>N-I</u> dated 1.11.1943............ F N	£95	£160
NI.623g	*Signatory: E. D. Hill*		
	Prefix <u>N-I</u> dated 1.10.1968 .... OO	£85	£150

Size 151 mm x 85 mm approximately

Obverse—brown on a multicoloured background; illustrations of agriculture, shipbuilding and weaving
Reverse—brown on a multicoloured background; Griffin emblem at the centre

		EF	UNC
NI.624a	*Signatory: W. S. Wilson*		
	Prefix E dated 1.7.1970	£150	£350
NI.624b	*Signatory: H. M. Gabbey*		
	Prefix E dated 1.10.1971	£150	£350
NI.624c	*Signatory: J. B. Newland*		
	Prefix E dated 1.7.1975 to 1.1.1978	£100	£180
NI.624d	*Signatory: W. Ervin*		
	Prefix E dated 1.3.1981 and 1.4.1982	£75	£120
NI.624e	*Signatory: J. Roberts*		
	Prefix E dated 2.1.1985 to 2.3.1987	£60	£90
NI.624f	*Signatory: S. H. Torrens*		
	Prefix E dated 15.6.1988	£60	£90

Size 142 mm x 75 mm approximately

Obverse—brown and red on a multicoloured background; portrait of J.B.Dunlop 1840-1921
Reverse—brown on a multicoloured background; images of satellite dish and computer systems

NI.625a	*Signatory: S.H.Torrens* (Chief Executive)		
	Prefix B dated 24.8.1988 to 24.8.1993	£45	£70
	Prefix Z—replacement note.	£90	£150
NI.625b	*Signatory: J.R.Wright* (Chief Executive)		
	Prefix B dated 30.8.1996.	£40	£60
	Prefix Z—replacement note	£90	£150

Obverse—brown and red on a multicoloured background; portrait of J.B.Dunlop 1840-1921
Reverse—brown on a multicoloured background; picture of façade of City Hall, Belfast

		EF	UNC
NI.626a	*Signatory: G. Savage* (Chief Executive)		
	Prefix BA and BB dated 24.2.1997	£25	£35
	Prefix ZZ—replacement note...	£80	£140
NI.626b	*Signatory: D. Price* (Chief Executive)		
	Prefix BC dated 8.10.1999	£25	£35
	Prefix ZZ—replacement note...	£80	£140

Similar to previous issue but change of colours to "Northern Bank" typeface and logo. This issue was quickly with drawn from circulation after a major robbery at the bank late in 2004
Obverse—brown and red on a multicoloured background; portrait of J.B.Dunlop 1840-1921
Reverse—brown on a multicoloured background; picture of façade of City Hall, Belfast

		EF	UNC
NI.627	*Signatory: D. Price* (Chief Executive)		
	Prefix BD dated 29.4.2004...	£45	£75
	Prefix ZZ—replacement note...	—	Rare

Similar to previous issue but change of colour
Obverse–mainly green on a multicolured background; portrait of J. B Dunlop 1840–1921
Reverse–green on a multicoloured background; picture of façade of City Hall, Belfast

		EF	UNC
NI.628	*Signatory: D. Price* (Chief Executive)		
	Prefix GE and GF dated 19.1.2005...	—	£25
	Prefix YY—replacement note...	—	£60

Similar to previous issue with minor design changes; The Bank title is now in a block at the top of the note
Obverse–mainly green on a multicoloured background; portrait of J. B Dunlop 1840–1921
Reverse–green on a multicoloured background; picture of façade of City Hall, Belfast

		EF	UNC
NI.629	*Signatory: G. Mallon* (Chief Executive)		
	Prefix GG dated 9.11.2008 and ongoing.	—	£18
	Prefix YY—replacement note...	£30	£45

TWENTY POUNDS

Size 203 mm x 117 mm approximately

Heading: Northern Bank Ltd. on earlier notes of the Northern Banking Company Limited
Obverse—black with "TWENTY" in a blue panel at the centre. Vignette with sailing ship above
Reverse—blue; "NBC" in a round panel at the centre with "20" in small round panels at either side

		F	VF
NI.631	*Signatory: Handsigned* Prefix A dated 20.10.1921 (but issued on or after 6th May 1929)	£650	£1250

Size 159 mm x 90 mm approximately

Obverse—purple on a multicoloured background; illustrations of agriculture, shipbuilding and weaving
Reverse—purple on a multicoloured background; Griffin emblem at the centre

		EF	UNC
NI.632a	*Signatory: W. S. Wilson* Prefix F dated 1.7.1970	£280	—
NI.632b	*Signatory: W. Ervin* Prefix F dated 1.3.1981 and 1.12.1984	£130	£220
NI.632c	*Signatory: J. Roberts* Prefix F dated 2.3.1987	£110	£190
NI632d	*Signatory: S. H. Torrens* Prefix F dated 15.6.1988	£80	£150

Size 150 mm x 80 mm approximately

Obverse—mauve and brown on a multicoloured background; portrait of H. Ferguson 1884–1960
Reverse—mauve on a multicoloured background; images of satellite dish and computer systems

		EF	UNC
NI.633a	*Signatory: S.H.Torrens* (Chief Executive)		
	Prefix C dated 24.8.1988 to 24.8.1993	£65	£100
	Prefix Z—replacement note	£150	—
NI.633b	*Signatory: J.R.Wright* (Chief Executive)		
	Prefix C dated 30.8.1996	£50	£85
	Prefix Z—replacement note	£150	£220

Obverse—mauve on a multicoloured background; portrait of H. Ferguson 1884–1960
Reverse—mauve on a multicoloured background; picture of façade of City Hall, Belfast

		EF	UNC
NI.634a	*Signatory: G. Savage* (Chief Executive)		
	Prefix CA and CB dated 24.2.1997	£40	£55
	Prefix ZZ—replacement note	£100	—
NI.634b	*Signatory: D. Price* (Chief Executive)		
	Prefix CB to CD dated 8.10.1999	£35	£50
	Prefix ZZ—replacement note	£100	—

Commemorative issue "175 Years of Banking 1824 – 1999"
Obverse—mauve on a multicoloured background; portrait of H.Ferguson 1884-1960
Reverse—mauve on a multicoloured background; picture of façade of City Hall, Belfast

		EF	UNC
NI.635	*Signatory: D. Price* (Chief Executive)		
	Prefix NB dated 1.9.1999..	£45	£65

Obverse–blue on a multicoloured background; portrait of H.Ferguson 1884-1960
Reverse–blue on a multicoloured background; picture of façade of City Hall, Belfast

NI.636	*Signatory: D. Price* (Chief Executive)		
	Prefix HE dated 19.1.2005 to prefix HG dated 6.11.2006..........	—	£40
	Prefix YY—replacement note...	£65	£85

FIFTY POUNDS

Size 195 mm x 108 mm approximately

Heading: Northern Bank Ltd. on earlier notes of the Northern Banking Company Limited
Obverse—black with "FIFTY" in a blue panel at the centre. Vignette with sailing ship above
Reverse—blue; "NBC" in a round panel at the centre with "50" in small round panels at either side.
These notes were issued on or after 6th May 1929

		F	VF
NI.641a	*Signatory: Handsigned (usually S. W. Knox)* No prefix letter, red serial numbers—dated 5.8.1914		from £750
NI.641b	*Signatory: Handsigned (usually H. J. Craig)* No prefix letter, black serial numbers—dated 25.4.1918		from £700

Size 185 mm x 110 mm approximately

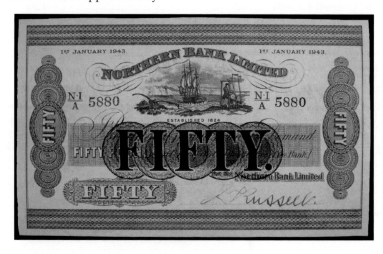

Obverse—black with "FIFTY" in a blue panel at the centre. Vignette with sailing ship above
Reverse—blue; "NBC" in a round panel at the centre with "50" in small round panels at either side

		VF	EF
NI.642a	*Signatory: Handsigned* Prefix <u>N-I</u> dated 1.1.1943 A	£650	£1200

Letters in central panel on the reverse changed to "NBL"	EF	UNC

NI.642b *Signatory: Handsigned*
Prefix <u>N-I</u> dated 1.10.1968 .... £600 £1100
B

Size 170 mm x 95 mm approximately

Obverse—orange/brown on a multicoloured background; illustrations of agriculture, shipbuilding and weaving
Reverse—reddish brown; Griffin emblem at the centre

NI.643a *Signatory: W. S. Wilson*
Prefix G dated 1.7.1970 .... £450 —

NI.643b *Signatory: J. B. Newland*
Prefix G dated 1.1.1975 (only 4000 issued) .... £550 —

NI.643c *Signatory: W. Ervin*
Prefix G dated 1.3.1981 .... £260 £450

Size 156 mm x 85 mm approximately

Obverse—green and multicoloured; portrait of Sir F. C. Davidson 1846-1921
Reverse—green and multicoloured; images of satellite dish and computer systems

NI.644 *Signatory: S. H. Torrens* (Chief Executive)
Prefix D dated 1.11.1990 .... £130 £180

Obverse—green, blue and multicoloured; portrait of Sir F. C. Davidson 1846–1921
Reverse—green, blue and multicoloured; picture of façade of City Hall, Belfast

		EF	UNC
NI.645	*Signatory: D. Price* (Chief Executive)		
	Prefix DA dated 8.10.1999	£100	£140
	Prefix ZZ—replacement note...	£200	—

Obverse—violet and multicoloured; portrait of Sir F. C. Davidson 1846–1921
Reverse—violet and multicoloured; picture of façade of City Hall, Belfast

		EF	UNC
NI.646	*Signatory: D. Price* (Chief Executive)		
	Prefix JB dated 19.1.2005..	—	£95
	Prefix YY—replacement note...	£150	£220

ONE HUNDRED POUNDS

Size 210 mm x 110 mm approximately

Heading: Northern Bank Ltd. on earlier notes of the Northern Banking Company Limited
Obverse—black with "£100" in a blue panel at the centre. Vignette with sailing ship above
Reverse—blue; "NBC" in a round panel at the centre with "100" in small round panels at either side

		F	VF
NI.651	*Signatory: handsigned*		
	No prefix letter—dated 2.6.1919	£750	£1250

Size 190 mm x 115 mm approximately

Obverse—black with "£100" in a blue panel at the centre. Vignette with sailing ship above
Reverse—blue; "NBC" in a round panel at the centre with "100" in small round panels at either side

		VF	EF
NI.652a	*Signatory: handsigned*		
	Prefix N-I dated 1.1.1943	£850	£1350
	A		

Letters in central panel on the reverse changed to "NBL"
NI.652b	*Signatory: handsigned*		
	Prefix <u>N-I</u> dated 1.10.1968	£750	£1250
	BB		

Size 170 mm x 95 mm approximately

Obverse—red on a multicoloured background; illustrations of agriculture, shipbuilding and weaving
Reverse—red; Griffin emblem at the centre

		EF	UNC
NI.653a	*Signatory: W. S. Wilson* Prefix H dated 1.7.1970	£550	—
NI.653b	*Signatory: H. M. Gabbey* Prefix H dated 1.10.1971	£550	—
NI.653c	*Signatory: J. B. Newland* Prefix H dated 1.1.1975 to 1.2.1977	£350	£550
NI.653d	*Signatory: W. Ervin* Prefix H dated 1.10.1978 and 1.1.1980	£300	£500

Size 164 mm x 90 mm approximately

Obverse—red, brown and multicoloured; portrait of Sir James Martin 1893–1981
Reverse—red, brown and multicoloured; images of satellite dish and computer systems

	EF	UNC
NI.654 *Signatory: S. H. Torrens* (Chief Executive)		
Prefix E dated 1.11.1990	£250	£350

Obverse—brown and multicoloured; portrait of Sir James Martin 1893-1981
Reverse—mauve and multicoloured; picture of façade of City Hall, Belfast

NI.655 *Signatory: D. Price* (Chief Executive)		
Prefix EA dated 8.10.1999	—	£250

Obverse—red, mauve and multicoloured; portrait of Sir James Martin 1893-1981
Reverse—red and multicoloured; picture of façade of City Hall, Belfast

		EF	UNC
NI.655	*Signatory: D. Price* (Chief Executive)		
	Prefix KB dated 19.1.2005	—	£190
	Prefix YY — replacement note	£300	£400

PROVINCIAL
BANK OF IRELAND LIMITED

The Provincial Bank of Ireland was formed in 1825 with its head office in London, and the majority of its initial shareholders were resident in England. It gradually took on a more Irish character, and in 1953 the Head Office was moved from London to Dublin. In 1966 the Provincial Bank merged with the Munster & Leinster Bank and the Royal Bank of Ireland to form Allied Irish Banks Limited, and the operations of the three banks were integrated under the Allied Irish name in 1969. Because of legal problems, however, the Provincial Bank retained an office in Royal Avenue, Belfast and continued to issue notes in its own name until 1981. By then the legal difficulties had been overcome and later note issues were in the name of Allied Irish Banks.

Some examples of early notes:

ONE POUND

Size 148mm x 85 mm approximately

Obverse—black with "£1" in a green panel at the centre; vignette with Bank building above
Reverse—blue panel with Britannia and Hibernia seated at the centre

		F	VF
NI.701a	*Signatory: Hume Robertson*		
	Prefix N dated 6.5.1929 and prefix N/A dated 1.8.1930	£250	£550
NI.701b	*Signatory: F. S. Forde*		
	Prefix N/A dated 1.2.1932 to prefix N/B dated 1.6.1934.........	£250	£550

Obverse—black with "£1" in a green panel at the centre; vignette with Bank building above
Reverse—green panel with Britannia and Hibernia seated at the centre

		F	VF
NI.702a	*Signatory: F. S. Forde* Prefix N/C dated 1.8.1935 and 2.11.1936	£180	£300
NI.702b	*Signatory: G. A. Kennedy* Prefix N/D dated 1.9.1937 to prefix N/J dated 1.5.1946..........	£65	£120

Size 150 mm x 85 mm approximately

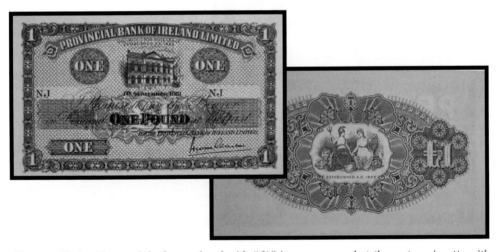

Obverse—black with a mesh background and with "£1" in a green panel at the centre; vignette with Bank building above
Reverse—green panel with Britannia and Hibernia seated at the centre

NI.703a	*Signatory: G. A. Kennedy* Prefix N/J dated 1.5.1946 .... Rare These notes were not issued. A few un-numbered specimen notes are known.
NI.703b	*Signatory: H. W. M. Clarke* Prefix NJ and NK dated 1.9.1951.. Rare These notes were not issued. A few un-numbered specimen notes are known, as well as a few numbered notes with prefix NJ.

Obverse — Olive green on a pale green underprint with a cameo at the centre
Reverse — green panel with the Bank's office building in Belfast at the centre

		VF	EF
NI.704a	Signatory: N. J. Shaw		
	Prefix KN dated 1.3.1954 to prefix LN dated 1.10.1954............	£160	£300
	(printed by Waterlow & Sons Limited)		
NI.704b	Prefix LN dated 1.12.1965...	£130	£220
	(printed by Thomas de la Rue & Co. Ltd.)		

Size 150 mm x 72 mm approximately

Obverse — Olive green on a pale green underprint with a cameo at the centre
Reverse — green panel with the Bank's office building in Belfast at the centre

		EF	UNC
NI.705	Signatory: J. G. McClay		
	Prefix LN dated 1.1.1968 to prefix UN dated 1.1.1972	£40	£75
	Prefix ZZ – replacement note...	£120	—

Size 135 mm x 67 mm approximately

Obverse—green and brown on a multicoloured underprint. Portrait of a boy to the right
Reverse—mainly green. Illustration of the Spanish galleass "The Girona" at the centre

		EF	UNC
NI.706a	*Signatory: J. G. McClay* (Manager)		
	Prefix PN dated 1.1.1977..	£22	£35
	Prefix ZY – replacement note......................................	£90	—
NI.706b	*Signatory: F.H. Hollway* (Manager)		
	Prefix PN dated 1.1.1979..	£20	£35
	Prefix ZY – replacement note......................................	£90	—

FIVE POUNDS

Size 148 mm x 86 mm approximately

Obverse—black with "£5" in a blue panel at the centre; vignette with Bank building above
Reverse—green panel with Britannia and Hibernia seated at the centre

		F	VF
NI.711a	*Signatory: Hume Robertson*		
	Prefix N dated 6.5.1929	£350	£650
NI.711b	*Signatory: F. S. Forde*		
	Prefix N dated 5.10.1933	£400	£800

Size 150 mm x 88 mm approximately

Obverse—blue/grey with "£5" in a brown panel at the centre; vignette with Bank building above
Reverse—brown panel with Britannia and Hibernia seated at the centre

		VF	EF
NI.712a	*Signatory: F. S. Forde*		
	Prefix N dated 5. 8.1935 and 5.5.1936	£500	£850
NI.712b	*Signatory: G. A. Kennedy*		
	Prefix N/A dated 5.5.1938 to prefix N/B dated 5.4.1946.........	£170	£320

Obverse—grey with a mesh background and with "£5" in a brown panel at the centre; vignette with Bank building above
Reverse—brown panel with Britannia and Hibernia seated at the centre

		VF	EF
NI.713	*Signatory: H. W. M. Clarke*		
	Prefix N/B dated 5.1.1948		Rare
	Prefix NB dated 5.12.1949 to 5.4.1952	£85	£170

Size 166 mm x 93 mm approximately

Obverse—Brown on a pale brown underprint with a cameo at the centre
Reverse—brown panel with the Bank's office building in Belfast at the centre

		VF	EF
	Signatory: N. J. Shaw		
NI.714a	Prefix CN dated from 5.10.1954 to 5.5.1959	£80	£140
	(printed by Waterlow & Sons Limited)		
NI.714b	Prefix DN dated from 5.7.1961 to 6.12.1965	£80	£140
	(printed by Thomas de la Rue & Co. Ltd.)		

Size 140 mm x 85 mm approximately

Obverse—Brown on a pale brown underprint with a cameo at the centre
Reverse—brown panel with the Bank's head office building at the centre

		EF	UNC
NI.715	Signatory: J. G. McClay		
	Prefix DN dated 5.1.1968 to prefix ON dated 5.1.1972.............	£45	£75
	Prefix ZZ—replacement note..	£200	—

Size 140 mm x 85 mm approximately

Obverse—blue and purple on a multicoloured underprint. Portrait of a girl to the right
Reverse—mainly blue. Illustration of Dunluce Castle at the centre

		EF	UNC
NI.716a	*Signatory: J. G. McClay* (Manager)		
	Prefix QN dated 1.1.1977	£55	£90
	Prefix ZY—replacement note	£150	—
NI.716b	*Signatory: F.H.Hollway* (Manager)		
	Prefix QN dated 1.1.1979	£50	£85
	Prefix ZY—replacement note	£140	—

TEN POUNDS

Size 150 mm x 87 mm approximately

Obverse—black with "£10" in a violet panel at the centre; vignette with Bank building above
Reverse—purple panel with Britannia and Hibernia seated at the centre

	F	VF
NI.721a *Signatory: Hume Robertson* Prefix N dated 6.5.1929		Rare
NI.721b *Signatory: F. S. Forde* Prefix N dated 10.12.1934	£250	£450

Obverse—green with "£10" in a red panel at the centre; vignette with Bank building above
Reverse—red panel with Britannia and Hibernia seated at the centre

	VF	EF
NI.722 *Signatory: G. A. Kennedy* Prefix N dated from 10.10.1938 to 10.4.1946	£280	£480

Obverse—green with a mesh background and with "£10" in a red panel at the centre; vignette with Bank building above
Reverse—red panel with Britannia and Hibernia seated at the centre

		VF	EF
NI.723	*Signatory: H. W. M. Clarke*		
	Prefix N dated 10.1.1948	£220	£450

Size 152 mm x 85 mm approximately

Obverse—brown on a multicoloured underprint. Portrait of a young man to the right
Reverse—mainly brown. Illustration of the sinking of the "Girona"

		EF	UNC
NI.724a	*Signatory: J. G. McClay (Manager)*		
	Prefix RN dated 1.1.1977	£75	£125
	Prefix ZY—replacement note...	£180	—
NI.724b	*Signatory: F. H. Hollway (Manager)*		
	Prefix RN dated 1.1.1979 and 1.1.1981.......................................	£70	£125
	Prefix ZY—replacement note...	£180	—

TWENTY POUNDS

Size 148 mm x 85 mm approximately

Obverse—black with "£20" in a brown panel at the centre; vignette with Bank building above
Reverse—rose-red panel with Britannia and Hibernia seated at the centre

		F	VF
NI.731a	*Signatory: Hume Robertson*		
	Prefix N dated 6.5.1929		Rare
NI.731b	*Signatory: G. A. Kennedy*		
	Prefix N dated 20.4.1943 and 20.11.1944.....................................	£280	£450

Size 160 mm x 90 mm approximately

Obverse—mauve on a multicoloured underprint; portrait of a mature lady to the right
Reverse—mauve on a multicoloured underprint. Illustration of rock chimney at Lacada Point, Giant's Causeway

		EF	UNC
NI.732	*Signatory: F. H. Hollway* (Manager)		
	Prefix SN dated 1.3.1981	£220	£350
	Prefix ZY—replacement note..		probably exists

ONE HUNDRED POUNDS

Size 160 mm x 90 mm approximately

Obverse—green on a multicoloured underprint. Portrait of a mature man to the right
Reverse—green on a multicoloured underprint. Illustration of the Spanish Armada at the centre

		EF	UNC
NI.741	*Signatory: F. H. Hollway* (Manager)		
	Prefix TN dated 1.3.1981...	£700	—
	Prefix ZY—replacement note..		possibly exists

ULSTER BANK LIMITED

The bank was formed in 1836 by investors who had intended to participate in the establishment of a branch of the National Bank of Ireland in Belfast, but who found the terms offered to them insufficiently inviting. They formed their own bank instead.

The Ulster Bank was acquired by the London County and Westminster Bank Ltd. in 1917, and is now part of the Royal Bank of Scotland group.

Examples of early notes:

ONE POUND

Size 153 mm x 85 mm approximately

Obverse—black with "ONE" in a blue panel at the centre; vignette with sailing ship above Uniface. Multiple rubber stamp overprints reading "ISSUED IN NORTHERN IRELAND AFTER 6TH MAY 1929"

		F	VF
NI.801	*Handsigned*		
	No prefix letters—dated 1.3.1926, 1.6.1927, 1.12.1927		Rare

(and possibly others)

The rubber stamp was probably applied to any notes dated prior to 1929 which passed through the Ulster Bank branch network in Northern Ireland.

Obverse—black with "ONE" in a blue panel at the centre; vignette with sailing ship above. Uniface.

		F	VF
NI.802	*Handsigned*		
	No prefix letters—dated from 6.5.1929 to 1.1.1934	£85	£140

Obverse—black with "ONE" in a blue panel at the centre; vignette with sailing ship above
Reverse—blue; unframed illustration of the Bank's head office building in Belfast

		F	VF
NI.803	*Handsigned*		
	No prefix letters—dated from 1.1.1935 to 1.2.1938	£65	£120

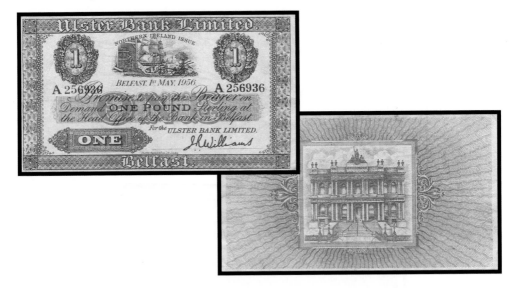

Obverse—black with "ONE" in a blue panel at the centre; vignette with sailing ship above
Reverse—blue; illustration of the Bank's head office building framed in a sunburst pattern

		VF	EF
NI.804a	*Handsigned*		
	No prefix letters—dated 1.9.1939, and	£90	£160
	Prefix A dated 1.9.1939 and 1.1.1940		
NI.804b	*Signatory: J. R. Williams*		
	No serial number dated 1.1.1948—specimen only...................		Rare
	Prefix A dated 1.5.1956...	£80	£145

Size 152 mm x 72 mm approximately

Obverse—blue/grey on a multicoloured underprint
Reverse—blue/grey on a red and purple underprint; Coat of Arms at the centre

		EF	UNC
NI.805	*Signatory: J. J. A. Leitch* No prefix letters—dated 4.10.1966.	£30	£50

Size 135 mm x 67 mm approximately

Obverse—blue/grey on a multicoloured underprint
Reverse—blue/grey on a red and purple underprint; Coat of Arms at the centre

		EF	UNC
NI.806a	*Signatory: A. E. G. Brain* (Chief Executive) Prefix A dated 15.2.1971	£55	£95
NI.806b	*Signatory: R. W. Hamilton* (Chief Executive) Prefix A dated 1.3.1973 and 1.3.1976	£15	£25

FIVE POUNDS

Size 205 mm x 115 mm approximately

Obverse—black with "FIVE" in a green panel at the centre; vignette with sailing ship above.
Uniface

		F	VF
NI.811	*Handsigned*		
	No prefix letters – dated 6.5.1929 to 1.1.1934............................	£110	£190

Obverse—black with "FIVE" in a green panel at the centre; vignette with sailing ship above
Reverse—green; unframed illustration of the Bank's head office building in Belfast

NI.812	*Handsigned*		
	No prefix letters—dated 1.1.1935 to 1.10.1937..........................	£110	£190

Obverse—black with "FIVE" in a green panel at the centre; vignette with sailing ship above
Reverse—green; illustration of the Bank's head office building framed in a sunburst pattern

		VF	EF
NI.813a	*Handsigned*		
	No prefix letters—dated from 1.2.1939 to 1.1.1943	£90	£180
NI.813b	*Signatory: J. R. Williams*		
	No prefix letters—dated 1.5.1956	£100	£200

Size 141 mm x 85 mm approximately

Obverse—brown on a light multicoloured underprint
Reverse—brown on a multicoloured underprint; Coat of Arms at the centre

		VF	EF
NI.814	*Signatory: J. J. A. Leitch*		
	No prefix letters—dated 4.10.1966.	£150	£300

Size 145 mm x 78 mm approximately

Obverse—brown on a light multicoloured underprint
Reverse—brown on a multicoloured underprint; Coat of Arms at the centre

		EF	UNC
NI.815a	*Signatory: A. E. G. Brain* (Chief Executive)		
	Prefix B dated 15.2.1971.	£100	£180
NI.815b	*Signatory: R. W. Hamilton* (Chief Executive)		
	Prefix B dated 1.3.1973 to 1.3.1977	£40	£70
NI.815c	*Signatory: V. Chambers* (Chief Executive)		
	Prefix B dated 1.10.1982 to prefix C dated 1.2.1988	£35	£65

Size 135 mm x 70 mm approximately

Obverse—brown on a multicoloured underprint
Reverse—brown on a multicoloured underprint; Coat of Arms at the centre

NI.816	*Signatory: D. Went* (Chief Executive)		
	Prefix D dated 1.12.1989 to prefix G dated 4.1.1993	£20	£30
	Prefix Z—replacement note		probably exists

Obverse–brown on a multicoloured underprint
Reverse–brown on a multicoloured underprint; Coat of Arms at the centre

		EF	UNC
NI.817	Signatory: M. J. Wilson (Group Chief Executive)		
	Prefix A dated 1.7.1998 to prefix C dated 1.1.2001	£12	£20
	Prefix Z—replacement note	£25	£45

1,000,000 notes issued December 2006 to commemorate the footballer George Best 1946–2005
Obverse—brown on a multicoloured underprint
Reverse—multicoloured with three picture of George Best

NI.818	Signatory: C. McCarthy (Group Executive)		
	Prefix GB dated 25.11.2006	—	£20

Design modification with new style heading and Royal Bank plc logo
Obverse—brown on a multicoloured underprint
Reverse—brown on multicoloured underprint; Coat of Arms in the centre

NI.819	Signatory: C. McCarthy (Group Chief Executive)		
	Prefix D dated 1.7.2007 and ongoing...	—	£10
	Prefix Z – replacement note	—	£25

TEN POUNDS

Size 205 mm x 120 mm approximately

Obverse—black with "TEN" in a red panel at the centre; vignette with sailing ship above.
Uniface

		F	VF
NI.821	*Handsigned*		
	No prefix letters—dated 1.6.1929 to 1.5.1933............................	£120	£240

Obverse—black with "TEN" in a red panel at the centre; vignette with sailing ship above
Reverse—red; unframed illustration of the Bank's head office building

NI.822	*Handsigned*		
	No prefix letters—dated 1.5.1936.	£250	£450

Obverse—black with "TEN" in a red panel at the centre; vignette with sailing ship above
Reverse—red; illustration of the Bank's head office building framed in a sunburst pattern

		VF	EF
NI.823	Handsigned		
	No prefix letters—dated from 1.2.1939 to 1.1.1948	£130	£270

Size 152 mm x 93 mm approximately

Obverse—green on a light multicoloured underprint
Reverse—green on a multicoloured underprint; Coat of Arms at the centre

NI.824	Signatory: J. J. A. Leitch	
	No prefix letters—dated 4.10.1966.	Rare

Size 151 mm x 85 mm approximately

Obverse—green on a light multicoloured underprint.
Reverse—green on a multicoloured underprint; Coat of Arms at the centre

		EF	UNC
NI.825a	*Signatory: A. E. G. Brain* (Chief Executive) Prefix C dated 15. 2.1971..	£400	£750
NI.825b	*Signatory: R. W. Hamilton* (Chief Executive) Prefix C dated 12.11.1972 to 2.6.1980.	£65	£110
NI.825c	*Signatory: V. Chambers* (Chief Executive) Prefix C dated 1.10.1982 to prefix D dated 1.2.1988.................	£50	£80
NI.825d	*Signatory: D. Went* (Chief Executive) Prefix D and prefix E dated 1.12.1989.........................	£40	£65

Size 142 mm x 75 mm approximately

Obverse—green on a multicoloured underprint
Reverse—green on a multicoloured underprint; Coat of Arms at the centre

		EF	UNC
NI.826	*Signatory: D. Went* (Chief Executive) Prefix F to prefix H dated 1.12.1990.	£35	£60
	prefix Z—replacement note—	£75	£120

Obverse—green on a multicoloured underprint
Reverse—green on a multicoloured underprint; Coat of Arms at the centre

		EF	UNC
NI.827a	*Signatory: R. D. Kells* (Group Chief Executive)		
	Prefix A and Prefix B dated 1.1.1997	£22	£35
	Prefix Z—replacement note	£45	£75
NI.827b	*Signatory: M. J. Wilson* (Group Chief Executive)		
	Prefix B and prefix C dated 1.7.1999	—	£30
	Prefix Z—replacement note.	£40	£60
NI.827c	*Signatory: L. McCarthy* (Group Chief Executive)		
	Prefix C dated 6.1.2004 to prefix E dated 1.1.2006	—	£25
	Prefix Z—replacement note.	£30	£50

Design modification with new style heading and Royal of Scotland plc Logo
Obverse–green on a multicoloured underprint
Reverse–green on a multicoloured underprint; Coat of arms in the centre

NI.828	*Signatory: L. McCarthy* (Group Chief Executive)		
	From prefix E5000001 dated 1.1.2007..	—	£20
	Prefix Z—replacement note	£25	£40

TWENTY POUNDS

Size 205 mm x 118 mm approximately

Obverse – black with "TWENTY" in a blue panel at the centre; vignette with sailing ship above. Uniface

		F	VF
NI.831	*Handsigned*		
	No prefix letters—dated 1.6.1929	£200	£400

Obverse—black with "TWENTY" in a blue panel at the centre; vignette with sailing ship above
Reverse—blue; illustration of the Bank's head office building framed in a sunburst pattern

		VF	EF
NI.832	*Handsigned*		
	No prefix letters—dated from 1.3.1941 to 1.1.1948	£300	£600

Size 161 mm x 90 mm approximately

Obverse—purple on a light multicoloured underprint
Reverse—purple on a multicoloured underprint; Coat of Arms at the centre

		VF	EF
NI.833a	*Signatory: J. J. A. Leitch*		
	No prefix letter – dated 1.7.1970..	£450	—
NI.833b	*Signatory: A. E. G. Brain* (Chief Executive)		
	Prefix D dated 15.2.1971	£350	£600

		EF	UNC
NI.833c	*Signatory: R. W. Hamilton* (Chief Executive)		
	Prefix D dated 1.3.1976 and 2.6.1980..	£100	£180
NI.833d	*Signatory: V. Chambers* (Chief Executive)		
	Prefix D dated 1.10.1982 to 1.2.1988..	£80	£140

Size 148 mm x 80 mm approximately

Obverse—purple and blue on a light multicoloured underprint
Reverse—purple on a multicoloured underprint; Coat of Arms at the centre

		EF	UNC
NI.834	*Signatory: D. Went* (Chief Executive)		
	Prefix E and prefix F dated 1.11.1990...	£65	£90

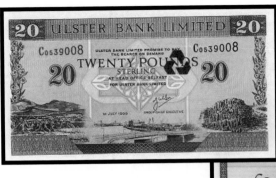

Obverse—purple and mauve on a multicoloured underprint
Reverse—purple on a multicoloured underprint; Coat of Arms at the centre

		EF	UNC
NI.835a	*Signatory: R. D. Kells* (Group Chief Executive)		
	Prefix A and prefix B dated 1.1.1996	£48	£75
	Prefix Z—replacement note	£100	£150
NI.835b	*Signatory: M. J. Wilson* (Group Chief Executive)		
	Prefix B dated 1.7.1999 to prefix D dated 1.7.2002	£38	£50
	Prefix Z—replacement note.	£75	£120
NI.835c	*Signatory: C. McCarthy* (Group Chief Executive)		
	Prefix D dated 6.1.2004 to prefix F dated 1.1.2006	—	£40
	Prefix Z—replacement note.	£65	£100

Design Modification with new style heading and Royal Bank of Scotland plc logo
Observe—purple and mauve on a multicoloured underprint
Reverse—purple on a multicoloured underprint; Coat of Arms at the centre

NI.836	*Signatory: C. McCarthy* (Group Chief Executive)		
	Prefix F dated 1.1.2007 to prefix H dated 1.1.2008 and ongoing	—	£40
	Prefix Z—replacement note	£45	£65

FIFTY POUNDS

Size 200 mm x 115 mm approximately

Obverse — black with "FIFTY" in a blue panel at the centre; vignette with sailing ship above
Uniface

		F	VF
NI.841	*Handsigned*		
	No prefix letters—dated 1.6.1929	£300	£550

Obverse — black with "FIFTY" in a blue panel at the centre; vignette with sailing ship above
Reverse — blue; illustration of the Bank's head office building framed in a sunburst pattern

NI.842	*Handsigned*		
	No prefix letters—dated 1.3.1941 and 1.1.1943	£200	£400

Size 168 mm x 95 mm approximately

Obverse—green and brown on a light multicoloured underprint
Reverse—green and brown on a multicoloured underprint; Coat of Arms at the centre

		EF	UNC
NI.843	*Signatory: V. Chambers* (Chief Executive)		
	Prefix E dated 1.10.1982.	£160	£250

Size 157 mm x 85 mm approximately

Obverse—green, brown and multicoloured on a light multicoloured underprint
Reverse—mainly green and brown on a multicoloured underprint; Coat of Arms at the centre

NI.844	*Signatory: R. D. Kells* (Chief Executive)		
	Prefix D dated 1.1.1997	£95	£120
	Prefix Z—replacement note	£140	£200

ONE HUNDRED POUNDS

Size 203 mm x 120 mm approximately

Obverse—black with "£100" in a blue panel at the centre; vignette with sailing ship above Uniface

		F	VF
NI.851	*Handsigned*		
	No prefix letters—dated 1.6.1929	£450	750

Obverse—black with "£100" in a blue panel at the centre; vignette with sailing ship above
Reverse—blue; illustration of the Bank's head office building framed in a sunburst pattern

		F	VF
NI.852	*Handsigned*		
	No prefix letters—dated 1.3.1941 and 1.1.1943	£350	£550

Size 157 mm x 100 mm approximately

Obverse—red on a light multicoloured underprint
Reverse—red on a light red and blue underprint; Coat of Arms at the centre

		EF	UNC
NI.853a	*Signatory: R. W. Hamilton* (Chief Executive) Prefix F dated 1.3.1973 and 1.3.1977.	£450	£850
NI.853b	*Signatory: V. Chambers* (Chief Executive) Prefix E dated 1.10.1982.	£400	£650

Size 162 mm x 90 mm approximately
Obverse—purple on a light multicoloured underprint.
Reverse—purple on a light multicoloured underprint; Coat of Arms at the centre

NI.854	*Signatory: D. Went* (Chief Executive) Prefix G dated 1.12.1990	£350	£480

The first Scottish notes appeared in 1695 in the year of the foundation of the Bank of Scotland and contemporary with the earliest notes of the Bank of England. They were released in values from £5 to £100 sterling; when pound notes appeared in 1704 they were denominated £12 Scots, reflecting the prevailing exchange rate. The Bank's monopoly expired in 1721 and within six years it was faced with a rival with the title of the Royal Bank of Scotland, although the general public referred to them simply as the Old and New Banks.

Both banks originated from a need to put banking on a proper footing and supply paper money for the convenience of the mercantile classes. The third bank, however, appeared in 1746 with the primary objective of stimulating the linen industry, and this was reflected in its name, the British Linen Company which did not change its title to the British Linen Bank until 1906. In the second half of the 18th century smaller banks appeared in various parts of the country, usually confined to a specific locality. Although these banks did much to foster trade and industry in their own areas, the spectacular crash of Douglas Heron & Company in 1772 bankrupted many of the leading families in the south-west of Scotland. Many of the smaller banks, confined to a single town, were fairly ephemeral, remembered by their elusive notes which are now much sought after by collectors of local history as well as notaphilists.

Early in the 19th century, however, there emerged a number of joint-stock banks which were destined to play a major role in the economic development of Scotland. These included the Caledonian Banking Company (1838–1907), the Central Bank (1834–68), the City of Glasgow Bank (1839–79), the Clydesdale Bank (1838), the Commercial Bank (1810–1959), the Eastern Bank (1838–63), the National Bank (1825–1959), the North of Scotland Bank (1836–1950), the Town & County Bank (1825–1908), the Union Bank (1843–1955) and the Western Bank (1832–57). Although the Bank Charter Act of 1844 severely restricted the note-issuing activities of the English provincial banks, the comparable legislation for Scotland a year later enabled the Scottish banks to continue to issue their own notes, although the act banned the foundation of any new note-issuing banks after that date.

Although banking in Scotland was on a sounder footing than in England, the failure of the West of Scotland Bank in 1857 and the City of Glasgow Bank in 1878 both had severe repercussions on the economy of the west of Scotland. The worst effects, so far as the general public possessing notes of these banks was concerned, were mitigated by the undertaking of the National Bank to redeem the notes of the West of Scotland, and by all the other banks acting in concert to redeem the City of Glasgow notes.

As a result of mergers and amalgamations the number of note-issuing banks gradually fell, although by the beginning of the 20th century there were still ten in existence. The Caledonian was absorbed by the Bank of Scotland in 1907 and the Town & County merged with the North of Scotland Bank the following year. In the period after World War II there were further amalgamations. For example, in 1959 the Commercial Bank joined forces with the National Bank to form the National Commercial Bank of Scotland which, in turn, combined with the Royal Bank of Scotland which now acquired the suffix "Limited" inscribed on notes since that date. In the same year the British Linen Bank (acquired by Barclays in 1919) was sold to the Bank of Scotland and the merger was completed the following year.

Of the 19th century joint-stock banks, only the Clydesdale has survived, although it, too, has undergone enormous changes. It was formed in 1838 by the union of the Greenock Union Bank, the Edinburgh & Glasgow Bank, the Eastern Bank and the Dundee Commercial Bank. In 1919 it was acquired by the Midland Bank which four years later also took over the North of Scotland Bank. These banks continued to operate separately until 1950 when they merged to form the Clydesdale & North of Scotland Bank which reverted to the shorter title of the Clydesdale Bank in 1963.

Today, therefore, Scotland enjoys the colourful variety of notes produced by three banks, a far cry from the relatively plain black and white notes of the 18th and early 19th centuries. Although many of the earlier notes were engraved and printed by local firms such as Kirkwood, Lizars and Johnston, later notes were produced by the great English security printers, from Perkins Bacon to De La Rue. Prior to the late 1960s there was no uniformity regarding size or colours but since then both have been brought into line with the notes of the Bank of England. In 1975 James Douglas estimated the total circulation of the three Scottish banks in excess of £250 million, or about 7 per cent of the total for the British Isles. The Royal Bank is now the only Scottish bank to continue issuing pound notes and all three have notes up to £100. Moreover, they have shown a penchant for commemorative notes in recent years, notably the Royal Bank's pounds honouring Alexander Graham Bell, Robert Louis Stevenson and the advent of the Scottish Parliament, and the Clydesdale's £20 notes for the Commonwealth Heads of Government Meeting (1997) and Glasgow and UK City of Architecture and Design (1999), not to mention the series of four £5 notes of 1996 marking the bicentenary of Robert Burns by including verses from his poems.

BANK OF SCOTLAND

Scotland's oldest bank, the Bank of Scotland was founded in 1695 and is thus just a year younger than the Bank of England. During its long history the Bank of Scotland has absorbed the Central Bank of Scotland (1866), the Caledonian Banking Co. Ltd. (1907), and more recently The Union Bank of Scotland Ltd (1955), and the British Linen Bank (1971). Elements of the designs of the banknotes of these two latter Banks can be seen in the contemporary notes of the Bank of Scotland.

ONE POUND

"A" size square notes   (175 mm x 128 mm approximately)

Obverse—brown with a yellow/brown underprint. Royal Arms in a Panel to the left, with the Bank's Coat of Arms towards the top of the note above a grey medallion. Uniface

		F	VF
SC101a *Signatory: Duncan McNeill (Secretary)*			
Prefix 70/H dated 18.2.1894 to prefix 59/X dated 19.12.1910 .... from £550			£1000
SC101b *Signatory: P. Macdonald (Secretary)*			
Prefix 60/X dated 3.1.1911 to prefix 59/AL dated 24.11.1920.....		£250	£550
SC101c *Signatory: A. J. Rose (Secretary)*			
Prefix 60/AL dated 8.12.1920 to prefix 9/AU dated 16.11.1927.		£220	£450

"B" size notes   (152mm x 84mm approximately)

Obverse—brown and grey with the Royal Coat of Arms in panel at the left; grey and brown medallion at centre
Reverse—grey; unframed illustration of Head Office building

SC102   *Signatories: (Lord) Elphinstone (Governor); G. J. Scott (Treasurer)*   *VF*   *EF*
         Prefix A dated 1.1.1927 to prefix J dated 17.7.1933 ....   £130   £250

Obverse—brown and grey with the Bank's Coat of Arms in panel at the left; grey medallion at centre
Reverse—grey; framed illustration of Head Office building

SC103a *Signatories: (Lord) Elphinstone (Governor); A. W. M. Beveridge (Treasurer)*
         Prefix K dated 15.1.1935 to prefix Q dated 15.9.1937 ....   £65   £130

SC103b *Signatories: (Lord) Elphinstone (Governor); J. Macfarlane (Treasurer)*
         Prefix R dated 5.1.1939 to prefix Y dated 7.5.1941 ....   £50   £100

SC103c *Signatories: (Lord) Elphinstone (Governor); J. B. Crawford (Treasurer)*
         Prefix Z dated 2.6.1942 to prefix AA dated 16.10.1943.................   £50   £100

Obverse—brown and grey; no panel at left; larger grey medallion at centre
Reverse—dark chocolate brown; Bank's Arms at centre

		VF	EF
SC104	*Signatories: (Lord) Elphinstone (Governor); J.B.Crawford (Treasurer)*		
	Prefix A dated 4.1.1945 to prefix B dated 6.2.1945.........................	£95	£180

Obverse—brown and grey; no panel at left; larger grey medallion at centre
Reverse—light brown; Bank's Arms at centre

		EF	UNC
SC105a	*Signatories: (Lord) Elphinstone (Governor); J.B.Crawford (Treasurer)*		
	Prefix B dated 6.2.1945 to prefix R dated 19.11.1952	£40	£70
SC105b	*Signatories: (Lord) Elphinstone (Governor); Sir William Watson (Treasurer)*		
	Prefix R dated 4.9.1953 to prefix T dated 9.11.1953	£45	£75

Obverse—brown with slate blue medallion at centre
Reverse—grey; sailing ship at centre surrounded by thistles

SC106a	*Signatories: (Lord) Elphinstone (Governor); Sir William Watson (Treasurer)*		
	Prefix A dated 1.3.1955 to prefix D dated 4.3.1955	£35	£50
SC106b	*Signatories: Sir John Craig (Governor); Sir William Watson (Treasurer)*		
	Prefix E dated 1.9.1955 to prefix N dated 14.9.1956	£25	£40
SC106c	*Signatories: Lord Bilsland (Governor); Sir William Watson (Treasurer)*		
	Prefix O dated 30.8.1957 to prefix B/A dated 30.11.1960	£25	£40

"C" size notes   (150mm x 70mm approximately)

Obverse—brown with slate blue medallion at centre
Reverse—grey; sailing ship at centre surrounded by thistles

		EF	UNC
SC107a	*Signatories: Lord Bilsland* (Governor); *Sir William Watson* (Treasurer)		
	Prefix A dated 16.11.1961 to prefix N dated 12.12.1962, and......	£25	£35
	Prefix A/A dated 3.2.1964 to prefix A/I dated 13.2.1964 (printer's imprint "LD")	£25	£35
	Prefix A/J dated 4.5.1965 to prefix A/O dated 11.5.1965 (printers imprint "LTD"	£25	£35
SC107b	*Signatories: Lord Polwarth* (Governor); *J. Letham* (Treasurer & General Manager)		
	Prefix A/P–A/U dated 1.6.1966 (w/o sorting symbols)............	£25	£35
	Prefix A/V–A/Y dated 3.3.1967 (with sorting symbols)............	£25	£35

Change of watermark

SC107c	*Signatories: Lord Polwarth* (Governor); *J. Letham* (Treasurer & General Manager)		
	Prefix A/Z to prefix B/C dated 3.3.1967 (with sorting symbols)	£25	£35

"D" size notes   (Size 135mm x 67mm approximately)

Obverse—multicoloured with Bank's Coat of Arms at the centre
Reverse—brown and purple; Shield and thistles flanked by Arms and sailing ship

SC108	*Signatories: Lord Polwarth* (Governor); *J. Letham* (Treasurer & General Manager)		
	Prefix A/1 to A/6 dated 17.7.1968; prefix A/7 to B/4 dated 18.8.1969..	£30	£50

Obverse—mainly green; Bank's Arms at the centre, portrait of Sir Walter Scott to the right
Reverse—mainly green; Shield and thistles at centre flanked by sailing ship and Pallas emblem

	EF	UNC
SC109a *Signatories: Lord Polwarth (Governor); T. W. Walker (Treasurer & General Manager)*		
Prefix A/1 dated 10.8.1970 to prefix B/20 dated 31.8.1971	£25	£40
Replacement note – prefix Z/1	£50	£80
SC109b *Signatories: Lord Clydesmuir (Governor); T. W. Walker (Treasurer & General Manager)*		
Prefix C/1 dated 1.11.1972 to prefix C/27 dated 30.8.1973	£20	£35
Replacement note – prefix Z/1	£50	£80
SC109c *Signatories: Lord Clydesmuir (Governor); A. M. Russell (Treasurer & General Manager)*		
Prefix C/28 dated 28.10.1974 to prefix D/1 dated 3.10.1978	£10	£16
Replacement note – prefix Z/1 and Z/2	£35	£65
SC109d *Signatories: Lord Clydesmuir (Governor); D. B. Pattullo (Treasurer & General Manager)*		
Prefix D/2 dated 15.10.1979 to prefix D/31 dated 4.11.1980	£9	£14
Replacement note – prefix Z/2 and Z/3	£25	£50
SC109e *Signatories: Sir T. N. Risk (Governor); D. B. Pattullo (Treasurer & General Manager)*		
Prefix D/32 to prefix D/42 dated 30.7.1981 (with sorting symbols) and	£8	£12
Prefix D/43 dated 7.10.1983 to prefix E/1 dated 18.11.1986 (without		
symbols)	£6	£10
Replacement note – prefix Z/3	£18	£30
SC109f *Signatories: Sir T. N. Risk (Governor); P. Burt (Treasurer & General Manager)*		
Prefix E/1 to prefix E/13 dated 19.8.1988	£4	£7
Replacement note – prefix Z/3	£18	£30

FIVE POUNDS

Size 220mm x 135mm approximately

Obverse—brown with black value panels. Royal Arms in a panel to the left, with the Bank's Coat of Arms towards the top of the note above a grey medallion. Uniface

		F	VF
SC111a	*Signatory: D. MacNeill (Secretary)* Prefix 17/B dated 5.5.1894 to prefix 8/F dated 17.10.1911		Rare
SC111b	*Signatory: P. Macdonald (Secretary)* Prefix 9/F dated 18.9.1912 to prefix 2/I dated 3.6.1919 .... from £320		£600
SC111c	*Signatory: A. J. Rose (Secretary)* Prefix 3/I dated 7.10.1920 to prefix 10/L dated 19.5.1931 (approx.)	£280	£500
SC111d	*Signatories: Lord Elphinstone (Governor) and G. J. Scott (Treasurer)* Prefix 11/L dated 26.6.1931 (approx.) to prefix 4/M dated 25.3.1933	£250	£450
SC111e	*Signatories: Lord Elphinstone (Governor) and A. W. M. Beveridge (Treasurer)* Prefix 5/M dated s17.1.1935 to prefix 8/M dated 23.1.1935	£250	£450

Obverse—brown with black value panels. A Scottish thistle replaces the Royal Shield in the left hand panel. The Bank's Coat of Arms towards the top of the note above a grey medallion. Uniface

		VF	EF
SC112a	*Signatories: Lord Elphinstone (Governor) and A. W. M. Beveridge (Treasurer)* Prefix 9/M dated 9.2.1935 to prefix 14/N dated 17.3.1938	£200	£400
SC112b	*Signatories: Lord Elphinstone (Governor) and J.Macfarlane (Treasurer)* Prefix 15/N dated 24.4.1939 to prefix 4/P dated 16.10.1941.............	£180	£350
SC112c	*Signatories: Lord Elphinstone (Governor) and J. B. Crawford (Treasurer)* Prefix 5/P dated 5.6.1942 to prefix 14/R dated 26.9.1944	£150	£300

Size 178mm x 102mm approximately

Obverse—brown on a light brown underprint. Thistle motif in a panel to the left with the Bank's Arms at the top of the note flanked by brown value panels. Grey medallion lower centre Reverse—Dark brown. Bank's Coat of Arms on a lined background with '£5' either side

		VF	EF
SC113	*Signatories: Lord Elphinstone (Governor) and J. B. Crawford (Treasurer)* Prefix 1/A dated 3.1.1945 to prefix 10/A dated 2.3.1945	£180	£300

Obverse—brown on a light brown underprint. Thistle motif in a panel to the left with the Bank's Arms at the top of the note flanked by brown value panels. Grey medallion lower centre
Reverse—Light brown. Bank's Coat of Arms on a lined background with '£5' either side

	VF	EF

SC114   Signatories: Lord Elphinstone (Governor) and J. B. Crawford (Treasurer)
Prefix 11/A dated 16.3.1945 to prefix 10/E dated 10.1.1948 .... £90   £170

Obverse—brown on a light brown underprint. Thistle motif in a panel to the left with the Bank's Arms at the top of the note flanked by black value panels. Grey medallion lower centre
Reverse—Light brown. Bank's Coat of Arms on a lined background with '£5' either side

SC115a   Signatories: Lord Elphinstone (Governor) and J. B. Crawford (Treasurer)
Prefix 11/E dated 16.11.1948 to prefix 10/M dated 21.11.1952 .... £60   £110

SC115b   Signatories: Lord Elphinstone (Governor) and Sir William Watson (Treasurer)
Prefix 11/M dated 10.12.1952 to prefix 20/O dated 4.12.1953 .... £60   £110

Obverse—brown on a light brown underprint. Thistle motif in a panel to the left with the Bank's Arms at the top of the note flanked by black value panels. Slate blue medallion lower centre
Reverse—Light brown. Bank's Coat of Arms on a lined background with '£5' either side

SC116a   Signatories: Lord Elphinstone (Governor) and Sir William Watson (Treasurer)
Prefix 1/A dated 1.3.1955 to prefix 6/D dated 7.4.1955 .... £50   £90

SC116b   Signatories: Sir John Craig (Governor) and Sir William Watson (Treasurer)
Prefix 7/D dated 7.4.1955 to prefix 10/G dated 3.9.1955 .... £50   £90

375

Obverse—brown on a light brown underprint. Thistle motif in a panel to the left with the Bank's Arms at the top of the note flanked by black value panels. Slate blue medallion lower centre Reverse—Dark brown. Redesigned following the merger with the Union Bank. The Bank's Shield at the centre is flanked by two circular panels bearing the Bank's Coat of Arms to the left and the Ship emblem to the right

		VF	EF
SC117a	*Signatories: Sir John Craig (Governor) and Sir William Watson (Treasurer)*		
	Prefix 11/G dated 9.4.1956 to prefix 20/L dated 17.4.1956.....................	£35	£70
SC117b	*Signatories: Lord Bilsland (Governor) and Sir William Watson (Treasurer)*		
	Prefix 1/M dated 1.5.1957 to prefix 20/KA dated 24.5.1960	£30	£60

Size 140mm x 84mm approximately

Obverse—brown on a light brown underprint. Thistle motif in a panel to the left with the Bank's Arms at the top of the note flanked by black value panels. Slate blue medallion lower centre. '£5' values at the bottom of the note are in hollow print Reverse—Dark brown. The Bank's shield at the centre is flanked by two circular panels bearing the Bank's Coat of Arms to the left and the ship emblem to the right

		EF	UNC
SC118	*Signatories: Lord Bilsland (Governor) and Sir William Watson (Treasurer)*		
	Prefix 1/A dated 14.9.1961 to prefix 20/G dated 22.9.1961.....................	£50	£70

Obverse—brown on a light brown underprint. Thistle motif in a panel to the left with the Bank's Arms at the top of the note flanked by black value panels. Slate blue medallion lower centre. '£5' values at the bottom of the note are in solid print
Reverse—Dark brown. The Bank's shield at the centre is flanked by two circular panels bearing the Bank's Coat of Arms to the left and the ship emblem to the right

		EF	UNC
SC119a	*Signatories: Lord Bilsland* (Governor) *and Sir William Watson* (Treasurer)		
	Prefix 1/H dated 25.9.1961 to prefix 15/N dated 14.8.1962...................	£40	£65
	Prefix A dated 7.10.1963 to prefix D dated 12.1.1965	£40	£65
SC119b	*Signatories: Lord Polwarth* (Governor) *and Sir William Watson* (Treasurer)		
	Prefix E dated 7.3.1966 and prefix F dated 8.3.1966	£40	£70
SC119c	*Signatories: Lord Polwarth* (Governor) *and J. Letham* (Treasurer and General Manager)		
	Prefix G dated 1.2.1967 and Prefix H dated 2.2.1967 (without symbols)	£40	£65
	Prefix I dated 1.11.1967 (Sorting symbols added to the reverse)...........	£45	£75

Size 146mm x 78mm approximately

Obverse—Multicoloured, blue, brown, green and yellow. Bank's Coat of Arms at the centre
Reverse—Dark and light green. The Bank's shield at the centre is flanked by two panels bearing the Bank's Coat of Arms to the left and the ship emblem to the right

SC120	*Signatories: Lord Polwarth* (Governor) *and J. Letham* (Treasurer & General Manager)		
	Prefix A dated 1.11.1968 to prefix D dated 9.12.1969.................................	£100	£150

Obverse—Mainly blue. Bank's Coat of Arms at the centre with a portrait of Sir Walter Scott to the right
Reverse—Mainly blue. Bank's shield above thistles at centre flanked by a sailing ship and Pallas emblem

	EF	UNC
SC121a *Signatories: Lord Polwarth* (Governor); *T. W. Walker* (Treasurer & General Manager)		
Prefix A dated 10.8.1970 to prefix K dated 2.9.1971............................	£70	£110
Replacement note—prefix ZA...	£100	£160
SC121b *Signatories: Lord Clydesmuir* (Governor); *T. W. Walker* (Treasurer & General Manager)		
Prefix L dated 4.12.1972 to prefix X dated 5.9.1973	£70	£110
Replacement note—prefix ZA...	£100	£160
SC121c *Signatories: Lord Clydesmuir* (Governor); *A. M. Russell* (Treasurer & General Manager)		
Prefix Y and prefix Z dated 4.11.1974, and		
Prefix AA dated 4.11.1974 to prefix BA dated 19.10.1978	£40	£60
Replacement note—prefix ZA...	£50	£70
SC121d *Signatories: Lord Clydesmuir* (Governor); *D. B. Pattullo* (Treasurer & General Manager)		
Prefix BB dated 28.9.1979 to prefix BS dated 28.11.1980....................	£35	£55
Replacement note—prefix ZA and ZB	£45	£60
SC121e *Signatories: Sir T. N. Risk* (Governor); *D. B. Pattullo* (Treasurer & General Manager)		
Prefix BT dated 27.7.1981 to prefix CK dated 25.6.1982 (with		
sorting symbols)	£30	£45
Prefix CL dated 13.10.1983 to prefix DZ dated 29.2.1988 (without		
symbols)...	£25	£35
Replacement note—prefix ZB	£30	£45

Size 136mm x 70mm approximately

Obverse—Mainly blue. Bank's Coat of Arms at the centre with a portrait of Sir Walter Scott to the right
Reverse—Mainly blue. Bank's shield above thistles at centre flanked by a sailing ship and Pallas emblem

SC122a *Signatories: Sir T. N. Risk* (Governer) *and P. Burt* (Treasurer & Chief General Manager)		
Prefix EA to prefix EJ dated 20.6.1990	£22	£35
Replacement note—prefix ZB	£40	£60

	EF	UNC

SC122b *Signatories: D. B. Pattullo* (Governor) *and P. Burt* (Treasurer & Chief General Manager)

Prefix EK dated 6.11.1991 to prefix FB dated 7.1.1994 .... £22 £35

Replacement note—prefix ZB £40 £60

Obverse—Blue and multicoloured. Bank's Arms at the centre of the note with a portrait of Sir Walter Scott to the left

Reverse—Blue and multicoloured. Illustration entitled "Oil and Energy" at the centre

SC123a *Signatories: D. B. Pattullo* (Governor) *and P. Burt* (Treasurer & Chief General Manager)

Prefix AA to prefix AM dated 4.1.1995 .... £12 £22

Replacement note—prefix ZZ.. £30 £50

SC123b *Signatories: D. B. Pattullo* (Governor) *and G. Masterton* (Treasurer & Chief General Manager)

Prefix AN to prefix AZ dated 13.9.1996.. £12 £20

Replacement note—prefix ZZ.. £30 £50

SC123c *Signatories: M. J. Grant* (Governor) *and G. Masterton* (Treasurer & Chief General Manager)

Prefix BA to prefix BR dated 5.8.1998 .... £10 £18

Replacement note—prefix ZZ.. £30 £50

SC123d *Signatories: P. Burt* (Governor) *and G. Mitchell* (Treasurer & Managing Director)

Prefix BS to CB dated 25.6.2002 .... — £15

Replacement note—prefix ZZ.. £25 £45

SC123e *Signatories: D. Stevenson* (Governor) *and C. Matthew* (Treasurer)

Prefix CC dated 1.1.2006 and ongoing. .... — £12

Replacement note—prefix ZZ.. £25 £45

Obverse—Mainly blue with a portrait of Sir Walter Scott at centre

Reverse—Mainly blue with an illustration of the Brig o' Doon

SC124 *Signatories: D. Stevenson* (Governor) *and C. Matthew* (Treasurer)

Prefix AA dated 17.9.2007 and ongoing .... — £9

Replacement note—prefix ZZ.. — £50

379

TEN POUNDS

Size 220mm x 135mm approximately

Obverse—brown with black value panels. Royal Arms in a Panel to the left, with the Bank's Coat of Arms towards the top of the note above a grey medallion. Uniface

	F	VF
SC131a *Signatory: D. MacNeill (Secretary)* Prefix 7/A dated 16.10.1894 to prefix 4/B dated 30.9.1909		Rare
SC131b *Signatory: P. Macdonald (Secretary)* Prefix 5/B dated 20.11.1912 to prefix 8/B dated 5.11.1919		Rare
SC131c *Signatory: A. J. Rose (Secretary)* Prefix 9/B dated 15.8.1921 to prefix 1/C dated 9.3.1929.................... from £700		£1200
SC131d *Signatories: Lord Elphinstone (Governor) and A. W. M. Beveridge (Treasurer)* Prefix 2/C dated 24.1.1935		Rare

Obverse—brown with black value panels. A Scottish thistle replaces the Royal shield in the left hand panel. The Bank's Coat of Arms towards the top of the note above a grey medallion. Uniface

	VF	EF
SC132a *Signatories: Lord Elphinstone (Governor) and A. W. M. Beveridge (Treasurer)* Prefix 3/C dated 28.1.1938 .... £750		£1350
SC132b *Signatories: Lord Elphinstone (Governor) and J. B. Crawford (Treasurer)* Prefix 4/C dated 16.7.1942 and prefix 5/C dated 15.10.1942............ £650		£1200

Obverse—brown on a light brown underprint. Thistle motif in a panel to the left with the Bank's Arms at the top of the note flanked by black value panels. Slate blue medallion lower centre. Uniface

                                                                     VF   *EF*

SC133 *Signatories: Lord Bilsland* (Governor) *and Sir William Watson* (Treasurer)
        Prefix 6/C dated 26.9.1963 and prefix 7/C dated 27.9.1963 .... £280   £450

Size 152mm x 85mm approximately

Obverse—Mainly brown. The Bank's Coat of Arms at the centre with a portrait of Sir Walter Scott to the right
Reverse—Mainly brown. The Bank's shield to the right with the sailing ship and Pallas emblem in round panels

                                                             EF   *UNC*

SC134a *Signatories: Lord Clydesmuir* (Governor); *A. M. Russell* (Treasurer & General Manager)
        Prefix A dated 1.5.1974 to prefix L dated 29.9.1978.............................. £70   £130
        Replacement note—prefix ZB... £100   £200

SC134b *Signatories: Lord Clydesmuir* (Governor); *D. B. Pattullo* (Treasurer & General Manager)
        Prefix M dated 10.10.1979 to prefix W dated 5.2.1981......................... £70   £130
        Replacement note—prefix ZB... £100   £200

SC134c *Signatories: Sir T.N.Risk* (Governor); *D. B. Pattullo* (Treasurer & General Manager)
        Prefix X dated 22.7.1981to prefix CX dated 6.8.1987 .... £40   £70
        Replacement note—prefix ZB... £55   £85

SC134d *Signatories: Sir T. N. Risk* (Governor) *and P. Burt* (Treasurer & Chief General Manager)
        Prefix CX dated 1.9.1989 to prefix EP dated 31.10.1990 .... £35   £60
        Replacement note—prefix ZB... £50   £80

Size 143mm x 75mm approximately

Obverse—Mainly brown. The Bank's Coat of Arms at the centre with a portrait of Sir Walter Scott to the right. The word "STERLING" added
Reverse—Mainly brown. The Bank's shield to the right with the sailing ship and Pallas emblem in round panels

	EF	UNC
SC135 *Signatories: D. B Pattullo (Governer) and P. Burt (Treasurer & Chief General Manager)*		
Prefix EQ dated 7.5.1992 to prefix GG dated 13.4.1994	£30	£55
Replacement note—prefix ZB and ZC(?)	£55	£90

Obverse—Mainly brown. Bank's Coat of Arms at the centre with a portrait of Sir Walter Scott to left
Reverse—Brown and multicoloured. Illustration entitled "Distilling and Brewing" at the centre

SC136a *Signatories: D. B. Pattullo (Governor) and P. Burt (Treasurer & Chief General Manager)*

	EF	UNC
Prefix AA to prefix BM dated 1.2.1995	—	£30
Replacement note—prefix ZZ	£45	£90

SC136b *Signatories: D. B. Pattullo (Governor) and G. Masterton (Treasurer & Chief General Manager)*

	EF	UNC
Prefix BN to prefix CF dated 5.8.1997	£20	£35
Replacement note—prefix ZZ	£45	£90

SC136c *Signatories: M. J. Grant (Governor) and G. Masterton (Treasurer & Chief General Manager)*

	EF	UNC
Prefix CG to prefix DT dated 18.8.1998	—	£30
Replacement note—prefix ZZ	£45	£85

SC136d *Signatories: Sir John Shaw (Governor) and G. Mitchell (Treasurer & Chief General Manager)*

	EF	UNC
Prefix DU to prefix EU dated 18.6.2001	—	£20
Replacement Note—prefox ZZ	£45	£70

	EF	UNC

SC136e *Signatories: G. Mitchell (Governor)*
Prefix EV dated 26.11.2003 to prefix FM dated 24.9.2004. .... — £20
Replacement note—prefix ZZ £45 £70

SC136f *Signatories: D. Stevenson (Governor) and C. Matthew (Treasurer)*
Prefix FN to FX dated 1.1.2006. .... — £20
Replacement note—prefix ZZ £45 £70

Obverse—Mainly brown with a portrait of Sir Walter Scott at the centre
Reverse—Mainly brown with an illustration of the Glenfinnan Viaduct

SC137 *Signatories: D. Stevenson (Governor) and C. Matthew (Treasurer)*
Prefix AA dated 17.9.2007 and ongoing.. — £18
Replacement note—prefix ZZ .... — £60

TWENTY POUNDS

Size 224mm x 135mm approximately

Obverse—brown with red value panels. Royal Arms in a panel to the left, with the Bank's Coat of Arms towards the top of the note above a grey medallion. Uniface

		F	VF
SC141a	*Signatory: D. MacNeill (Secretary)* Prefix 5/B dated 26.5.1894 to prefix 6/D dated 2.9.1910.....................		Rare
SC141b	*Signatory: P. Macdonald (Secretary)* Prefix 7/D dated 26.10.1911 to prefix 10/E dated 29.12.1920............		Rare
SC141c	*Signatory: A. J. Rose (Secretary)* Prefix 1/F date unknown, to prefix 10/F dated 21.6.1932..................	£500	£950
SC141d	*Signatories: Lord Elphinstone (Governor) and G. J. Scott (Treasurer)* Prefix 1/G dated 2.12.1932...	£500	£950
SC141e	*Signatories: Lord Elphinstone (Governor) and A. W. M. Beveridge (Treasurer)* Prefix 2/G dated 11.1.1935 and prefix 3/G dated 16.2.1935..............	£400	£650

Obverse—brown with red value panels. A Scottish thistle replaces the Royal Shield in the left hand panel. The Bank's Coat of Arms towards the top of the note above a grey medallion. Uniface

		VF	EF
SC142a	*Signatories: Lord Elphinstone (Governor) and A. W. M. Beveridge (Treasurer)* Prefix 4/G dated 28.3.1936 to prefix 7/G dated 22.7.1938................	£380	£650
SC142b	*Signatories: Lord Elphinstone (Governor) and J. Macfarlane (Treasurer)* Prefix 8/G dated 16.5.1939 and prefix 9/G dated 12.9.1939.............	£380	£650
SC142c	*Signatories: Lord Elphinstone (Governor) and J. B. Crawford (Treasurer)* Prefix 10/G dated 5.6.1942 to prefix 5/J dated 11.8.1952.............from £160		£350
SC142d	*Signatories: Lord Elphinstone (Governor) and Sir W. Watson (Treasurer)* Prefix 6/J dated 5.12.1952 to prefix 10/J dated 24.4.1953..................	£150	£320

Obverse—brown with red value panels. Thistle motif in the left hand panel. The Bank's Coat of Arms towards the top of the note above a slate blue medallion. Uniface

		VF	EF
S143a	*Signatories: Sir John Craig (Governor) and Sir W. Watson (Treasurer)* Prefix 1/A dated 6.4.1955 to prefix 5/B dated 12.6.1956	£110	£220
S143b	*Signatories: Lord Bilsland (Governor) and Sir W. Watson (Treasurer)* Prefix 6/B dated 25.3.1958 to prefix 4/H dated 3.10.1963	£85	£180

Size 212mm x 134mm approximately

Obverse—brown with red value panels. Thistle motif in the left hand panel. The Bank's Coat of Arms towards the top of the note above a slate blue medallion. Uniface

SC144	*Signatories: Lord Polwarth (Governor) and J. Letham (Treasurer)* Prefix 5/H to prefix 9/H dated 5.5.1969	£170	£350

Size 160mm x 90mm approximately

Obverse—Mainly purple. The Bank's Coat of Arms at the centre with a portrait of Sir Walter Scott to the right
Reverse—Purple and red. Illustration of the Bank's head office building at the centre with the shield, sailing ship and Pallas emblem to the left

		EF	UNC
SC145a	*Signatories: Lord Polwarth (Governor) and T. W. Walker (Treasurer & General Manager)* Prefix A dated 1.10.1970...	£190	£380
SC145b	*Signatories: Lord Clydesmuir (Governor); T. W. Walker (Treasurer & General Manager)* Prefix A dated 3.1.1973..	£180	£350
SC145c	*Signatories: Lord Clydesmuir (Governor); A. M. Russell (Treasurer & General Manager)* Prefix A dated 8.11.1974 and 14.1.1977	£150	£280
SC145d	*Signatories: Lord Clydesmuir (Governor); D. B. Pattullo (Treasurer & General Manager)* Prefix A and B dated 16.7.1979, and prefix B dated 2.2.1981	£100	£200
SC145e	*Signatories: Sir T. N. Risk (Governor); D. B. Pattullo (Treasurer & General Manager)* Prefix B dated 4.8.1981 to prefix K dated 15.12.1987	£90	£140

Size 150mm x 80mm approximately

Obverse—Mainly purple. The Bank's Coat of Arms at the centre with a portrait of Sir Walter Scott to the right
Reverse—Purple and red. Illustration of the Bank's head office building at the centre with the shield, sailing ship and Pallas emblem to the left

		EF	UNC
SC146	*Signatories: D. B. Pattullo (Governor) and P. Burt (Treasurer & Chief General Manager)* Prefix K dated 1.7.1991 to prefix AU dated 12.1.1993	£70	£100

Obverse—Mainly purple. Bank's Coat of Arms at centre with portrait of Sir Walter Scott to left
Reverse—Purple, red and brown. Illustration entitled "Education and Research" at the centre

		EF	UNC
SC147a	*Signatories: D. B. Pattullo (Governor) and P. Burt (Treasurer & Chief General Manager)*		
	Prefix AA to prefix AY dated 1.5.1995	£40	£60
	Replacement note—prefix ZZ	£100	£180
SC147b	*Signatories: D. B. Pattullo (Governor) and G. Masterton (Treasurer & Chief General Manager)*		
	Prefix AY dated 25.10.1996 to prefix CE dated 1.4.1998	—	£50
	Replacement note—prefix ZZ	£80	£150
SC147c	*Signatories: M. J. Grant (Governor) and G. Masterton (Treasurer & Chief General Manager)*		
	Prefix CE to prefix DL dated 22.3.1999	—	£45
	Replacement note—prefix ZZ	£70	£120
SC147d	*Signatories:Shaw (Governor) and G. Mitchell (Treasurer & Managing Director)*		
	Prefix DM to prefix DW (DW 900000) dated 18.6.2001	—	£40
	Replacement note—prefix ZZ	£70	£120
SC147e	*Signatory: G. Mitchell (Governor)*		
	Prefix DW 900001 dated 26.11.2003 to prefix FN dated 24.9.2004	—	£40
	Replacement note—prefix ZZ	£60	£100

Obverse—Mainly mauve with portrait of Sir Walter Scott at centre
Reverse—Mainly mauve with illustration of the Forth Bridge

SC148	*Signatories: D. Stevenson (Governor) and C. Matthew (Treasurer)*		
	Prefix AA dated 17.9.2007 and ongoing	—	£35
	Replacement note—prefix ZZ	—	£80

FIFTY POUNDS

Size 156mm x 85mm approximately

Obverse—Mainly green. Bank's Coat of Arms at centre with portrait of Sir Walter Scott to left
Reverse—Green, brown and multicoloured. Illustration entitled "Arts and Culture" at the centre

	EF	UNC
SC161a *Signatories: D. B. Pattullo (Governor) and P. Burt (Treasurer & Chief General Manager)*		
Prefix AA dated 1.5.1995	£90	£150
SC161b *Signatories: M. J. Grant (Governor) and G. Masterton (Treasurer & Chief General Manager)*		
Prefix AA to prefix AB dated 15.4.1999	—	£120
SC161c *Signatories: G. Mitchell (Governor)*		
Prefix AB dated 29.1.2003 to prefix AC 500000 dated 24.9.2004	—	£110
SC161d *Signatories: D. Stevenson (Governor) and C. Matthew (Treasurer)*		
Prefix AC 500001 to prefix AD 100000 dated 1.1.2006	—	£110

Obverse—Mainly green with portrait of Sir Walter Scott at centre
Reverse—Mainly green with an illustration of the Falkirk Wheel

SC162 *Signatories: D. Stevenson (Governor) and C. Matthew (Treasurer)*		
Prefix AA dated 17.9.2007 and ongoing	—	£85
Replacement note — prefix ZZ	—	£160

ONE HUNDRED POUNDS

Size 220mm x 135mm approximately

Obverse—brown with red value panels. Royal Arms in a panel to the left, with the Bank's Coat of Arms towards the top of the note above a grey medallion. Uniface

		F	VF
SC171a *Signatory: D. MacNeill (Secretary)* Prefix 7/C dated 12.7.1894 to prefix 1/G dated 9.12.1910			Rare
SC171b *Signatory: P. Macdonald (Secretary)* Prefix 2/G dated 11.12.1911 to prefix 4/H dated 17.4.1919			Rare
SC171c *Signatory: A. J. Rose (Secretary)* Prefix 5/H dated 7.7.1920, to prefix 8/I dated 8.6.1930....................			Rare
SC171d *Signatories: Lord Elphinstone (Governor) and G. J. Scott (Treasurer)* Prefix 9/I dated 28.5.1932 and prefix 10/I dated 8.11.1932			Rare
SC171e *Signatories: Lord Elphinstone (Governor) and A. W. M. Beveridge (Treasurer)* Prefix 1/J dated 8.1.1935 and prefix 2/J dated 31.1.1935			Rare

Obverse—brown with red value panels. A Scottish thistle replaces the Royal Shield in the left hand panel. The Bank's Coat of Arms towards the top of the note above a grey medallion. Uniface

SC172a *Signatories: Lord Elphinstone (Governor) and A. W. M. Beveridge (Treasurer)* Prefix 3/J dated 23.3.1937 and prefix 4/J dated 12.8.1937			Rare
SC172b *Signatories: Lord Elphinstone (Governor) and J.Macfarlane (Treasurer)* Prefix 5/J dated 2.4.1940 to prefix 8/J dated 25.9.1942......................			Rare
SC172c *Signatories: Lord Elphinstone (Governor) and J. B. Crawford (Treasurer)* Prefix 9/J dated 16.8.1946 to prefix 9/K dated 14.12.1951	£600		£1100

Obverse—brown with red value panels. Thistle motif in the left hand panel. The Bank's Coat of Arms towards the top of the note above a slate blue medallion. Uniface

		VF	EF
SC173a *Signatories: Sir John Craig (Governor) and Sir W. Watson (Treasurer)* Prefix 10/K dated 14.9.1956 to prefix 3/L dated 3.12.1956	£650	£1250
SC173b *Signatories: Lord Bilsland (Governor) and Sir W. Watson (Treasurer).* Prefix 4/L dated 24.3.1959 to prefix 8/N dated 30.11.1962...............	£650	£1250

Size 160mm x 90mm approximately

Obverse—mainly red and orange. Bank's Coat of Arms centre with Sir Walter Scott to right
Reverse—mainly red. Illustration of the Bank's head office building at the centre with the shield,
sailing ship, Ditat emblem and £100 in the four corners

	EF	UNC
SC174a *Signatories: Lord Polwarth (Governor) and T. W. Walker (Treasurer & General Manager)* Prefix A dated 6.12.1971	£650	£1100
SC174b *Signatories: Lord Clydesmuir (Governor); T. W. Walker (Treasurer & General Manager)* Prefix A dated 6.9.1973	£650	£1100
SC174c *Signatories: Lord Clydesmuir (Governor); A. M. Russell (Treasurer & General Manager)* Prefix A dated 11.10.1978	£500	£850
SC174d *Signatories: Lord Clydesmuir (Governor); D. B. Pattullo (Treasurer & General Manager)* Prefix A dated 26.1.1981	£500	£850
SC174e *Signatories: Sir T. N. Risk (Governor); D. B. Pattullo (Treasurer & General Manager)* Prefix A dated 10.6.1982 to prefix A dated 26.11.1986	£400	£700
SC174f *Signatories: Sir T. N. Risk (Governor); P. Burt (Treasurer & Chief General Manager)* Prefix A dated 14.2.1990	£380	£600

Obverse—mainly red and orange. Bank's Coat of Arms centre with Sir Walter Scott to right. The
word "STERLING" added
Reverse—mainly red. Illustration of the Bank's head office building at the centre with the shield,
sailing ship, Ditat emblem and £100 in the four corners

SC175 *Signatories: D. B. Pattullo (Governor) and P. Burt (Treasurer & Chief General Manager)* Prefix A dated 22.1.1992 to prefix A dated 9.2.1994	£250	£400

Obverse—mainly red. Bank's Coat of Arms centre with Sir Walter Scott to left
Reverse—red, brown and multicoloured. Illustration entitled "Leisure and Tourism" at the centre

		EF	UNC
SC176a	*Signatories: D. B. Pattullo* (Governor) *and P. Burt* (Treasurer & Chief General Manager)		
	Prefix AA dated 17.7.1995..	£280	£400
	Replacement note—prefix ZZ...		Rare
SC176b	*Signatories: D. B. Pattullo* (Governor) *and G. Masterton* (Treasurer & Chief General Manager)		
	Prefix AA dated 18.8.1997..	£220	£300
	Replacement note—prefix ZZ...		Rare
SC176c	*Signatories: M. J. Grant* (Governor) *and G. Masterton* (Treasurer & Chief General Manager)		
	Prefix AA dated 19.5.1999..	£220	£300
	Replacement note—prefix ZZ...		Rare
SC176d	*Signatory: G. Mitchell* (Governor) Prefix AA to prefix AD dated 26.11.2003		
	to prefix AB 400000 dated 24.9.2004...................................	—	£250
	Replacement note—prefix ZZ...		Rare
SC176e	*Signatories: D. Stevenson* (Governor) *and C. Matthew* (Treasurer)		
	Prefix AB 400001 to AB 720000 dated 1.1.2006	—	£200

Obverse—Mainly red/purple with portrait of Sir Walter Scott centre
Reverse—Mainly red/purple with an illustration of Kessock Bridge

SC177	*Signatories: D. Stevenson* (Governor) *and C. Matthew* (Treasurer)		
	Prefix AA dated 17.9.2007 and ongoing	—	£180
	Replacement note—prefix ZZ..	—	£260

BRITISH LINEN BANK

Formerly known as The British Linen Company, the Bank was incorporated in 1746 during the reign of George II. The round seal with the figure of Pallas was adopted as the Company's emblem from the outset, and appears on most of the banknotes. In 1906 the name was changed to The British Linen Bank, and the first notes with the new title are dated 1907. Notes of The British Linen Bank were printed initially by Waterlow and Sons Ltd., whose banknote printing business was purchased by Thomas de la Rue in 1961. This change can be seen in the printer's imprint which appears on the notes. The British Linen Bank was merged with the Bank of Scotland in 1970.

ONE POUND

"A" size square notes (150mm x 130mm approximately)

Obverse — Blue with "B.L.B." in large red letters at centre; panel to the left; Royal Coat of Arms at the top. Uniface.

		F	VF
SC201a	*Signatories: F. Gordon Brown (p. Manager) and handsigned p. Accountant* Prefix T dated 15.1.1907 and prefix U dated 26.12.1907		Rare
SC201b	*Signatories: A. S. Aikman (p. Manager) and handsigned p. Accountant* Prefix V dated 2.11.1908		Rare
SC201c	*Signatories: E. G. Galletley (p. Manager) and handsigned p. Accountant* Prefix W dated 15.7.1910 and prefix X dated 11.8.1911	£450	£800
SC201d	*Signatories: E. G. Galletley (p. General Manager) and handsigned p. Accountant* Prefix Y dated 29.10.1912 and prefix Z dated 17.9.1913	£400	£800

*Obverse—Blue with a red sunburst underprint and "B.L.B." in large red letters; panel at left and
Royal Arms at top.*
Reverse—Blue panel with "DITAT" emblem at centre.

		F	VF
SC202a	*Signatories: E. G. Galletley* (p. General Manager) *and handsigned p. Accountant*		
	Prefix A dated 23.9.1914 to prefix G dated 5.11.1918.........................	£220	£450
SC202b	*Signatories: C.J.Grant* (p. General Manager) *and handsigned p. Accountant*		
	Prefix H dated 19.8.1919 to prefix L dated 31.7.1924.........................	£220	£450

"B" size notes. (150mm x 85mm approximately)

*Obverse—Blue with a red sunburst underprint and "B.L.B." in large red letters; panel at left and
Royal Arms at top.*
Reverse—Blue panel with "DITAT" emblem at centre

		VF	EF
SC203	*Signatory: J. Waugh* (Cashier)		
	Prefix N dated 1.6.1926 to prefix Z dated 26.1.1933, and	£95	£180
	Prefix A dated 3.4.1933 to prefix G dated 2.8.1934	£90	£170

Obverse—Blue with a red sunburst underprint and "B.L.B." in large red letters; panel at left and the Bank's Coat of Arms at top.
Reverse—Blue panel with "DITAT" emblem at centre.

	VF	EF

SC204 *Signatory: J. Waugh* (Cashier)
Prefix H dated 18. 1.1935 to prefix R dated 26.4.1937 .... £65 £120

Obverse—Blue with a red sunburst underprint and "B.L.B." in large red letters; panel at left and the Bank's Coat of Arms at top. Silk fibres added to paper.
Reverse—Blue panel with "DITAT" emblem at centre.

SC205a *Signatory: J. Waugh* (Cashier)
Prefix S dated 4.7.1937 to prefix Z dated 8.11.1938, and.................... £55 £85
Prefix A dated 12.6.1939 to prefix D dated 13.11.1939, and.............. £55 £85
Prefix E/1 dated 7.3.1940 to prefix U/1 dated 7.4.1944..................... £50 £80

SC205b *Signatory: G.Mackenzie* (General Manager)
Prefix V/1 dated 4.1.1946 to prefix R/2 dated 5.8.1950.................... £32 £50

SC205c *Signatory: A. P. Anderson* (General Manager)
Prefix S/2 dated 4.6.1951 to prefix L/3 dated 12.5.1959................... £20 £35

Obverse—Blue with a red sunburst underprint and "B.L.B." in large red letters; panel at left and the Bank's Coat of Arms at top. "No." is omitted from the serial number.
Reverse—Blue panel with "DITAT" emblem at centre.

	VF	EF
SC206 *Signatory: A. P. Anderson* (General Manager)		
Prefix M/3 to prefix P/3 dated 15.4.1960.	£22	£40

Obverse—Blue with a red sunburst underprint and "B.L.B." in large red letters; panel at left and the Bank's Coat of Arms at top. Change of printer to Thomas de la Rue & Co. Ltd.
Reverse—Blue panel with "DITAT" emblem at centre.

SC207 *Signatory: A. P. Anderson* (General Manager)
Prefix Q/3 to prefix T/3 dated 30.9.1961 .... £22 £40

"C" size notes. (150mm x 70mm approximately)

Obverse—Blue with a red sunburst underprint and "B.L.B." in large red letters; panel at left and the Bank's Coat of Arms at top.
Reverse—Blue panel with "DITAT" emblem at centre.

		EF	UNC
SC208a	*Signatory: A. P .Anderson* (General Manager) Prefix U/3 to prefix Y/3 dated 31.3.1962	£35	£50
SC208b	*Signatory: T. W. Walker* (General Manager) Prefix Z/3 dated 1.7.1963 to prefix P/4 dated 13.6.1967.	£25	£40

Obverse—Blue with a red sunburst underprint and "B.L.B." in large red letters; panel at left and the Bank's Coat of Arms at top—similar to previous issue.
Reverse—Revised blue panel with "ONE" either side of DITAT emblem at centre and sorting symbols added.

SC209	*Signatory: T. W. Walker* (General Manager) Prefix Q/4 to prefix T/4 dated 13.6.1967.	£35	£50

"D" size notes. (Size 135mm x 67mm approximately)

Obverse—Blue with multicoloured underprint. Portrait of Sir Walter Scott to the left.
Reverse—Blue panel with "ONE" either side of DITAT emblem at centre.

SC210	*Signatory: T. W. Walker* (General Manager) Prefix U/4 dated 29.2.1968 to prefix D/5 dated 20.7.1970.	£28	£40

FIVE POUNDS

Size: 206mm x 130mm approximately

Obverse—Blue with "B.L.B." in large red letters at centre; panel to the left; Royal Coat of Arms at the top. Uniface.

		F	VF
SC211a	*Signatories: handsigned p. Manager and p. Accountant.*		
	Prefix A/3 dated 3.9.1907 to prefix H/3 dated 4.12.1911.................		Rare
SC211b	*Signatories: handsigned p. General Manager and p. Accountant*		
	Prefix I/3 dated 30.10.1912 to prefix M/3 dated 12.9.1915..............	£450	£800

Obverse—Blue with a red sunburst underprint and "B.L.B." in large red letters; panel at left and Royal Arms at top.
Reverse—Blue panel with "DITAT" emblem at centre.

SC212	*Signatories: Handsigned p. General Manager and p. Accountant.*		
	Prefix N/3 dated 1.2.1916 to prefix W/5 dated 3.8.1933.................from £200		£450

Obverse—Blue with a red sunburst underprint and "B.L.B." in large red letters; panel at left and the Bank's Coat of Arms at top.
Reverse—Blue panel with "DITAT" emblem at centre.

		VF	EF
SC213a	*Signatories: A. Dempster (General Manager) and handsigned p. Accountant* Prefix X/5 dated 16.9.1935 to prefix P/6 dated 30.12.1940	£220	£450
SC213b	*Signatories: G. Mackenzie (General Manager) and handsigned p. Accountant* Prefix Q/6 dated 16.7.1941 to prefix B/7 dated 12.1.1943	£220	£450
SC213c	*Signatories: J. Waugh (Accountant and Cashier) and G. Mackenzie (General Manager)* Prefix C/7 dated 11.2.1943 to prefix O/7 dated 28.1.1944	£200	£400

Size 182mm x 100mm approximately

Obverse—Blue with a red sunburst underprint and "B.L.B." in large red letters; panel at left and the Bank's Coat of Arms at top.
Reverse—Blue panel with "DITAT" emblem at centre.

		VF	EF
SC214a	*Signatories: J. Waugh (Accountant & Cashier) and G. Mackenzie (General Manager)* Prefix P/7 dated 29.5.1944 to prefix U/7 dated 3.11.1944	£140	£250
SC214b	*Signatory: G. Mackenzie (General Manager)* Prefix V/7 dated 10.9.1946 to prefix Z/8 dated 2.8.1950	£70	£140
SC214c	*Signatory: A. P. Anderson (General Manager)* Prefix A/9 dated 5.12.1950 to prefix Y/11 dated 4.8.1959	£55	£110

Size 158mm x 90mm approximately

Obverse—Blue with a red sunburst underprint and "B.L.B." in large red letters; panel at left and the Bank's Coat of Arms at top. Printed by De la Rue.
Reverse—Blue panel with "DITAT" emblem at centre.

		VF	EF
SC215	*Signatory: A. P. Anderson* (General Manager)		
	Prefix Z/11 dated 2.1.1961 and prefix A/12 dated 3.2.1961	£130	£250

Size 140mm x 84mm approximately

Obverse—Blue on a red sunburst underprint; portrait of Sir Walter Scott.
Reverse—Revised blue panel with "DITAT" emblem at centre.

		EF	UNC
SC216a	*Signatory: A. P. Anderson* (General Manager)		
	Prefix D/12 dated 21.9.1962 to prefix F/12 dated 19.11.1962..........	£30	£55
SC216b	*Signatory: T. W. Walker* (General Manager)		
	Prefix G/12 dated 16.6.1964 to prefix I/12 dated 18.8.1964	£30	£55

Size 146mm x 78mm approximately.

Obverse—Blue on a red sunburst underprint; portrait of Sir Walter Scott.
Reverse—Revised blue panel with "DITAT" emblem at centre.

SC217	*Signatory: T. W. Walker* (General Manager)		
	Prefix K/12 dated 22.3.1968 to prefix M/12 dated 24.5.1968..........	£45	£70

TEN POUNDS

Size: 206mm x 130mm approximately

Obverse—Blue with "B.L.B." in large red letters at centre; panel to the left; Royal Coat of Arms at the top. Uniface.

	F	VF
SC221 *Signatories: handsigned p. Manager and p. Accountant* Prefix S/1 dated 30.1.1907..		Rare

Obverse—Blue with a red sunburst underprint and "B.L.B." in large red letters; panel at left and Royal Arms at top.
Reverse—Blue panel with "DITAT" emblem at centre.

SC222   *Signatories: Handsigned p. General Manager and p. Accountant.*
Prefix T/1 dated 15.2.1916 to prefix V/1 dated 15.3.1920............   from £650

TWENTY POUNDS

Size: 206mm x 130mm approximately

Obverse—Blue with "B.L.B." in large red letters at centre; panel to the left; Royal Coat of Arms at the top. Uniface.

SC231   *Signatories: handsigned p. Manager and p. Accountant*
Prefix X/2 dated 2.1.1907 to prefix B/3 dated 31.3.1911 ....   Rare

Obverse—Blue with "B.L.B." in large red letters at centre; panel to the left; Royal Coat of Arms at the top. Uniface.

SC232   *Signatories: handsigned p. General Manager and p. Accountant.*
Prefix C/3 dated 20.10.1912 and prefix D/3 dated 18.11.1912 ....   Rare

Obverse—Blue with a red sunburst underprint and "B.L.B." in large red letters; panel at left and Royal Arms at top.
Reverse—Blue panel with "DITAT" emblem at centre.

SC233   *Signatories: Handsigned p. General Manager and p. Accountant*
Prefix E/3 dated 3.5.1916 to prefix X/3 dated 4.9.1933....................from £300   £600

Obverse—Blue with a red sunburst underprint and "B.L.B." in large red letters; panel at left and the Bank's Coat of Arms at top.
Reverse—Blue panel with "DITAT" emblem at centre.

		VF	EF

SC234a *Signatories: A. Dempster* (General Manager) *and handsigned p.Accountant*
(Printed on plain paper without silk threads)
Prefix Y/3 dated 6.8.1935 to prefix Z/3 dated 3.10.1935 .... £480 £800

SC234a *Signatories: A. Dempster* (General Manager) *and handsigned p.Accountant*
(Printed on granite paper with silk threads)
Prefix A/4 dated 21.7.1939 to prefix D/4 dated 2.8.1940 .... £320 £550

SC234b *Signatories: G. Mackenzie* (General Manager) *and handsigned p. Accountant*
Prefix E/4 dated 25.5.1942 to prefix K/4 dated 24.2.1945 .... £220 £450

Obverse—Blue with a red sunburst underprint and "B.L.B." in large red letters; panel at left and the Bank's Coat of Arms at top.
Reverse—Blue panel with "DITAT" emblem at centre.

SC235a *Signatory: G. Mackenzie* (General Manager)
Prefix L/4 dated 2.9.1946 to prefix Q/4 dated 4.8.1949 .... £220 £400

SC235b *Signatory: A. P.Anderson* (General Manager)
Prefix R/4 dated 12.5.1952 to prefix F/5 dated 11.12.1957 .... £180 £350

Obverse—Blue with a red sunburst underprint and "B.L.B." in large red letters; panel at left and the Bank's Coat of Arms at top. Printed by De la Rue.
Reverse—Blue panel with "DITAT" emblem at centre.

	VF	EF
SC236 *Signatory: A. P. Anderson* (General Manager)		
Prefix G/5 dated 14.2.1962 to prefix I/5 dated 4.4.1962..................	£200	£360

ONE HUNDRED POUNDS

Size: 206mm x 130mm approximately

Obverse—Blue with "B.L.B." in large red letters at centre; panel to the left; Royal Coat of Arms at the top. Uniface.

	F	VF
SC241 *Signatories: handsigned p. Manager and p. Accountant.*		
Prefix E/3 dated 3.1.1906 to prefix H/3 dated 15.5.1912..................		Rare

Obverse—Blue with a red sunburst underprint and "B.L.B." in large red letters; panel at left and Royal Arms at top.
Reverse—Blue panel with "DITAT" emblem at centre.

SC242 *Signatories: Handsigned p. General Manager and p. Accountant*
Prefix I/3 dated 7.1.1916 to prefix N/3 dated 18.7.1933................... Rare

Obverse—Blue with a red sunburst underprint and "B.L.B." in large red letters; panel at left and the Bank's Coat of Arms at top.
Reverse—Blue panel with "DITAT" emblem at centre

	F	VF

SC243a *Signatories: A. Dempster (General Manager) and handsigned p.Accountant*
Prefix O/3 dated 24.6.1935... Rare

SC243b *Signatories: G. Mackenzie (General Manager) and handsigned p.Accountant*
Prefix P/3 dated 4.2.1942 and prefix Q/3 dated 3.3.1943................. Rare

Obverse—Blue with a red sunburst underprint and "B.L.B." in large red letters; panel at left and the Bank's Coat of Arms at top.
Reverse—Blue panel with "DITAT" emblem at centre.

	VF	EF

SC244 *Signatory: A. P. Anderson (General Manager)*
Prefix R/3 dated 6.4.1951 to prefix T/3 dated 27.11.1957 .... £1100 £1800

(Actual size 206mm x 130mm)

Obverse—Blue with a red sunburst underprint and "B.L.B." in large red letters; panel at left and the Bank's Coat of Arms at top. Printed by De la Rue.
Reverse—Blue panel with "DITAT" emblem at centre.

SC245 *Signatory: A. P. Anderson (General Manager)*
Prefix U/3 dated 9.5.1962 and V/3 dated 1.6.1962........................... £1100 £1800

THE CLYDESDALE BANK LIMITED

The Bank was founded in Glasgow in 1838 and expanded rapidly during the 19th century by absorbing a number of other Scottish banks including the Greenock Union Bank, the Edinburgh and Glasgow Bank and the Eastern Bank of Scotland. In 1919 ownership of the Bank passed to the Midland Bank who also purchased the North of Scotland Bank Ltd., but it was not until 1950 that the two Scottish Banks merged to form The Clydesdale & North of Scotland Bank Ltd. In 1987 the Clydesdale Bank was sold by the Midland Bank to the National Australia Bank, and it remains as one the three issuers of paper money in Scotland today.

ONE POUND

"A" size square notes (165mm x 120mm approximately)

Obverse—black and red. The Arms of Glasgow surrounded by three female figures at the top with further female figure to the left and right; uniface.

	F	VF
SC301 *Signatories: D. Dewar* (Accountant) *and handsigned p. General Manager*		
From 4.7.1882 to 30.10.1912 without prefix letter, and .... from £480		£850
Prefix A dated 8.10.1913 to prefix A dated 9.2.1921. .... £300		£550

Obverse — Blue with a red overlay. Similar to previous design with the Arms of Glasgow and female figures.
Reverse — Blue. A large panel with the Arms of Glasgow at the centre.

		F	VF
SC302a	*Signatories: A. Swanson* (Cashier) *and J. D. Dewar* (Accountant)		
	Prefix A dated 4.1.1922 and 14.6.1922	£260	£450
SC302b	*Signatories: A. Swanson* (Cashier) *and R. Young* (Accountant)		
	Prefix A dated 14.3.1923 to prefix A dated 27.10.1926..........................	£260	£450

"B" size notes (152mm x 85mm approximately)

Obverse — Blue with red overlay. Arms of Glasgow with female figures at the top; female figures to the left and right.
Reverse — Blue. A large panel with the Arms of Glasgow at the centre.

		VF	EF
SC303a	*Signatories: A. Swanson* (Cashier) *and R. Young* (Accountant)		
	Prefix A dated 3.1.1927 to prefix A dated 7.10.1931...............................	£95	£180
SC303b	*Signatories: A. Mitchell* (General Manager) *and R. Young* (Accountant & Cashier)		
	Prefix A dated 2.3.1932 to prefix B dated 24.10.1945............................	£65	£100
SC303c	*Signatories: A. Mitchell* (General Manager) *and J. W. Pairmain* (Accountant & Cashier)		
	Prefix C dated 1.5.1946.	£110	£200
SC303d	*Signatories: J. J. Campbell* (General Manager) *and J. W. Pairmain* (Accountant & Cashier)		
	Prefix C dated 20.11.1946 to prefix C dated 3.9.1947.............................	£60	£100
SC303e	*Signatories: J. J. Campbell* (General Manager) *and R. R. Houston* (Accountant & Cashier)		
	Prefix C dated 7.4.1948 to prefix C dated 14.12.1949	£60	£100

FIVE POUNDS

Size 225mm x 125mm approximately

Obverse—black with "Clydesdale Bank Limited" and value panels overlaid in red. Arms of Glasgow at the top of the note; ornate panel to the left. Uniface

	F	VF
SC304 *Signatories: D. Dewar (Accountant) and handsigned p. General Manager* From 4.7.1882 (prefix unknown) to prefix Q²/B dated 9.2.1921..............		Rare

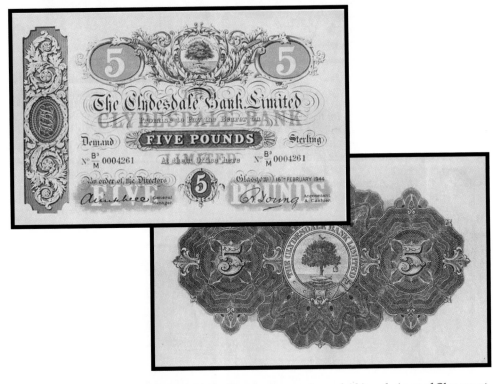

Obverse—blue with "Clydesdale Bank Limited" and value panels overlaid in red. Arms of Glasgow at the top of the note; ornate panel to the left
Reverse—large blue value panel with the Arms of Glasgow at the centre surrounded by "The Clydesdale Bank Limited"

SC305a *Signatories: A. Swanson (Cashier) and J. D. Dewar (Accountant)*
Prefix Q²/C dated 15.2.1922 to prefix R²/J dated 14.6.1922 .... Rare

SC305b *Signatories: A. Swanson (Cashier) and R. Young (Accountant)*
Prefix R²/K dated 31.1.1923 to prefix U²/O dated 9.12.1931................ £280   £450

SC305c *Signatories: A. Mitchell (General Manager) and R. Young (Accountant & Cashier)*   VF   EF
Prefix U²/P dated 16.11.1932 to prefix W²/H dated 27.10.1937, then.   £380   £600
printers imprint is removed from the bottom left of the note, and

SC305d Prefix W²/J dated 25.5.1938 to prefix D³/A dated 24.10.1945 ....   £300   £500

SC305e *Signatories: J. J. Campbell (General Manager) and J. W. Pairmain (Accountant & Cashier)*
Prefix D²/B to prefix D³/R dated 10.7.1946 ....   £350   £550

Obverse—blue with "Clydesdale Bank Limited" and value panels overlaid in red, and with an additional light blue overlay. Arms of Glasgow at the top of the note; ornate panel to the left Reverse—large blue value panel with the Arms of Glasgow at the centre surrounded by "The Clydesdale Bank Limited"

		VF	*EF*
SC306a	*Signatories: J. J. Campbell* (General Manager) *and J. W. Pairmain* (Accountant & Cashier)		
	Prefix AA to prefix AQ dated 3.3.1948...	£340	£650
SC306b	*Signatories: J. J. Campbell* (General Manager) *and R. R. Houston* (Accountant & Cashier)		
	Prefix AR to prefix BG dated 12.1.1949...	£340	£650

TWENTY POUNDS

Size 225mm x 125mm approximately

Obverse—black with "Clydesdale Bank Limited" and value panels overlaid in red. Arms of Glasgow at the top of the note; ornate panel to the left. Uniface

SC307 *Signatories: D.Dewar (Accountant) and handsigned p. General Manager*
From 4.7.1882 (prefix unknown) to prefix P/B dated 9.6.1920 ....   Rare

Obverse—blue with "Clydesdale Bank Limited" and value panels overlaid in red. Arms of Glasgow at the top of the note; ornate panel to the left.
Reverse—large blue value panel with the Arms of Glasgow at the centre surrounded by "The Clydesdale Bank Limited".

	F	VF
SC308a *Signatories: A. Swanson (Cashier) and J. D. Dewar (Accountant)* Prefix P/C dated 15.2.1922 to prefix Q/A dated 31.1.1923		Rare
SC308b *Signatories: A. Swanson (Cashier) and R. Young (Accountant)* Prefix Q/B dated 2.5.1923 to prefix Q/Z dated 3.6.1931......................from £450		£900

	VF	EF
SC308c *Signatories: A. Mitchell (General Manager) and R. Young (Accountant & Cashier)* Prefix R/A dated 16.11.1932 to prefix U/A dated 15.11.1944...................	£750	£1250
SC308d *Signatories: J. J. Campbell (General Manager) and J. W. Pairmain (Accountant & Cashier)* Prefix U/B to prefix U/J dated 4.6.1947.......................................	£750	£1150

ONE HUNDRED POUNDS

Size 225mm x 125mm approximately

Obverse—black with "Clydesdale Bank Limited" and value panels overlaid in red. Arms of Glasgow at the top of the note; ornate panel to the left. Uniface

	F	VF
SC309 *Signatories: D. Dewar* (Accountant) *and handsigned p.General Manager*		
Final prefix E/V dated 5.8.1914..		Rare

Obverse—blue with "Clydesdale Bank Limited" and value panels overlaid in red. Arms of Glasgow at the top of the note; ornate panel to the left.
Reverse—large blue value panel with the Arms of Glasgow at the centre surrounded by "The Clydesdale Bank Limited".

SC310a *Signatories: A. Swanson* (Cashier) *and J. D. Dewar* (Accountant)
Prefix E/W to prefix F/A dated 15.2.1922   Rare

SC310b *Signatories: A. Swanson* (Cashier) *and R. Young* (Accountant)
Prefix F/B dated 16.12.1925 to prefix F/L dated 3.6.1931 .... Rare

SC310c *Signatories: A. Mitchell* (General Manager) *and R. Young* (Accountant & Cashier)
Prefix F/M dated 19.6.1935 to prefix G/D dated 3.2.1943 .... Rare

SC310d *Signatories: J. J. Campbell* (General Manager) *and J. W. Pairmain* (Accountant & Cashier)
Prefix G/E to prefix G/H dated 26.3.1947 .... Rare

THE CLYDESDALE & NORTH OF SCOTLAND BANK LIMITED

ONE POUND

"B" size notes (152mm x 85mm approximately)

Obverse—blue/grey with a red/orange underprint. New Coat of Arms at the top of the note; vignettes of shipping and agricultural scenes at the bottom corners.
Reverse—blue with an illustration of a highland river scene.

		VF	EF
SC311a *Signatory: J. J. Campbell* (General Manager)...			
Prefix A dated 1.11.1950 to prefix M dated 1.6.1955, and		£35	£70
Prefix A/N to prefix A/Q dated 1.11.1956..		£35	£70
SC311b *Signatory: R. D. Fairbairn* (General Manager)			
Prefix A/R dated 1.5.1958 to prefix A/U dated 1.11.1960		£35	£70

"C" size notes (152mm x 72mm approximately)

Obverse—mainly green with an orange/brown underprint. Coat of Arms to the right.
Reverse—green; illustration of a ship launching scene.

		EF	UNC
SC312 *Signatory: R. D. Fairbairn* (General Manager)			
Prefix B/A dated 1.3.1961 to prefix B/H dated 1.2.1963............................		£35	£55

FIVE POUNDS

Size 179mm x 98mm approximately

Obverse—purple on a green and pink underprint. Illustrations of King's College, Aberdeen to the left, and Glasgow Cathedral to the right
Reverse—large purple panel with the new Coat of Arms at the centre with the value to the left and right

		VF	EF
SC313a *Signatory: J. J. Campbell* (General Manager)			
Prefix A dated 2.5.1951 to prefix P dated 1.6.1955, and		£60	£120
Prefix A/Q dated 1.11.1956 to prefix A/X dated 1.2.1958.......................		£60	£120
SC313b *Signatory: R. D. Fairbairn* (General Manager)			
Prefix A/Y, A/Z, A/A and A/B dated 1.3.1960		£70	£130

Size 141mm x 84mm approximately

Obverse—mainly blue with an orange/brown underprint. Coat of Arms to the right.
Reverse—blue; illustration of King's College, Aberdeen.

SC314 *Signatory: R. D. Fairbairn* (General Manager*)*			
Prefix B/A dated 20.9.1961 to prefix B/M dated 1.2.1963		£45	£85

TWENTY POUNDS

Size 179mm x 98mm approximately

Obverse—green on a pale yellow underprint. Illustrations of King's College, Aberdeen to the left, and Glasgow Cathedral to the right.
Reverse—large green panel with the new Coat of Arms at the centre with the value to the left and right.

SC315a *Signatory: J. J. Campbell* (General Manager)   *VF*   *EF*
    Prefix A dated 2.5.1951 to prefix B dated 1.2.1958..................................... £120 £250

SC315b *Signatory: R. D. Fairbairn* (General Manager)
    Prefix C dated 1.12.1960 to prefix E dated 1.8.1962.................................. £120 £250

ONE HUNDRED POUNDS

Size 179mm x 98mm approximately

Obverse—blue on a pale yellow/green underprint. Illustrations of King's College, Aberdeen to the left, and Glasgow Cathedral to the right.
Reverse—large blue panel with the new Coat of Arms at the centre with the value to the left and right.

SC316a *Signatory: J. J. Campbell* (General Manager)
    Prefix A dated 2.5.1951.. £700 £1200

SC316b *Signatory: R. D. Fairbairn* (General Manager)
    Prefix A dated 1.12.1960.. £850 £1300

CLYDESDALE BANK LIMITED

ONE POUND

"C" size notes (152mm x 72mm approximately)

Obverse—mainly green with an orange/brown underprint. Coat of Arms to the right.
Reverse—green; illustration of a ship launching scene.

		EF	UNC
SC317a *Signatory: R. D. Fairbairn (General Manager)*			
Prefix C/A dated 2.9.1963 to prefix C/K dated 3.4.1967		£30	£50
SC317b *Sorting symbols added to reverse of the notes*			
Prefix C/L dated 3.4.1967 to prefix C/U dated 1.9.1969..........................		£30	£50

"D" size notes (135mm x 67mm approximately)

Obverse—green with a multicoloured underprint. Portrait of Robert the Bruce to the left.
Reverse—mainly green with an illustration of Robert the Bruce at the battle of Bannockburn.

SC318a *Signatory: R. D. Fairbairn (General Manager)*			
Prefix D/A to prefix D/F dated 1.3.1971......................................		£25	£35
SC318b *Signatory: A. R. MacMillan (General Manager)*			
Prefix D/G dated 1.5.1972 to prefix D/Q dated 1.8.1973........................		£20	£30
SC318c *Signatory: A. R. MacMillan (Chief General Manager)*			
Prefix D/R dated 1.3.1974 to prefix D/BT dated 27.2.1981		£12	£18

FIVE POUNDS

Size 141mm x 84mm approximately

Obverse—mainly blue with an orange/brown underprint. Coat of Arms to the right.
Reverse—blue; illustration of King's College, Aberdeen.

		EF	*UNC*
SC319a *Signatory: R. D. Fairbairn* (General Manager)			
Prefix C/A dated 2.9.1963 to prefix C/R dated 1.5.1967		£55	£85
SC319b *Sorting symbols added to reverse of the notes*			
Prefix C/S dated 1.5.1967 to prefix C/GG dated 1.9.1969		£55	£85

Size 146mm x 78mm approximately

Obverse—blue with a multicoloured underprint. Portrait of Robert Burns to the left.
Reverse—mainly blue. Illustration of a field mouse and wild roses.

SC320a *Signatory: R. D. Fairbairn* (General Manager)			
Prefix D/A to prefix D/K dated 1.3.1971		£55	£85
SC320b *Signatory: A. R. MacMillan* (General Manager)			
Prefix D/L dated 1.5.1972 to prefix D/AA dated 1.8.1973		£55	£85
SC320c *Signatory: A. R. MacMillan* (Chief General Manager)			
Prefix D/AB dated 1.3.1974 to prefix D/DX dated 27.2.1981		£45	£65

TEN POUNDS

Size 151mm x 93mm approximately

Obverse—mainly brown with a multicoloured underprint. Coat of Arms to the right.
Reverse—brown; illustration of the University of Glasgow.

		EF	UNC
SC321	*Signatory: R. D. Fairbairn* (General Manager)		
	Prefix C/A dated 20.4.1964 to prefix C/D dated 1.12.1967..................	£240	£350

Size 150mm x 85mm approximately

Obverse—brown; portrait of David Livingstone to the left.
Reverse—brown; scene with three African slaves.

SC322a	*Signatory: A. R. MacMillan* (General Manager)
	Prefix D/A dated 1.3.1972 to prefix D/F dated 1.8.1973 .... £160 £250

SC322b	*Signatory: A. R. MacMillan* (Chief General Manager)
	Prefix D/G dated 1.3.1974 to prefix D/DZ dated 27.2.1981.................... £140 £200

TWENTY POUNDS

Size 162mm x 93mm approximately

Obverse—mainly red with a multicoloured underprint. Coat of Arms to the right.
Reverse—red; view of George Square, Glasgow.

		EF	UNC
SC323	*Signatory: R. D. Fairbairn* (General Manager)		
	Prefix C/A dated 19.11.1964 to prefix C/H dated 1.12.1967. .... £250		£320

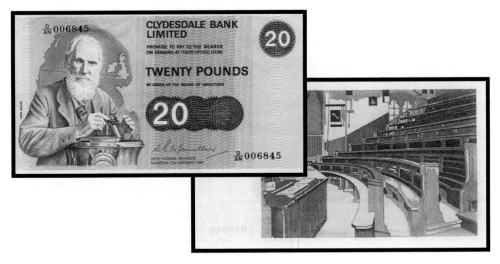

Obverse—purple with a portrait of Lord Kelvin to the left.
Reverse—purple; illustration of Lord Kelvin's lecture room at the University of Glasgow.

SC324a *Signatory: A. R. MacMillan* (General Manager)
Prefix D/A to prefix D/J dated 1.3.1972 .... £300   £450

SC324b *Signatory: A. R. MacMillan* (Chief General Manager)
Prefix D/K dated 2.2.1976 to prefix D/AV dated 27.2.1981 .... £200   £300

FIFTY POUNDS

Size 169mm x 95mm approximately

Obverse—olive green with a portrait of Adam Smith to the left.
Reverse—olive green; illustration of a group of old industrial and agricultural tools with sailing ships in the background.

SC325	*Signatory: A. R. MacMillan* (Chief General Manager)	*EF*	*UNC*
	Prefix D/A to prefix D/Q dated 1.9.1981.	£280	£400

ONE HUNDRED POUNDS

Size 162mm x 93mm approximately

Obverse—mainly purple with a multicoloured underprint. Coat of Arms to the right.
Reverse—purple; river scene with bridge and hills in the background.

SC326	*Signatory: R. D. Fairbairn* (General Manager)	*VF*	*EF*
	Prefix C/A dated 1.2.1964 to prefix C/B dated 1.2.1968	£1050	£1950

Size 169mm x 95mm approximately

Obverse — red with a portrait of Lord Kelvin to the left.
Reverse — mainly red; illustration of Lord Kelvin's lecture room at the University of Glasgow.

		EF	UNC
SC327a *Signatory: A. R. MacMillan* (General Manager)			
Prefix D/A dated 1.3.1972 to prefix D/E dated 6.1.1975		£850	£1400
SC327b *Signatory: A. R. MacMillan* (Chief General Manager)			
Prefix D/E and D/F dated 1.2.1976		£850	£1400

CLYDESDALE BANK PLC

ONE POUND

"D" size notes (135mm x 67mm approximately)

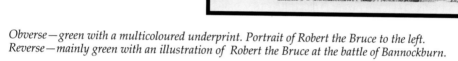

Obverse—green with a multicoloured underprint. Portrait of Robert the Bruce to the left.
Reverse—mainly green with an illustration of Robert the Bruce at the battle of Bannockburn.

		EF	UNC
SC328a	*Signatory: A. R. MacMillan* (Chief General Manager)		
	Prefix D/BU to prefix D/CD dated 29.3.1982..	£10	£16
SC328b	*Signatory: A. R. Cole Hamilton* (Chief General Manager)		
	Prefix D/CE to prefix D/CR dated 5.1.1983	£8	£13
SC328c	*Sorting symbols removed from reverse of the notes*		
	Prefix D/CS dated 8.4.1985 to prefix D/DK dated 25.11.1985	£8	£12
	Replacement note—prefix D/ZZ..	£28	£40
SC328d	*Signatory: A. R. Cole Hamilton* (Chief Executive)		
	Prefix D/DL dated 18.9.1987 to prefix D/DW dated 9.11.1988...............	£5	£9
	Replacement note—prefix D/ZZ..	£28	£45

FIVE POUNDS

Size 146mm x 78mm approximately

Obverse—blue with a multicoloured underprint. Portrait of Robert Burns to the left.
Reverse—mainly blue. Illustration of a field mouse and wild roses.

		EF	UNC
SC329a *Signatory: A. R. MacMillan* (Chief General Manager)			
Prefix D/DY to prefix D/FP dated 29.3.1982.		£40	£60
SC329b *Signatory: A. R. Cole Hamilton* (Chief General Manager)			
Prefix D/FQ to prefix D/HP dated 5.1.1983.		£40	£60
SC329c *Sorting symbols removed from reverse of the notes*			
Prefix D/HQ to prefix D/JG dated 18.9.1986		£25	£45
SC329d *Signatory: A. R. Cole Hamilton* (Chief Executive)			
Prefix D/JH dated 18.9.1987 to prefix D/LU dated 28.6.1989		£22	£35

Size 136mm x 70mm approximately

Obverse—blue with a multicoloured underprint. Revised portrait of Robert Burns to the left.
Reverse—mainly blue. Illustration of a field mouse and wild roses.

SC330a *Signatory: A. R. Cole Hamilton* (Chief Executive)			
Prefix E/AA to prefix E/CM dated 2.4.1990.		£18	£30
SC330b *Signatory: F. Cicutto* (Chief Executive)			
Prefix E/CN to prefix E/DN dated 1.9.1994		£12	£18
Replacement note—prefix D/ZZ			Rare
SC330c *Signatory: F. Goodwin* (Chief Executive)			
Prefix E/DP dated 21.7.1966 to prefix E/DY dated 1.12.1997		£9	£14
SC330d *Signatory: G. Savage* (Chief Executive)			
Prefix E/DZ to Prefix E/EB dated 19.6.2002		—	£10

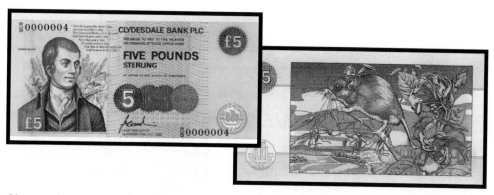

Obverse—blue with a multicoloured underprint. Portrait of Robert Burns to the left. A set of four notes, to commemorate the 200th anniversary of the poet, Robert Burns. Each note has a different Burns poem printed towards the top left corner.
Reverse—mainly blue. Illustration of a field mouse and wild roses.

These were originally issued as a set with similar serial numbers—
Prefix RB, and with the first digit running sequentially.

		EF	UNC
SC331	*Signatory: F. Goodwin* (Chief Executive)		
	Prefix RB dated 21.7.1996. Set of four notes with matched numbers.....	—	£90
	Prefix RB dated 21.7.1996. Single note	—	£20

Obverse—mainly blue on a multicoloured underprint. Portrait of Sir Alexander Fleming to the centre right.
Reverse—mainly blue. Illustration of St Kilda—Scottish World Site, inscribed 1986 & 2005.

SC332	*Signatory: D. Thorburn* (Chief Operating Officer)		
	Prefix W/HS dated 6.8.2009	—	£9
	Prefix E/ZZ—replacement note	—	£20

TEN POUNDS

Size 150mm x 85mm approximately

Obverse—brown; portrait of David Livingstone to the left.
Reverse—brown; scene with three african slaves.

		EF	UNC
SC341a *Signatory: A. R. MacMillan* (Chief General Manager) Prefix D/EA to prefix D/GW dated 29.3.1982................................. (prefix D/GW splits at or below 030000)		£130	£200
SC341b *Signatory: A. R. Cole Hamilton* (Chief General Manager) Prefix D/GW dated 5.1.1983 to prefix D/PZ dated 18.9.1986....... Replacement note—prefix D/ZZ..		£100	£160 Rare
SC341c *Signatory: A. R. Cole Hamilton* (Chief Executive) Prefix D/QA to prefix D/SW dated 18.9.1987................................		£90	£150

Size 150mm x 85mm approximately

Obverse—brown on a multicoloured underprint. Revised portrait of David Livingstone to the left.
Reverse—mainly brown. Illustration of the birthplace of Livingstone in Blantyre.

SC342 *Signatory: A. R. Cole Hamilton* (Chief Executive) Prefix D/SW dated 7.5.1988 to prefix E/GR dated 3.9.1990 Replacement note—prefix D/ZZ..		£45	£75 Rare

Size 143mm x 75mm approximately

Similar to previous issue, but reduced size.

Obverse—brown on a multicoloured underprint. Portrait of David Livingstone to the left.
Reverse—mainly brown. Illustration of the birthplace of Livingstone in Blantyre.

SC343a *Signatory: A. R. Cole Hamilton* (Chief Executive)   *EF* *UNC*
    Prefix E/GR to prefix E/QZ dated 3.9.1992... £40 £65
    Replacement note—prefix E/ZZ ....   Rare

SC343b *Signatory: C. Love* (Chief Executive)
    Prefix E/QZ to prefix E/VC dated 5.1.1993... £35 £60
    Replacement note—prefix E/ZZ ....   Rare

SC343c *Signatory: F. Goodwin* (Chief Executive)
    Prefix E/VD dated 22.3.1996 to prefix E/WZ dated 27.2.1997............... £22 £40
    Replacement note—prefix E/ZZ ....   Rare

Size 143mm x 75mm approximately

Obverse—brown on a multicoloured underprint. Portrait of Mary Slessor to the left.
Reverse—representation of Mary Slessor's missionary work in Africa during the late 19th Century.

SC344a *Signatory: F. Goodwin* (Chief Executive)
    Prefix A/AA to prefix A/AK dated 1.5.1997.   £24 £40
    Replacement note—prefix E/ZZ..   Rare

SC344b Prefix NAB dated 1.5.1997 .... £65 £90
    Notes with prefix NAB were encapsulated in a block of acrylic and issued to
    members of the Bank's staff to commemorate 10 years of ownership of the National
    Australia Bank. Surplus, un-encapsulated notes were subsequently issued due to a
    shortage of new notes, and a few have found their way onto the collectors market.

EF UNC

SC344c *Signatory: J. Wright* (Chief Executive)
Prefix A/AK dated 5.11.1998 to prefix A/CA dated 12.10.1999 .... — £25

SC344d *Signatory: S. Targett* (Chief Executive)
Prefix A/CA to prefix A/CL 800000 dated 26.1.2003 .... — £25

SC344e *Signatory: R. Pinney* (Chief Executive)
Prefix A/CL to prefix A/CZ (split at 300,000) dated 25.4.2003 .... — £25
Prefix E/ZZ—replacement note... £65

SC344f *Signatory: D. Thorburn* (Chief Operating Officer)
Prefix A/CZ 300,001 to prefix A/DS (split at 800,000) dated 21.11.2004.. — £20

Similar to previous issue with commemorative overprint.

Obverse—brown on a multicoloured underprint. Portrait of Mary Slessor to the left. Overprint to the right reads "Commemorating the year 2000"
Reverse—representation of Mary Slessors missionary work in Africa during the late 19th Century.

SC345 *Signatory: J. Wright* (Chief Executive)
Prefix MM dated 1.1.2000 .... £20 £45

Issued to commemorate the Commonwealth Games in Melbourne, March 2006. (5 million notes issued).
Obverse–brown on a multicoloured underprint. Portrait of Mary Slessor to the left. Overprint to the right reads "Commonwealth Games – Scotland – Melbourne 2006. Proud Partner".
Reverse–multicoloured; stylised representation of events in the Games.

SC346 *Signatory: D. Thorburn* (Chief Operating Officer).
Prefix CG/1 to CG/5 dated 15.3.2006 — £35

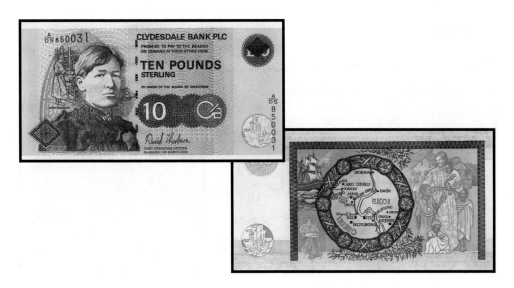

Obverse - brown on a multicoloured underprint. Portrait of Mary Slessor to the left. (Change of logo design).
Reverse—representation of Mary Slessor's missionary work in Africa during the late 19th century.

		EF	UNC
SC347	*Signatory: D.Thorburn (Chief Operating Officer)*		
	Prefix A/DS 800001 to prefix A/FP 800000 dated 14.3.2006	—	£20

Obverse—mailnly brown on a multicoloured underprint. Portrait of Robert Burns to the centre right.
Reverse—brown and green. Illustration of the old & New towns of Edinburgh—Scottish World Heritage Site.

		EF	UNC
SC348a	*Signatory: D. Thorburn (Chief Operating Officer)*	—	£18
	Prefix W/HS dated 25.1.2009		
	Prefix E/ZZ—Replacement note	—	£30

TWENTY POUNDS

Size 162mm x 93mm approximately

Obverse—purple with a portrait of Lord Kelvin to the left.
Reverse—purple; illustration of Lord Kelvin's lecture room at the University of Glasgow.

		EF	UNC
SC351a	*Signatory: A. R. MacMillan* (Chief General Manager)		
	Prefix D/BH to prefix D/BR dated 29.3.1982..	£170	£300
SC351b	*Signatory: A. R. Cole Hamilton* (Chief General Manager)		
	Prefix D/BS dated 5.1.1983 to prefix D/ED dated 8.4.1985	£140	£220
SC351c	*Signatory: A. R. Cole Hamilton* (Chief Executive)		
	Prefix D/EE dated 18.9.1987 to prefix D/FV dated 2.8.1990	£120	£200

Size 162mm x 93mm approximately

Obverse—purple and orange/brown on a multicoloured underprint. Portrait of Robert the Bruce in armour to the left.
Reverse—purple and brown. Illustration of Robert the Bruce in full battle armour on horseback.

		EF	UNC
SC352a	*Signatory: A. R. Cole Hamilton* (Chief Executive)		
	Prefix E/AA dated 30.11.1990 to prefix E/NM dated 3.9.1992	£65	£100
	Replacement note—prefix E/ZZ..		Rare
SC352b	*Signatory: C. Love* (Chief Executive)		
	Prefix E/NN to prefix E/SR dated 5.1.1993..	£90	£180
	Replacement note—prefix E/ZZ..		Rare

Obverse—purple and orange/brown on a multicoloured underprint. Portrait of Robert the Bruce in armour to the left. Somewhat bolder colours and new design elements added
Reverse—purple and brown. Illustration of Robert the Bruce in full battle armour on horseback. Bolder colours and new design element to the left.

		EF	UNC
SC353a	*Signatory: F. Ciccutto (Chief Executive)*		
	Prefix E/SS to prefix F/AX dated 1.9.1994	£50	£85
	Replacement note—prefix E/ZZ..		Rare
SC353b	*Signatory: F. Goodwin (Chief Executive)*		
	Prefix F/AY to prefix F/BC dated 2.12.1996....................................	£45	£65
	Replacement note—prefix E/ZZ..		Rare

Commemorates the Commonwealth Heads of Government meeting which took place in Edinburgh in October 1997.

Obverse—purple and orange/brown on a multicoloured underprint. Portrait of Robert the Bruce in armour to the left.
Reverse—Illustrations of the Edinburgh International Conference Centre and the new Clydesdale Bank Plaza, with Edinburgh Castle in the background.

SC354	*Signatory: F. Goodwin (Chief Executive)*		
	Prefix F/BD to F/BF, and prefix C/HG dated 30.9.1997	£50	£85

Obverse—purple and orange/brown on a multicoloured underprint. Portrait of Robert the Bruce in armour to the left. Some design elements changed.
Reverse—purple and brown. Illustration of Robert the Bruce in full battle armour on horseback.

		EF	UNC
SC355a	*Signatory: F. Goodwin* (Chief Executive)		
	Prefix A/AA to prefix A/AQ (split at 950,000) dated 1.11.1997. .... £35		£60
	Replacement note—prefix E/ZZ..		Rare
SC355b	*Signatory: J. Wright* (Chief Executive)		
	Prefix A/AQ to prefix A/BL (split at 450,000) dated 12.10.1999. .... £35		£55
	NB—Prefix A/AQ starts at A/AQ 950001 and is scarce		
SC355c	*Signatory: G. Savage* (Chief Executive)		
	Prefix A/BL to prefix A/BP dated 19.6.2002 .... —		£55
SC355d	*Signatory: S. Targett* (Chief Executive)		
	Prefix A/BQ to prefix A/BW (split at 450,000) dated 26.1.2003 .... —		£45
SC355e	*Signatory: R. Pinney* (Chief Executive)		
	Prefix A/BW to prefix A/CS (split at 450,000) dated 25.4.2003........... —		£45
SC355f	*Signatory: D. Thorburn* (Chief Operating Officer)		
	Prefix A/CS to prefix AD/K dated 21.11.2004 .... —		£40

Comemorates the 19th Century architect Alexander "Greek" Thomson 1817–75, and Glasgow as the UK City of Architecture and Design, 1999.

Obverse—purple and orange/brown on a multicoloured underprint. Portrait of Alexander "Greek" Thomson to the left.
Reverse—stylised illustration of architecture in Glasgow.

SC356	*Signatory: J. Wright* (Chief Executive)		
	Prefix A/AL to A/AQ, 950,000 and G/AD dated 9.4.1999. .... £45		£85

Obverse—purple and orange/brown on a multicoloured underprint. Portrait of Robert the Bruce in armour to the left. Similar to the 1999 issue above with additional overprint—"Commemorating the Year 2000".

Reverse—purple and brown. Illustration of Robert the Bruce in full battle armour on horseback.

SC357 *Signatory: J. Wright* (Chief Executive)

	EF	UNC
Prefix MM dated 1.1.2000.	£40	£65

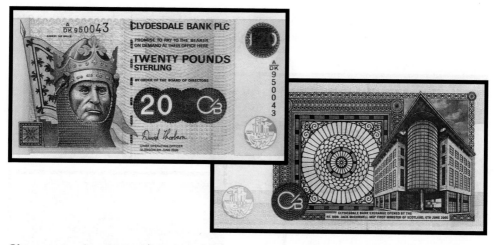

Obverse —purple and orange/brown on a multicoloured underprint. Portrait of Robert the Bruce in armour to the left. Similar to the earlier 1997 issue (SC355) with the addition of the Bank logo and extra security features.

Reverse—purple and brown. Illustration of the Clydesdale Bank Exchange which opened 6th. June 2005.

SC358 *Signatory: D. Thorburn* (Chief Operating Officer)

Prefix A/DK 950001 to prefix A/EJ 450000 dated 6.5.2005........................ £35   £50

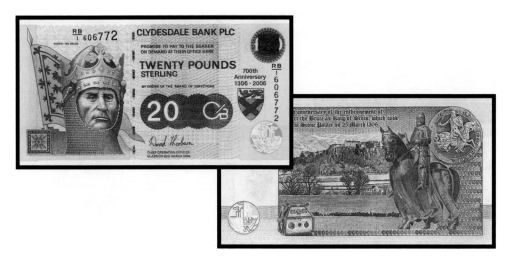

Issued in December 2006 to commemorate the 700th Anniversary of the enthronement of Robert the Bruce.

Obverse— purple and orange/brown on a multicoloured underprint. Portrait of Robert the Bruce in armour to the left. Similar to the earlier issues with the addition of a shield and commemorative text to the right.

Reverse—purple and brown. Picture of Robert the Bruce on horseback with commemorative text at top.

		EF	*UNC*
SC359 *Signatory: D. Thorburn* (Chief Operating Officer)			
Prefix RB/1 to prefix RB/5 dated 25.3.2005		£40	£60

Obverse— purple and orange/brown on a multicoloured underprint. Portrait of Robert the Bruce in armour to the left. Similar to the 2005 issue (SC358).

Reverse—purple and brown. Picture of Robert the Bruce on horseback (as SC355).

SC360 *Signatory: D. Thorburn* (Chief Operating Officer)			
Prefix A/EJ (from 450001) dated 24.6.2006 and ongoing		—	£40

Obverse—mainly purple on a multicoloured underprint. Portrait of Robert the Bruce in armour to the centre right
Reverse—purple on a green and brown background. Illustration of New Lanark—Scottish World Heritage Site.

		EF	UNC
SC360A *Signatory: D. Thorburn* (Chief Operating Officer)			
Prefix W/HS dated 11.7.2009		—	£36
Prefix E/ZZ—replacement note			£55

FIFTY POUNDS

Size 169mm x 95mm approximately

Obverse—olive green with a portrait of Adam Smith to the left.
Reverse—olive green; illustration of a group of old industrial and agricultural tools with sailing ships in the background.

SC361 *Signatory: A. R. Cole Hamilton* (Chief Executive)			
Prefix D/R dated 3.9.1989 to prefix D/AV dated 20.4.1992		£200	£350

Size 156mm x 85mm approximately

Obverse—green, brown and multicolour with a portrait of Adam Smith to the left.
Reverse—mainly green and brown; illustration of a group of old industrial and agricultural tools with sailing ships in the background.

		EF	UNC
SC362a *Signatory: F. Goodwin (Chief Executive)*			
Prefix A/AA to A/CB dated 22.3.1996		£110	£180
SC362b *Signatory: R. Pinney (Chief Executive)*			
Prefix A/CC dated 25.4.2003		£100	£170

Commemorates 550 years of the University of Glasgow

Obverse—green, brown and multicolour with a portrait of Adam Smith to the left and with an additional overprint—"University of Glasgow 1451–2001"
Reverse—mainly green and brown; illustration of a group of old industrial and agricultural tools, with sailing ships in the background.

SC363 *Signatory: S. Grimshaw (Chief Executive)*
Prefix GU dated 6.1.2001 (100,000 notes issued) £125   £200

The Bank logo is now added to the front of the note

Obverse—green, brown and multicolour with a portrait of Adam Smith to the left.
Reverse—mainly green and brown; illustration of a group of old industrial and agricultural tools, with sailing ships in the background.

SC364 *Signatory: D. Thorburn* (Chief Operating Officer)
Prefix A/CC dated 9.1.2006 Series ends at AC/CC 750000 ....

	EF	UNC
	—	£100

Obverse—mainly gree on a multicoloured underprint. Portrait of Elsie Inglis to the centre right.
Reverse—mailnly shades of green. Illustration of Antonine Wall—Scottish World Heritage Site.

SC365 *Signatory: D. Thorburn* (Chief Operating Officer)
Prefix W/HS dated 16.8.2009 .... — £90
Prefix E/ZZ—Replacement note.. — £150

ONE HUNDRED POUNDS

Size 160mm x 90mm approximately

Obverse—mainly red with a portrait of Lord Kelvin to the left.
Reverse—red and yellow; illustration of Lord Kelvin's lecture room at the University of Glasgow.

SC371a *Signatory: A. R. Cole Hamilton* (Chief General Manager)   *EF*   *UNC*
Prefix D/G to prefix D/L dated 8.4.1985 .... £500   £1000

SC371b *Signatory: A. R. Cole Hamilton* (Chief Executive)
Prefix D/M to prefix D/R dated 9.11.1991 .... £400   £800

Size 162mm x 90mm approximately

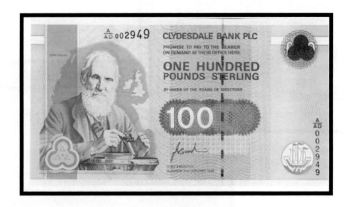

Obverse—red, purple and multicolour with a portrait of Lord Kelvin to the left.
Reverse—red, purple and multicolour; illustration of the University of Glasgow.

SC372   *Signatory: F. Goodwin* (Chief Executive)
Prefix A/AA to prefix A/BA dated 2.10.1996 .... —   £240

Commemorating 550 years of the University of Glasgow

Obverse—red, purple and multicolour with a portrait of Lord Kelvin to the left and with an additional overprint—"University of Glasgow 1451–2001"
Reverse—red, purple and multicolour; illustration of the University of Glasgow.

		EF	UNC
SC373	*Signatory: S. Grimshaw* (Chief Executive)		
	Prefix GU dated 6.1.2001 (100,000 notes issued).................................	£160	£350

Obverse—red, purple and multicolour with a portrait of Charles Rennie Mackintosh to the right of centre.
Reverse—red, green and grey; illustration of the Heart of Neolithic Orkney—Scottish World Heritage Site.

SC374	*Signatory: D. Thorburn* (Chief Operating Officer)		
	Prefix W/HS dated 7.6.2009 and ongoing	—	£185
	Prefix E/ZZ		£260

THE COMMERCIAL BANK OF SCOTLAND LIMITED

Founded in 1810 as The Commercial Banking Company of Scotland, the Bank developed during the 19th Century the largest branch system in Scotland. The name was changed to the Commercial Bank of Scotland Limited in 1882 by which time the bank had absorbed the Caithness Bank and the Arbroath Banking Company. In 1959 it amalgamated with the National Bank of Scotland Ltd. to form the National Commercial Bank of Scotland Limited.

ONE POUND

"A" size square notes (160mm x 120mm approximately)

Obverse—mainly black with the value in a yellow and blue underprint. Illustrations of the Bank's principal offices in Edinburgh, Glasgow and London.
Reverse—large blue panel with the Bank's emblem at the centre.

SC401   *Signatories: L. M. Mackay (Accountant) and handsigned p. Cashier.*
Prefix 18/A dated 2.1.1907 to prefix 18/E dated 2.1.1908. ....   Rare

Obverse—blue on a yellow and light blue underprint. Illustrations of the Bank's principal offices in Edinburgh, Glasgow and London.
Reverse—large blue panel with the Bank's emblem at the centre.

	F	VF
SC402a *Signatories: L. M. Mackay (Accountant) and handsigned p. Cashier.* ...		
Prefix 18/F dated 2.1.1909 to prefix 18/Q dated 3.1.1911..................	£380	£650
Prefix 19/A dated 2.1.1912 to prefix 19/Q dated 2.1.1915 (red serial Nos.)	£280	£550
SC402b *Signatories: L. M. Mackay (Accountant) and G. Riddell (Cashier)*		
Prefix 19/A dated 2.1.1912 to prefix 19/Q dated 2.1.1915 (red serial Nos.)	£280	£550
Prefix 20/A dated 2.1.1915 to prefix 20/Q dated 2.1.1917 (black serial Nos.)	£280	£550
Prefix 21/A dated 2.1.1918 (red serial No.)..	£300	£600
Prefix 21/B dated 2.1.1918 to prefix 21/I dated 2.1.1923 (black serial Nos.).	£280	£500

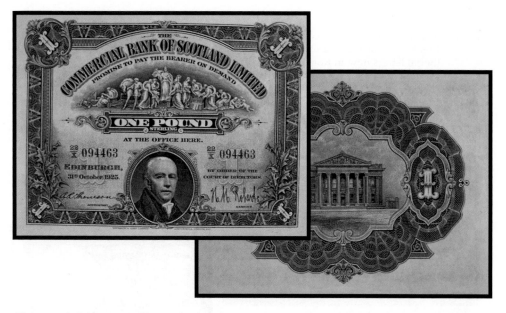

Obverse—dark blue on a yellow and red underprint. Portrait of Lord Pitcairn, the first Chairman of the Bank, at lower centre.
Reverse—dark blue panel with the Bank's Head Office building at the centre.

	F	VF

SC403   *Signatories: R. R. Thomson* (Accountant) *and H. M. Roberts* (Cashier)
Prefix 22/Z dated 31.10.1924 to prefix 22/W dated 1.11.1926........ £300 £500

"B" size notes (150mm x 85mm approximately)

Obverse—dark blue on a yellow and red underprint. Portrait of Lord Pitcairn, the first Chairman of the Bank, at lower centre.
Reverse—dark blue panel with the Bank's Head Office building at the centre.

	VF	EF

SC404a   *Signatories: R. R. Thomson* (Accountant) *and H. M. Roberts* (Cashier)
Prefix 23A dated 1.12.1927 (Serial letter in Gothic capitals) £250 £400

SC404b   *Signatories: P. Irving* (Accountant) *and R. R. Thomson* (Cashier)
Prefix 23B dated 1.6.1928 to prefix 23C dated 1.12.1928 (Gothic capitals)£100 £220

			VF	EF

SC404c *Signatories: P. Irving (Accountant) and R. R. Thomson (Cashier)*

Prefix 23D dated 2.12.1929 to prefix 23Z dated 30.11.1936, ... £65 £110
(Serial letters now in Roman capitals), and
Prefix A/24 dated 2.9.1937 to prefix P/24 dated 4.5.1939............. £65 £110

SC404d *Signatories: P. Irving (Chief Accountant) and James Thomson (Cashier)*

Prefix Q/24 dated 6.8.1940 to prefix Z/24 dated 4.6.1941, and..... £40 £85
Prefix A/25 dated 4.6.1941, and.. £45 £90
Prefix 25B dated 4.6.1941 to prefix 25N dated 2.12.1944 .... £40 £85

Obverse—mainly purple. Portrait of Lord Cockburn in a round panel to the right.
Reverse—purple; large panel with the Bank's Arms at the centre.

			EF	UNC

SC405 *Signatory: Sir J. M. Erskine (General Manager)*

Prefix 26A dated 2.1.1947 to prefix 26V dated 2.1.1953 .... £45 £85

Obverse—mainly blue. Portrait of Lord Cockburn in a round panel to the right
Reverse—blue; large panel with the Bank's Arms at the centre

SC406 *Signatory: I. W. Macdonald (General Manager)*

Prefix 27A dated 2.1.1954 to prefix 27R dated 1.7.1958 .... £40 £75

FIVE POUNDS

Size 220mm x 130mm approximately

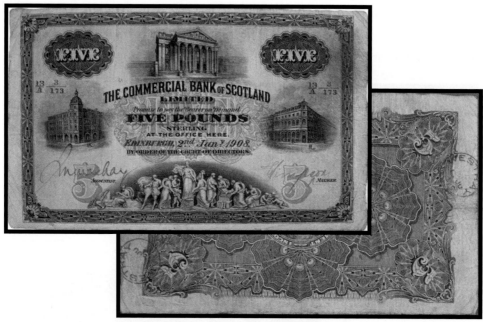

Obverse—mainly black with the value in a yellow and blue underprint. Illustrations of the Bank's principal offices in Edinburgh, Glasgow and London.
Reverse—large blue panel with the Bank's emblem at the centre.

SC411   *Signatories: handsigned p. Accountant and handsigned p. Manager*
               Prefix13/A dated 2.1.1908...   Rare

Obverse—blue on a yellow and light blue underprint. Illustrations of the Bank's principal offices in Edinburgh, Glasgow and London.
Reverse—large blue panel with the Bank's emblem at the centre.

	F	VF
SC412a *Signatories: handsigned p. Accountant and handsigned p. Manager*..... Prefix 13/A dated 2.1.1909 to prefix 13/B dated 2.1.1913	£600	£1050
SC412b *Signatories: L. M. Mackay* (Accountant) *and handsigned p. Manager* Prefix 13/C dated 2.1.1913 to prefix 13/M dated 2.1.1923	£550	£900

Size 207mm x 130mm approximately

Obverse—dark blue on a yellow and red underprint. Portrait of Lord Pitcairn, the first Chairman of the Bank, at lower centre.
Reverse—dark blue panel with the Bank's head office building at the centre.

	F	VF
SC413a *Signatories: R. R. Thomson* (Accountant) *and handsigned p. Manager* Prefix 14/Z dated 31.10.1924 to prefix 14/W dated 1.11.1926.	£300	£550

	VF	EF
SC413b *Signatories: R. R. Thomson* (Cashier) *and A. Robb* (General Manager) Prefix 14/W dated 1.12.1928 to prefix 14/R dated 1.8.1931.............	£300	£450
SC413c *Signatories: R. R. Thomson* (Cashier) *and Sir J. M. Erskine* (General Manager) Prefix 14/R dated 30.4.1934 to prefix 14/K dated 20.11.1937	£160	£350
SC413d *Signatories: James Thomson* (Cashier) *and Sir J. M. Erskine* (General Manager) Prefix 14/K dated 3.8.1940 to prefix 14/A dated 5.1.1943, and.......	£130	£320
Prefix 15/Z dated 5.1.1943 to prefix 15/M dated 1.12.1944	£130	£320

Size 179mm x 102mm approximately

Obverse — mainly purple. Portrait of Lord Cockburn at top flanked by two female figures representing agriculture and shipping.
Reverse — purple. Illustration of an Edinburgh street scene in Victorian times with the Bank's head office building in the background.

		VF	EF
SC414a	*Signatory: Sir J. M. Erskine* (General Manager)		
	Prefix 16A dated 2.1.1947 to prefix 16Z dated 2.1.1953	£50	£100
SC414b	*Signatory: I. W. Macdonald* (General Manager)		
	Prefix 17A dated 2.1.1954 to prefix 17Z dated 2.1.1957, and	£50	£100
	Prefix 18A to prefix 18F dated 2.1.1958	£50	£100

TWENTY POUNDS

Size 220mm x 130mm approximately

Obverse — mainly black with the value in a yellow and blue underprint. Illustrations of the Bank's principal offices in Edinburgh, Glasgow and London
Reverse — large blue panel with the Bank's emblem at the centre

SC421 *Signatories: handsigned p. Accountant and handsigned p. Manager*
Prefix 11/A dated 2.1.1907 .... no known examples extant

Obverse — blue on a yellow and light blue underprint. Illustrations of the Bank's principal offices in Edinburgh, Glasgow and London.
Reverse — large blue panel with the Bank's emblem at the centre.

		F	VF
SC422a	*Signatories: handsigned p. Accountant and handsigned p. Manager*		
	Prefix 11/A dated 3.1.1910 to prefix 11/A dated 2.1.1913		Rare
SC422b	*Signatories: L. M. Mackay* (Accountant) *and handsigned p. Manager*		
	Prefix 11/A dated 2.1.1914 to prefix 11/B dated 2.1.1923		Rare

Size 207mm x 130mm approximately

Obverse—dark blue on a yellow and red underprint. Portrait of Lord Pitcairn, the first Chairman of the Bank, at lower centre.
Reverse—dark blue panel with the Bank's head office building at the centre.

		F	VF
SC423a	*Signatories: R. R. Thomson* (Accountant) *and handsigned p. Manager* Prefix 12/Z dated 31.10.1924 and 1.5.1925...		Rare
SC423b	*Signatories: R. R. Thomson* (Cashier) *and A. Robb* (General Manager) Prefix 12/Z dated 1.5.1928 to prefix 12/X dated 1.8.1931.	£400	£700
SC423c	*Signatories: R. R. Thomson* (Cashier) *and Sir J. M. Erskine* (General Manager) Prefix 12/X dated 31.7.1935 to prefix 12/V dated 25.10.1937	£280	£550
SC423d	*Signatories: James Thomson* (Cashier) *and Sir J. M. Erskine* (General Manager) Prefix 12/V dated 2.8.1940 to prefix 12/Q dated 4.1.1943.................	£250	£450

Size 179mm x 102mm approximately

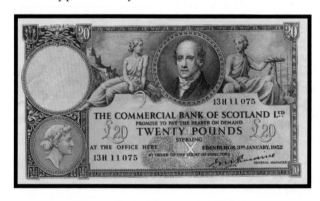

Obverse—mainly blue. Portrait of Lord Cockburn at top flanked by two female figures representing agriculture and shipping.
Reverse—blue. Illustration of an Edinburgh street scene in Victorian times with the Bank's head office building in the background.

		VF	EF
SC424a	*Signatory: Sir J. M. Erskine* (General Manager) Prefix 13A dated 2.1.1947 to prefix 13K dated 2.1.1953....................	£180	£400
SC424b	*Signatory: I. W. Macdonald* (General Manager) Prefix 13K dated 2.1.1954 to prefix 13P dated 2.1.1958.	£180	£400

ONE HUNDRED POUNDS

Size 220mm x 130mm approximately

Obverse—mainly black with the value in a yellow and blue underprint. Illustrations of the Bank's principal offices in Edinburgh, Glasgow and London
Reverse—large blue panel with the Bank's emblem at the centre

SC431   *Signatories: handsigned p. Accountant and handsigned p. Manager*
Prefix 10/A dated 2.1.1907..   no known examples extant

Obverse—blue on a yellow and light blue underprint. Illustrations of the Bank's principal offices in Edinburgh, Glasgow and London.
Reverse—large blue panel with the Bank's emblem at the centre.

SC432a   *Signatories: handsigned p. Accountant and handsigned p. Manager*
Prefix 10/A dated 2.1.1908 to prefix 10/A dated 2.1.1913 ....   Rare

SC432b   *Signatories: L. M. Mackay* (Accountant) *and handsigned p. Manager*
Prefix 10/A dated 2.1.1914 to prefix 10/A dated 2.1.1923 ....   Rare

Size 207mm x 130mm approximately

Obverse—dark blue on a yellow and red underprint. Portrait of Lord Pitcairn, the first Chairman of the Bank, at lower centre.
Reverse—dark blue panel with the Bank's head office building at the centre.

	F	VF
SC433a *Signatories: R. R. Thomson* (Accountant) *and handsigned p. Manager.* Prefix 11/Z dated 31.10.1924 and 1.12.1928.		Rare
SC433b *Signatories: R. R. Thomson* (Cashier) *and A. Robb* (General Manager). Prefix 11/Z dated 30.9.1937..	£1100	£2000
SC433c *Signatories: James Thomson* (Cashier) *and Sir J. M. Erskine* (General Manager) Prefix 11/Z dated 1.8.1940 to prefix 11/Y dated 2.1.1943.	£750	£1400

Size 179mm x 102mm approximately

Obverse—mainly green. Portrait of Lord Cockburn at top flanked by two female figures representing agriculture and shipping.
Reverse—green. Illustration of an Edinburgh street scene in Victorian times with the Bank's head office building in the background.

	VF	EF
SC434 *Signatory: Sir J. M. Erskine* (General Manager) Prefix 12A dated 2.1.1947 to prefix 12B dated 2.1.1953	£1000	£1800

THE NATIONAL BANK OF SCOTLAND LIMITED

The National Bank of Scotland was founded in 1825 and rapidly developed a branch system throughout Scotland. It absorbed the Commercial Banking Company of Aberdeen in 1833 and the Perth Union Bank in 1836. The title of the Bank was changed to The National Bank of Scotland Limited in 1882. In 1959 it merged with the Commercial Bank of Scotland Ltd. to form the National Commercial Bank of Scotland Limited.

ONE POUND

"A" size square notes (160mm x 120mm approximately)

Obverse—black lettering on a blue design with a red and yellow sunburst underprint. Royal Coat of Arms at the centre of the note; portrait of the Marquess of Lothian to the left and view of Edinburgh castle to the right.
Reverse—blue Elaborate panel with a view of Edinburgh at the centre.

		F	VF
SC501a	*Signatories: Thomas Shaw* (p. Manager) *and handsigned p. Accountant* Prefix A dated 2.1.1893 to prefix D dated 2.1.1905.		Rare
SC501b	*Signatories: W. Samuel* (p. General Manager) *and handsigned p. Accountant* Prefix F dated 15.5.1908 to prefix L dated 15.5.1919...................... from £220		£400
SC501c	*Signatories: W. Samuel* (p. General Manager) *and A. McKissock* (Accountant) Prefix L dated 11.11.1919 to prefix N dated 15.5.1924........................	£200	£400
SC501d	*Signatories: W. Lethbridge* (Cashier) *and A. McKissock* (Accountant) Prefix N dated 15.5.1925 to prefix O dated 1.7.1926...........................	£200	£400

"B" size notes (150mm x 85mm approximately)

Obverse—black on a red and yellow sunburst underprint. Royal Arms at the centre; illustrations of Glasgow Cathedral to the left and the Palace of Holyroodhouse to the right.
Reverse—large brown panel on a red and yellow sunburst underprint with a view of Edinburgh at the centre.

		VF	EF
SC502a	*Signatory: W. Lethbridge* (Cashier)		
	Prefix A/A dated 2.11.1927 to prefix A/C dated 1.11.1929...............	£110	£250
SC502b	*Signatory: George Drever* (Cashier)		
	Prefix A/D dated 2.2.1931..	£110	£250
	Change of printer from Waterlow & Sons Ltd to W. & A.K.Johnston Ltd.		
SC502c	Prefix A/D dated 2.2.1931 to prefix A/F dated 11.11.1933................	£95	£200

Obverse—black on a red and yellow sunburst underprint. Bank's Coat of Arms at the centre; illustrations of Glasgow Cathedral to the left and the Palace of Holyroodhouse to the right.
Reverse—large brown panel on a red and yellow sunburst underprint with a view of Edinburgh at the centre.

		VF	EF
SC503a	*Signatory: George Drever* (Cashier)		
	Prefix A/G dated 12.11.1934 to prefix A/S dated 1.5.1942	£40	£80
SC503b	*Signatory: J. T. Leggat* (General Manager)		
	Prefix A/T dated 15.3.1943 to prefix A/V dated 15.6.1946...............	£35	£75
SC503c	*Signatory: J. A. Brown* (General Manager)	EF	UNC
	Prefix A/W dated 1.3.1947 to prefix B/G dated 2.1.1953	£55	£90
	Change of printer's imprint to W. & A. K.Johnston & G. W. Bacon Ltd.		
SC503d	Prefix B/H dated 1.6.1953 to prefix B/K dated 1.10.1954.................	£50	£85
SC503e	*Signatory: D. Alexander* (General Manager)		
	Prefix B/L dated 1.3.1955 to prefix B/Z dated 2.2.1959, and	£45	£80
	Prefix C/A dated 1.5.1959		Rare

FIVE POUNDS

Size 210mm x 126mm approximately

Obverse—blue with a red and yellow underprint. Royal Coat of Arms at the centre of the note; portrait of the Marquess of Lothian to the left and view of Edinburgh Castle to the right.
Reverse—blue. Elaborate panel with a view of Edinburgh at the centre.

		F	VF
SC511a	*Signatories: handsigned p.General Manager and handsigned p. Accountant.* Prefix A dated 15.5.1909 to prefix A dated 11.11.1919................. from £280		£600
SC511b	*Signatories: W. Samuel (p. General Manager) and handsigned p. Accountant* Prefix A dated 11.11.1919 and prefix A dated 8.7.1920 .... £260		£550
SC511c	*Signatories: W. Lethbridge (Cashier) and handsigned p. Accountant* Prefix A dated 1.7.1927 to prefix A dated 11.11.1930......................... £220		£450
SC511d	*Signatories: George Drever (Cashier) and handsigned p. Accountant* Prefix A dated 11.11.1932. .... £200		£400

Obverse—blue with a red and yellow underprint. The Bank's Coat of Arms at the centre of the note; portrait of the Marquess of Lothian to the left and view of Edinburgh Castle to the right.
Reverse—blue, elaborate panel with a view of Edinburgh at the centre.

		VF	EF
SC512a	*Signatories: George Drever* (Cashier) *and handsigned p.Accountant* Prefix A and Prefix B dated 1.7.1936	£220	£380
SC512b	*Signatories: George Drever* (Cashier) *and A. A. Bremner* (Accountant) Prefix B dated 1.8.1939 to prefix B dated 1.3.1941	£180	£320
SC512c	*Signatories: George Drever* (Cashier) *and A. A. Bremner* (Chief Accountant) Prefix B dated 6.7.1942	£180	£320
SC512d	*Signatories: George Drever* (Cashier) *and J. T. Leggatt* (General Manager) Prefix B dated 11.1.1943	£180	£320
SC512e	*Signatories: A.S.O.Dandie* (Cashier) *and J. T. Leggatt* (General Manager) Prefix B dated 3.1.1944 to prefix C dated 2.1.1945	£150	£260
SC512f	*Signatories: A.S.O.Dandie* (Cashier) *and J.A.Brown* (General Manager) Prefix C dated 3.6.1947 to prefix D dated 1.5.1954	£95	£180
SC512g	*Signatories: A.S.O.Dandie* (Cashier) *and D.Alexander* (General Manager) Prefix D dated 1.7.1955 to prefix E dated 31.12.1956	£95	£180

Size 178mm x 102mm approximately

Obverse—green, Bank's Coat of Arms to the bottom left with thistles above.
Reverse—green, illustration of the Forth rail bridge.

		EF	UNC
SC513	*Signatories: A.S.O.Dandie* (Cashier) *and D.Alexander* (General Manager) Prefix A and prefix B dated 1.11.1957	£120	£170

TWENTY POUNDS

Size 210mm x 126mm approximately

Obverse—blue with a red yellow and pink underprint. Royal Coat of Arms at the centre of the note; portrait of the Marquess of Lothian to the left and view of Edinburgh Castle to the right.
Reverse—blue. Elaborate panel with a view of Edinburgh at the centre.

		F	VF
SC521a	*Signatories: handsigned p.General Manager and handsigned p. Accountant* Prefix A dated 1.8.1914.		Rare
SC521b	*Signatories: W. Lethbridge* (Cashier) *and handsigned p. Accountant* Prefix A dated 1.3.1928 and 2.1.1930.	£450	£750
SC521c	*Signatories: George Drever* (Cashier) *and handsigned p. Accountant* Prefix A dated 11.11.1932.	£450	£750

Obverse—blue with a red yellow and pink underprint. The Bank's Coat of Arms at the centre of the note; portrait of the Marquess of Lothian to the left and view of Edinburgh Castle to the right. Reverse—blue, elaborate panel with a view of Edinburgh at the centre.

		VF	EF
SC522a	*Signatories: George Drever* (Cashier) *and handsigned p. Accountant* Prefix A dated 16.5.1935 to prefix A dated 1.4.1941	£450	£850
SC522b	*Signatories: A. A. Bremner* (Chief Accountant) *and handsigned p. Cashier* Prefix A dated 8.12.1941 and 6.7.1942	£450	£800
SC522c	*Signatories: George Drever* (Cashier) *and J. T. Leggatt* (General Manager) Prefix A dated 11.1.1943	£450	£850
SC522d	*Signatories: A. S. O. Dandie* (Cashier) *and J. T. Leggatt* (General Manager) Prefix A dated 1.6.1944 and 2.1.1945	£420	£750
SC522e	*Signatories: A. S. O. Dandie* (Cashier) *and J. A. Brown* (General Manager) Prefix A dated 2.6.1947 to prefix A dated 1.5.1954	£350	£650
SC522f	*Signatories: A. S. O. Dandie* (Cashier) *and D. Alexander* (General Manager) Prefix A dated 31.12.1956	£340	£600

Size 178mm x 102mm approximately

Obverse—red, bank's Coat of Arms to the bottom left with thistles above.
Reverse—red, illustration of the Forth rail bridge.

SC523	*Signatories: A. S. O. Dandie* (Cashier) *and D. Alexander* (General Manager) Prefix A dated 1.11.1957.. £150		£300

ONE HUNDRED POUNDS

Size 210mm x 126mm approximately

Obverse—blue with a red yellow and pink underprint. Royal Coat of Arms at the centre of the note; portrait of the Marquess of Lothian to the left and view of Edinburgh Castle to the right. Reverse—blue. Elaborate panel with a view of Edinburgh at the centre.

	F	VF
SC531 *Signatories: handsigned p. General Manager and handsigned p. Accountant.* Prefix A dated 16.5.1935.		Rare

Obverse—blue with a red yellow and pink underprint. The Bank's Coat of Arms at the centre of the note; portrait of the Marquess of Lothian to the left and view of Edinburgh Castle to the right. Reverse—blue, elaborate panel with a view of Edinburgh at the centre.

SC532a *Signatories: George Drever* (Cashier) *and J. T. Leggat* (General Manager)
Prefix A dated 11.1.1943 .... Rare

SC532b *Signatories: A. S. O. Dandie* (Cashier) *and J. A. Brown* (General Manager)
Prefix A dated 2.6.1947 to prefix A dated 1.3.1952.............................. Rare

SC532c *Signatories: A. S. O. Dandie* (Cashier) *and D. Alexander* (General Manager)
Prefix A possibly exists.. Rare

Size 178mm x 102mm approximately

Obverse—green, bank's Coat of Arms to the bottom left with thistles above.
Reverse—green, illustration of the Forth rail bridge.

	VF	EF
Signatories: A. S. O.Dandie (Cashier) *and D. Alexander* (General Manager) Prefix A dated 1.11.1957...	£950	£2000

THE NATIONAL COMMERCIAL
BANK OF SCOTLAND LTD

The National Commercial Bank of Scotland Limited was formed in 1959 as the result of a merger between The Commercial Bank of Scotland Ltd. and the National Bank of Scotland Ltd. It was the largest bank in Scotland at that time. Its lifespan however was limited as in 1970 it merged with the Royal Bank of Scotland to form the Royal Bank of Scotland Limited.

ONE POUND
"B" size notes (152mm x 84mm approximately)

Obverse—blue; illustration of the Forth rail bridge
Reverse—blue; large panel with the Bank's Coat of Arms at the centre

	EF	UNC

SC601 *Signatory: D. Alexander* (General Manager)
Prefix A to prefix 1F dated 16.9.1959 .... £35 £55

"C" size notes (152mm x 72mm approximately)

Obverse—green; illustration of the Forth rail bridge
Reverse—green; large panel with the Bank's Coat of Arms at the centre

SC602a *Signatory: D. Alexander* (General Manager)
Prefix A dated 1.11.1961 to prefix 2F dated 4.1.1966 .... £24 £35
SC602b *Electronic sorting symbols added to the reverse.*
Prefix 2G to prefix 2T dated 4.1.1967.. £30 £45

"D" size notes (136mm x 68mm approximately)

Obverse—green; illustration of the Forth rail bridge with the new Forth road bridge in the background.
Reverse—green; large panel with the Bank's Coat of Arms at the centre.

		EF	UNC
SC603	*Signatory: J. B. Burke* (General Manager)		
	Prefix A to prefix K dated 4.1.1968	£26	£45

FIVE POUNDS

Size 178mm x 102mm approximately

Obverse—mainly green; Bank's Coat of Arms at lower right.
Reverse—green; illustration of the Forth rail bridge.

		EF	UNC
SC611	*Signatory: D. Alexander* (General Manager)		
	Prefix A to prefix G dated 16.9.1959	£75	£125

Size 159mm x 90mm approximately

Similar to previous issue but smaller size
Obverse—mainly green; Bank's Coat of Arms at lower right.
Reverse—green; illustration of the Forth rail bridge.

		EF	UNC
SC612	*Signatory: D. Alexander (General Manager)*		
	Prefix G to prefix J dated 3.1.1961	£95	£200

Size 140mm x 85mm approximately

Obverse—blue on a multicoloured underprint. Bank's coat of Arms at lower centre.
Reverse—blue; view of Edinburgh with the Castle in the background.

SC613a	*Signatory: D. Alexander (General Manager)*		
	Prefix A dated 2.1.1963 to prefix N dated 1.8.1966	£45	£75
SC613b	*Signatory: J. B. Burke (General Manager)*		
	Electronic sorting symbols added to the reverse.		
	Prefix N to prefix R dated 4.1.1968	£55	£85

TEN POUNDS

Size 150mm x 90mm approximately

Obverse—brown on a multicoloured underprint. Bank's coat of Arms at bottom centre.
Reverse—illustration of the Tay road bridge with Dundee in the background.

SC621	*Signatory: D. Alexander (General Manager)*		
	Prefix A dated 18.8.1966	£650	£850

TWENTY POUNDS

Size 178mm x 102mm approximately

Obverse—mainly green; Bank's Coat of Arms at lower right.
Reverse—green; illustration of the Forth rail bridge.

		EF	UNC
SC631	*Signatory:* D. Alexander (General Manager)		
	Prefix A dated 16.9.1959...	£180	£250

A second printing, also prefix A and dated 1.6.1967 was prepared but not issued. One or two have come on to the market in the intervening years but they remain very rare.

ONE HUNDRED POUNDS

Size 178mm x 102mm approximately

Obverse—mainly purple; Bank's Coat of Arms at lower right.
Reverse—purple; illustration of the Forth rail bridge.

		VF	EF
SC641	*Signatory:* D. Alexander (General Manager)		
	Prefix A dated 16.9.1959...	£1000	£2000

THE NORTH OF SCOTLAND &
TOWN & COUNTY BANK LIMITED

The North of Scotland Banking company was founded in Aberdeen in 1836. In 1907 the Bank merged with the Town & County Bank Limited, and from 1910 issued notes under the heading The North of Scotland & Town & County Bank Limited. In 1923 the name reverted to The North of Scotland Bank Ltd. which remained until 1950 when the Bank merged with the Clydesdale bank Ltd. to form The Clydesdale & North of Scotland Bank Limited.

ONE POUND

"A" size square notes (174mm x 130mm approximately)

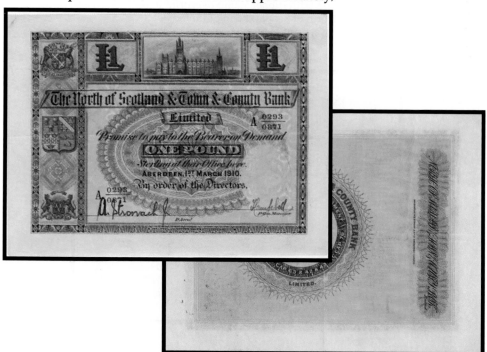

Obverse—black printing on a blue design with a yellow underprint. Illustration of the Marischal College in Aberdeen at top centre with three Coats of Arm in a panel to the left.
Reverse—blue and yellow; Bank's Coat of Arms at the centre.

	F	VF
SC701a *Signatories: handsigned p. Accountant and p. General Manager*		
Prefix A dated 1.3.1910 to prefix B dated 1.3.1916	£380	£750
SC701b *Signatories: handsigned p. Accountant and Mitchell Stuart (p. General Manager)*		
Prefix C dated 1.3.1918	£380	£750

	F	VF
SC701c Prefix C dated 1.3.1918 with rubber stamp overprint in red, reading "Now the North of Scotland Bank Limited" .... (*This rubber stamp overprint may exist on earlier dates*)	£380	£750

	F	VF
SC701d Prefix C dated 1.3.1918 with printed overprint in black, reading "Now the North of Scotland Bank Limited"	£400	£700

FIVE POUNDS

Size 217mm x 135mm approximately

Obverse—black printing on a blue design with a yellow underprint. Illustration of the Marischal College in Aberdeen at top centre with three Coats of Arm in a panel to the left.
Reverse—blue and yellow; Bank's Coat of Arms at the centre. Later notes have the denomination "£5" printed six times.

		F	VF
SC702a *Signatories: handsigned p.Accountant and p.General Manager* Prefix A dated 1.3.1910 to prefix A dated 1.3.1918.....................................		£450	£850
SC702b *Prefix A dated 1.3.1918 with rubber stamp overprint in red, reading "Now the North of Scotland Bank Limited"* .... *(This rubber stamp overprint may exist on earlier dates)*		£450	£850
SC702c *Prefix A dated 1.3.1918 and 1.3.1921 with printed overprint in black, reading "Now the North of Scotland Bank Limited"*		£480	£850

TWENTY POUNDS

Size 217mm x 135mm approximately

Obverse—black printing on a blue design with a yellow underprint. Illustration of the Marischal College in Aberdeen at top centre with three Coats of Arm in a panel to the left.
Reverse—blue and yellow; Bank's Coat of Arms at the centre.

SC703a *Signatories: handsigned p.Accountant and p.General Manager*
Prefix A dated 1.3.1910 to prefix A dated 1.3.1918... From £900

SC703b *Prefix A dated 1.3.1918 with rubber stamp overprint in red, ...* From £900
reading "Now the North of Scotland Bank Limited"
(This rubber stamp overprint may exist on earlier dates)

SC703c *Prefix A dated 1.3.1918 and 1.3.1921with printed overprint in black,*
reading "Now the North of Scotland Bank Limited" .... From £900

ONE HUNDRED POUNDS

Whilst £100 notes in this series were almost certainly printed and issued, no issued example has ever been seen. Specimens dated 1910 and 1921 exist.

THE NORTH OF SCOTLAND BANK LIMITED

ONE POUND

"B" size notes (155mm x 85mm approximately)

Obverse—black printing on a blue design with a yellow underprint. Illustration of the Marischal College in Aberdeen at top centre with three Coats of Arm in a panel to the left. Value panels with "£1". Reverse—blue and yellow; Bank's Coat of Arms at the centre.

		F	VF
SC710a	*Signatories: handsigned p. Accountant and Mitchell Stuart* (p. General Manager*)*		
	Prefix D dated 1.3.1924 to prefix E dated 1.3.1926............................. £180		£350
SC710b	*Signatories R.W.W. (Accountant) and Mitchell Stuart* (p. General Manager)		
	Prefix E and prefix F dated 1.3.1926 .... £180		£350

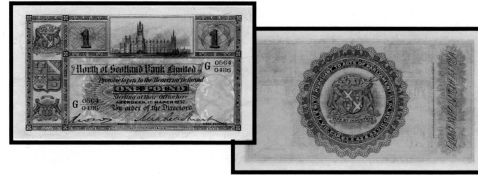

Obverse—black printing on a blue design with a yellow underprint. Illustration of the Marischal College in Aberdeen at top centre with three Coats of Arm in a panel to the left. Value panels with "1". Reverse—blue and yellow; Bank's Coat of Arms at the centre.

		VF	EF
SC711a	*Signatories R.W.W. (Accountant) and Mitchell Stuart* (p. General Manager)		
	Prefix F dated 1.3.1928 to prefix H dated 1.3.1932.............................. £100		£200
SC711b	*Signatories: J.D.P. (Accountant) and R.W.Wath* (p. General Manager)		
	Prefix J dated 1.3.1935 .... £100		£200

Obverse—blue on a pale yellow underprint. Illustration of King's College, Aberdeen at the centre.
Reverse—blue on a pale yellow underprint. Bank's Coat of Arms at the centre.

		VF	EF
SC712a	*Signatory: Harvey Smith* (General Manager)		
	Prefix A dated 1.7.1938 to prefix C dated 1.7.1940..............................	£45	£75
SC712b	*Signatory: G. L. Webster* (General Manager)		
	Prefix D dated 1.7.1945 to prefix F dated 1.7.1949..............................	£45	£75

FIVE POUNDS

Size 215mm x 135mm approximately

Obverse—black printing on a blue design with a yellow underprint. Illustration of the Marischal
College in Aberdeen at top centre with three Coats of Arm in a panel to the left.
Reverse—blue and yellow; Bank's Coat of Arms at the centre with the denomination "£5" printed six
times around it.

		F	VF
SC713	*Signatory: handsigned p. Accountant and Harvey Smith* (General Manager)		
	Prefix A dated 2.3.1925..	£550	£850

Size 191mm x 130mm approximately

Obverse—black printing on a blue design with a yellow underprint. Illustration of the Marischal College in Aberdeen at top centre with three Coats of Arm in a panel to the left.
Reverse—blue and yellow; Bank's Coat of Arms at the centre with the denomination "5" printed five times around it.

		VF	EF
SC714a	*Signatory: handsigned p. Accountant and Harvey Smith* (General Manager)		
	Prefix A dated 1.3.1928 to prefix A dated 1.3.1932............................	£250	£450
SC714b	*Signatory: Thomas Brown* (Accountant) *and Harvey Smith* (General Manager)		
	Prefix A dated 1.3.1934	£250	£450

Size 180mm x 98mm approximately

Obverse—red; illustration of King's College, Aberdeen at the centre.
Reverse—red; Bank's Coat of Arms at the centre.

		VF	EF
SC715a	*Signatory: Harvey Smith* (General Manager)		
	Prefix AE dated 1.7.1940..	£170	£350
SC715b	*Signatory: G. L. Webster* (General Manager)		
	Prefix BE dated 1.7.1943 to prefix EE dated 1.7.1949........................	£170	£350

TWENTY POUNDS

Size 190mm x 130mm approximately

Obverse—black printing on a purple design with an olive underprint. Illustration of the Marischal College in Aberdeen at top centre with three Coats of Arm in a panel to the left.
Reverse—purple and olive; Bank's Coat of Arms at the centre with the denomination "20" printed five times around it.

		F	VF
SC716	*Signatory: handsigned p.Accountant and Harvey Smith* (General Manager)		
	Prefix A dated 1.3.1930 and 1.3.1934	£250	£450

Size 181mm x 98mm approximately

Obverse—green on a light mauve underprint; illustration of King's College, Aberdeen at the centre.
Reverse—green on a light mauve underprint; Bank's Coat of Arms at the centre.

		VF	EF
SC717a	*Signatory: Harvey Smith* (General Manager)		
	Prefix AT to prefix ET dated 1.7.1940...	£180	£300
SC717b	*Signatory: G.L.Webster* (General Manager)		
	Prefix FT dated 1.7.1943 to prefix PT dated 1.7.1949	£180	£300

ONE HUNDRED POUNDS

Size 190mm x 130mm approximately

Obverse—black printing on a brown design with a green and brown underprint. Illustration of the Marischal College in Aberdeen at top centre with three Coats of Arms in a panel to the left Reverse—brown and green; Bank's Coat of Arms at the centre with the denomination "100" printed five times around it.

		F	VF
SC718	*Signatory: handsigned p. Accountant and Harvey Smith* (General Manager)		
	Prefix A dated 1.3.1930 and 1.3.1934..		From £1,000

Size 181mm x 98mm approximately

Obverse—dark purple on a light purple underprint; illustration of King's College, Aberdeen at the centre
Reverse—dark purple on a light purple underprint; Bank's Coat of Arms at the centre

		F	VF
SC719	*Signatory: Harvey Smith* (General Manager)		
	Prefix AC to prefix EC dated 1.7.1940.	£850	£1200

THE ROYAL BANK OF SCOTLAND

The Royal Bank of Scotland was founded in 1727 and immediately competed strongly with the already well established Bank of Scotland. It took over the Dundee Banking Company in 1864, and then in the 1920's and 1930's acquired several English Banks— namely Drummonds Bank in 1924, Williams Deacons Bank as well as the Western Branch of the Bank of England in 1930, and Glyn Mills & Co. in 1939. More recently, it merged with the National Commercial Bank of Scotland Ltd. in 1969 when it became The Royal Bank of Scotland Limited.

ONE POUND

"A" size square notes (65mm x 120mm approximately)

Obverse—blue on a yellow background with R.B.S. in brown/red letters at the centre. Portrait of George I flanked by Lion and Unicorn at the top. Female figures in the bottom corners. Uniface

		F	VF
SC801a	*Signatories: W. Templeton* (Accountant) *and handsigned p. Cashier* Prefix P dated 2.2.1888 (and perhaps earlier) to prefix Z dated ? Prefix A dated 1.11.1900 to prefix H dated 3.1.1908.....................From £300		£550
SC801b	*Signatories: D. S. Lunan* (Accountant) *and handsigned p. Cashier* Prefix H dated 5.5.1908 to prefix Z dated 29.6.1919, and Prefix A dated 24.3.1920...	£200	£400
SC801c	*Signatories: D. Speed* (Accountant) *and handsigned p. Cashier* Prefix A dated 14.5.1920 to prefix M dated 14.5.1926	£180	£400

"B" size notes (152mm x 85mm approximately)

Obverse—blue on a yellow background with a red/brown underprint. Portrait of George I flanked by Lion and Unicorn at the top. Female figures in the bottom corners
Reverse—blue panel with illustrations of the Bank's head office buildings in Edinburgh and Glasgow

	VF	EF
Signatories: D. Speed (Accountant) and handsigned p. Cashier		
SC802a Suffix A dated 2.2.1927 (just over 100,000 notes issued), then.........		Rare
SC802b Prefix A dated 2.2.1927 to prefix L dated 24.12.1936	£75	£150
SC802c *Signatory: D. Speed* (Chief Accountant)		
Prefix A/1 dated 2.1.1937 to prefix G/1 dated 1.7.1942, also	£40	£85
Prefix D/1 with suffix A dated 1.9.1939.............................. only one example known		
SC802d *Signatory: T. Brown* (Chief Accountant).		
Prefix H/1 dated 1.3.1943 to prefix T/1 dated 1.7.1951....................	£30	£70
SC802e *Signatory: J. D. C. Dick* (Chief Accountant).		
Prefix U/1 dated 16.7.1951 to prefix X/1 dated 1.11.1952, then		
change of printer's imprint to "W. and A. K. Johnston and G. W. Bacon		
Ltd., Edinburgh"	£25	£55
SC802f Prefix Y/1 dated 1.4.1953 and Z/1 dated 1.8.1953, and		
Prefix AA dated 1.12.1953 to prefix AE dated 3.1.1955.....................	£25	£55

Obverse—blue/black on a darker yellow background with a red/brown underprint. Portrait of George I flanked by Lion and Unicorn at the top. Female figures in the bottom corners
Reverse—blue/black panel with illustrations of the Bank's head office buildings in Edinburgh and Glasgow

	EF	UNC
SC803 *Signatory: W. R. Ballantyne* (General Manager)		
Prefix AF dated 1.4.1955 to prefix BS dated 1.7.1964.......................	£25	£40

"C" size notes (152mm x 72mm approximately)

Obverse—blue/black on a yellow background with a red/brown underprint. Portrait of George I flanked by Lion and Unicorn at the top. Female figures in the bottom corners
Reverse—blue/black panel with illustrations of the Bank's head office buildings in Edinburgh and Glasgow

		EF	UNC
SC804a	*Signatory: W. R. Ballantyne* (General Manager)		
	Prefix CA dated 1.8.1964 to prefix CG dated 1.6.1965.........................	£25	£40
SC804b	*Signatory: G. P. Robertson* (General Manager)		
	Prefix CH dated 2.8.1965 to prefix CX dated 1.11.1967......................	£25	£40

"D" size notes (135mm x 67mm approximately)

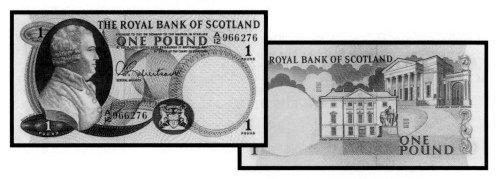

Obverse—mainly green on a multicoloured underprint. Portrait of David Dale to the left
Reverse—mainly green with illustrations of the Bank's head offices in Edinburgh and Glasgow

		EF	UNC
SC805	*Signatory: G. P. Robertson* (General Manager)		
	Prefix A/1 to prefix A/24 dated 1.9.1967	£25	£50

FIVE POUNDS

Size 228mm x 128mm approximately

Obverse—blue on a yellow background with red/brown overprint. Blue panel to the left; portrait of George I flanked by Lion and Unicorn at the top. Uniface

		F	VF
SC806a	*Signatories: handsigned p. Accountant and p. Cashier*		
	Various handwritten dates:		
	Prefix D to 26.12.1907...		Rare
	Prefix E from 23.12.1909 to 3.1.1922......................................From £260		£550

		VF	EF
SC806b	*Signatories: D. Speed* (Accountant) *and handsigned p. Cashier*		
	Prefix E dated 29.6.1923 to 10.1.1942 ....From £240		£400

SC806c	*Signatories: W. Whyte* (Cashier & General Manager) *and D. Speed* (Chief Accountant)		
	Signatories: I. M. Thomson (Cashier & General Manager) *and T. Brown* (Chief Accountant)		
	Prefix F dated 1.7.1942 to 16.10.1950 .... £200		£360

Size 178mm x 104mm approximately

Obverse—blue on a yellow background with red/brown overprint. Blue panel to the left; portrait of George I flanked by Lion and Unicorn at the top. Uniface. Similar to previous issue

		EF	UNC
SC807a	*Signatories: I. M. Thomson (Cashier & General Manager) and J. D. C. Dick* (Chief Accountant)		
	Prefix G dated 2.1.1952 to 1.7.1953	£100	£180
SC807b	*Signatories: W. A. Watt and W. R. Ballantyne (joint Chief Cashiers and* General Managers) *and J. D. C. Dick* (Chief Accountant)		
	Prefix G dated 1.7.1953 and 1.3.1955	£120	£200
SC807c	*Signatories: W. R. Ballantyne (Cashier & General Manager) and A. G. Campbell* (Chief Accountant)		
	Prefix G dated 1.4.1955 to 2.1.1964	£100	£180
	Series traced to G34321 dated 2.1.1964		

Size 146mm x 78mm approximately

Obverse—blue on a yellow background with red/brown overprint. Blue panel to the left; portrait of George I flanked by Lion and Unicorn at the top. Uniface. Similar to previous issue

SC808a	*Signatories: W. R. Ballantyne (Cashier & General Manager) and* A. G. Campbell (Chief Accountant)		
	Prefix H dated 2.11.1964	£90	£160
SC808b	*Signatories: G. P. Robertson (Cashier & General Manager) and* A. G. Campbell (Chief Accountant)		
	Prefix H dated 2.8.1965 and 1.10.1965.	£90	£160

Obverse—mainly blue on a multicoloured underprint. Portrait of David Dale to the left
Reverse—blue. Illustration on the Bank's head office in Edinburgh

		EF	UNC
SC809	*Signatories: G. P. Robertson* (General Manager) *and A. G. Campbell* (Chief Accountant)		
	Prefix J/1 dated 1.11.1966 to prefix J/5 dated 1.3.1967	£75	£120

TEN POUNDS

Size 228mm x 128mm approximately

Obverse—blue on a yellow background with red/brown overprint. Blue panel to the left; portrait of
George I flanked by Lion and Unicorn at the top. Uniface

		F	VF
SC810	*Signatories: handsigned p. Accountant and p. Cashier*		
	Various hand written dated, including:		
	Prefix C dated 3.3.1914 to 10.4.1917, and		Rare
	Prefix D dated 5.4.1921 to 1.8.1940...		From £650

TWENTY POUNDS

Size 228mm x 128mm approximately

Obverse—blue on a yellow background with red/brown overprint. Blue panel to the left; portrait of George I flanked by Lion and Unicorn at the top. Uniface

	F	VF

SC811a *Signatories: handsigned p. Accountant and p. Cashier*
Various hand written dated, including:
Prefix C to 1912 .... Rare
Prefix D from 1912 to 3.1.1947 (the earlier notes have higher
values) ....From £200 £400

SC811b *Signatories: I. M. Thomson (Cashier & General Manager) and T. Brown*
  (Chief Accountant)   *VF*   *EF*
Prefix E dated 1.7.1947 to 2.7.1951 .... £250   £500

SC811c *Signatories: I. M. Thomson (Cashier & General Manager) and J. D. C. Dick*
(Chief Accountant)
Prefix F dated 1.12.1952 .... £220   £450

SC811d *Signatories: W. R. Ballantyne (General Manager) and A. G. Campbell*
(Chief Accountant)
Prefix G dated 1.5.1957 .... £220   £450

SC811e *Signatories: G. P. Robertson (General Manager) and A. G. Campbell*
  (Chief Accountant)
Prefix H .... Possibly exists

ONE HUNDRED POUNDS
Size 228mm x 128mm approximately

Obverse—blue on a yellow background with red/brown overprint. Blue panel to the left; portrait of George I flanked by Lion and Unicorn at the top. Uniface

	F	VF
SC812a *Signatories: handsigned p. Accountant and p. Cashier* Various hand written dated, including: Prefix C to 1912		Rare
Prefix D from 1912 to 1.8.1940 (perhaps later)..................................	from £800	
SC812b *Signatories: I. M. Thomson* (Cashier & General Manager) *and T. Brown* (Chief Accountant) Prefix E dated 1.10.1949	£750	£1450

	VF	EF
SC812c *Signatories: W. R. Ballantyne* (General Manager) *and A. G. Campbell* (Chief Accountant) Prefix F dated 1.10.1960	£850	£1500

Obverse – blue on a yellow background with red/brown overprint. Blue panel to the left; portrait of George I flanked by Lion and Unicorn at the top. Uniface. (The note has guillotined rather than deckled edges)

SC813 *Signatories: G. P. Robertson* (General Manager) *and A. G. Campbell* (Chief Accountant) Prefix G dated 3.2.1966..	£800	£1450

THE ROYAL BANK
OF SCOTLAND LIMITED

ONE POUND

"D" size notes (135mm x 67mm approximately)

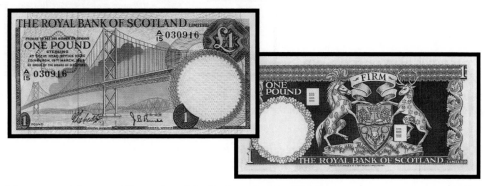

Obverse—mainly green. Illustration of the Forth road and rail bridges
Reverse—green, Bank's Coat of Arms at the centre

		EF	UNC
SC814a	*Signatories: A. P. Robertson and J. B. Burke* (General Managers) Prefix A/1 to prefix A/45 dated 19.3.1969	£18	£35
SC814b	*Signatory: J. B. Burke* (Managing Director) Prefix A/46 to prefix A/68 dated 15.7.1970	£18	£35

Obverse—green on a multicoloured underprint. Bank's Arms to the right
Reverse—green, illustration of Edinburgh Castle

SC815	*Signatory: J. B. Burke* (Managing Director) Prefix A/1 dated 5.1.1972 to prefix C/57 dated 1.5.1981	£12	£20

FIVE POUNDS

Size 146mm x 79mm approximately

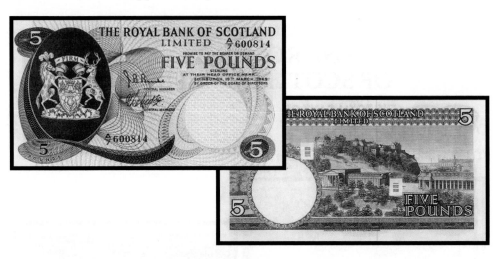

Obverse—blue on a multicoloured underprint. Bank's Arms to the left
Reverse—blue, view over Edinburgh with the Castle at the centre

		EF	UNC
SC816a *Signatories: A. P. Robertson and J. B. Burke* (General Managers)			
Prefix A/1 to prefix A/14 dated 19.3.1969		£50	£90
SC816b *Signatory: J. B. Burke* (Managing Director)			
Prefix A/15 to prefix A/19 dated 15.7.1970.		£50	£90

Obverse—blue on a multicoloured underprint. Bank's Arms to the right
Reverse—blue, illustration of Culzean Castle

SC817 *Signatory: J. B. Burke* (Managing Director)
Prefix A/1 dated 5.1.1972 to prefix B/13 dated 1.5.1981 .... £40 £65

TEN POUNDS

Size 151mm x 84mm approximately

Obverse—brown on a multicoloured underprint. Bank's Coat of Arms at bottom centre
Reverse—brown, illustration of the Tay bridge

	EF	UNC

SC818 *Signatories: A. P. Robertson and J. B. Burke* (General Managers)
Prefix A/1 dated 19.3.1969 .... £160   £240

Obverse—brown on a multicoloured underprint. Bank's Coat of Arms to the right
Reverse—brown, illustration of Glamis Castle

SC819 *Signatory: J. B. Burke* (Managing Director)
Prefix A/1 dated 5.1.1972 to prefix A/49 dated 1.12.1981 .... £80   £120

TWENTY POUNDS

Size 160mm x 90mm approximately

Obverse—purple on a multicoloured underprint. Bank's Coat of Arms at bottom centre
Reverse—purple, illustration of the Forth road and rail bridges

	EF	UNC
SC820 *Signatories: A. P. Robertson and J. B. Burke* (General Managers)		
Prefix A/1 dated 19.3.1969	£180	£320

Obverse—purple on a multicoloured underprint. Bank's Coat of Arms to the right
Reverse – purple. Illustration of Brodick Castle

	EF	UNC
SC821 *Signatory: J. B. Burke* (Managing Director)		
Prefix A/1 dated 5.1.1972 to prefix A/6 dated 1.5.1981	£160	£280

ONE HUNDRED POUNDS

Size 160mm x 90mm approximately

Obverse—red on a multicoloured underprint. Bank's coat of Arms at bottom centre
Reverse—red, illustration of the Forth road and rail bridges

	EF	UNC
SC822 *Signatories: A. P. Robertson and J. B. Burke* (General Managers)		
Prefix A/1 dated 19.3.1969		Rare

Obverse—red on a multicoloured underprint. Bank's Coat of Arms to the right
Reverse—red, illustration of Balmoral Castle

	EF	UNC
SC823 *Signatory: J. B. Burke* (Managing Director)		
Prefix A/1 dated 5.1.1972 to 1.5.1981	£750	£1250

THE ROYAL BANK
OF SCOTLAND PLC

ONE POUND

"D" size notes (135mm x 67mm approximately)

Obverse—green on a multicoloured underprint. Bank's Arms to the right
Reverse—green, illustration of Edinburgh Castle

		EF	UNC
SC831a	*Signatory: C. R. Winter* (Managing Director)		
	Prefix C/58 to prefix C/66 dated 3.5.1982..	£20	£40
	Sorting symbols removed from reverse.		
SC831b	Prefix C/67 dated 1.10.1983 to prefix D/32 dated 3.1.1985	£9	£18
SC831c	*Signatory: C. R. Winter* (Chief Executive)		
	Prefix D/33 to prefix D/67 dated 1.5.1986	£8	£15
SC831d	*Signatory: R. M. Maiden* (Managing Director)		
	Prefix D/68 to prefix D/84 (maybe higher) dated 17.12.1986	£8	£15
	Replacement note—prefix Z/1	£45	£80

Obverse—green on a multicoloured underprint. Portrait of Lord Ilay, first Governor of the Bank, to the right
Reverse—green on a multicoloured underprint. Illustration of Edinburgh Castle

.

SC832	*Signatory: R. M. Maiden* (Managing Director)		
	Prefix A/1 to prefix A/40 dated 25.3.1987..	£5	£9
	Replacement note—prefix Z/1	£20	£40

"E" size notes (129mm x 65mm approximately)

Similar to previous issue
Obverse—green on a multicoloured underprint. Portrait of Lord Ilay, first Governor of the Bank, to the right
Reverse—green on a multicoloured underprint. Illustration of Edinburgh Castle

		EF	UNC
SC833a *Signatory: R. M. Maiden* (Managing Director)			
Prefix A/41 dated 13.12.1988 to prefix B/21 dated 19.12.1990		£3	£6
Replacement note—prefix Z/1		£16	£25
SC833b *Signatory: C. M. Winter* (Chief Executive)			
Prefix B/22 to prefix B/51 dated 24.7.1991		£3	£8
Replacement note—prefix Z/1		£20	£45
SC833c *Signatory: G. R. Mathewson* (Chief Executive)			
Prefix B/52 dated 24.3.1992 to prefix C/72 dated 1.10.1997		£3	£6
Replacement note—prefix Z/1		£16	£25
SC833d Notes printed on un-watermarked paper, sometimes known as the "headless" notes.			
Prefix C/28 to prefix C/31 dated 23.3.1994		£25	£40
SC833e *Signatory: G. R. Mathewson* (Group Chief Executive)			
Prefix C/73 to prefix C/82 dated 30.3.1999		£3	£6
Replacement note—prefix Z/1		£16	£25
SC833f *Signatory: F. Goodwin* (Group Chief Executive)			
Prefix C/83 dated 27.6.2000 to prefix C/97 dated 1.10.2001		—	£4
Replacement note—prefix Z/1		£10	£15

Obverse—mainly green with portrait of Lord Ilay. Similar to regular issue but with overprint to the left to commemorate the European Summit in Edinburgh, December 1992
Reverse—green on a multicoloured underprint. Illustration of Edinburgh Castle

	EF	UNC
SC834 *Signatory: G. R. Mathewson* (Chief Executive) Prefix EC dated 8.12.1992	£3.50	£6

Obverse—mainly green with portrait of Lord Ilay. Similar to regular issue but with overprint to the left to commemorate the death of Robert Louis Stevenson 1850–94
Reverse—portrait of Robert Louis Stevenson

SC835 *Signatory: G. R. Mathewson* (Chief Executive) Prefix RLS dated 3.12.1994	£2.50	£6

Obverse—mainly Green with portrait of Lord Ilay. Similar to regular issue but with overprint to the left to commemorate the 150th anniversary of the birth of Alexander Graham Bell 1847–1922
Reverse—portrait of Alexander Graham Bell and a representation of his work

SC836 *Signatory: G. R. Mathewson* (Chief Executive) Prefix AGB dated 3.3.1997	£2.50	£6

Obverse—mainly green with portrait of Lord Ilay. Similar to regular issue but with overprint to the left to commemorate the first meeting of the Scottish Parliament
Reverse—illustration of the Scottish Parliament building

		EF	UNC
SC837	*Signatory: G. R. Mathewson* (Group Chief Executive)		
	Prefix SP dated 12.5.1999	£2.50	£6

FIVE POUNDS

Size 145mm x 78mm approximately

Obverse—blue on a multicoloured underprint. Bank's Arms to the right
Reverse—blue, illustration of Culzean Castle

SC841a	*Signatory: C. R. Winter* (Managing Director)		
	Prefix B/13 dated 3.5.1982 to prefix B/36 dated 5.1.1983................	£35	£60
	Sorting symbols removed from reverse.		
SC841b	Prefix B/37 dated 4.1.1984 to prefix B/58 dated 3.1.1985................	£35	£60
SC841c	*Signatory: R. M. Maiden* (Managing Director)		
	Prefix B/59 to prefix B/82 (possibly higher) dated 17.12.1986.......	£35	£60
	Replacement note—prefix Z/1..		Rare

Obverse—blue on a multicoloured underprint. Portrait of Lord Ilay to the right
Reverse—blue on a multicoloured underprint. Illustration of Culzean Castle

		EF	UNC
SC842	*Signatory: R. M. Maiden* (Managing Director)		
	Prefix A/1 dated 25.3.1987 to prefix A/54 dated 22.6.1988	£20	£35
	Replacement note—prefix Z/1	£45	£75

Size 135mm x 70mm approximately

Similar to previous issue but reduced size

Obverse—blue on a multicoloured underprint. Portrait of Lord Ilay to the right
Reverse—blue on a multicoloured underprint. Illustration of Culzean Castle

SC843a	*Signatory: R. M. Maiden* (Managing Director)		
	Prefix A/55 dated 13.12.1988 to prefix B/5 dated 24.1.1990	£15	£25
	Replacement note—prefix Z/1	£40	£65
SC843b	*Signatory: G. R. Mathewson* (Chief Executive)		
	Prefix B/6 dated 23.3.1994 to prefix B/57 dated 29.4.1998	£12	£20
	Replacement note—prefix Z/1	£40	£65
SC843c	*Signatory: G. R. Mathewson* (Group Chief Executive)		
	Prefix B/58 to prefix B/67 dated 30.3.1999	£11	£16
	Replacement note—prefix Z/1	£40	£65
SC843d	*Signatory: F. Goodwin* (Group Chief Executive)		
	Prefix B/68 dated 27.6.2000 to prefix B/96 dated 20.1.2005 and		
	ongoing..	—	£9
	Replacement note—prefix Z/1	£25	£40

Issued to commemorate the Queen's Golden Jubilee 2002

Obverse—similar to regular issue. Mainly blue; portrait of Lord Ilay to the right. Gold overprint "The Queen's Golden Jubilee 2002" to the left
Reverse—blue and multicolour. Portrait of the Queen with an earlier portrait from 1952

		EF	UNC
SC844	Signatory: F. Goodwin (Group Chief Executive)		
	Prefix TQGJ dated 6.2.2002...	£10	£20

Issued to commemorate the 250th anniversary of the Royal and Ancient Golf Club of St. Andrews, established 1754.

Obverse—similar to regular issue. Mainly blue; portrait of Lord Ilay to the right. Gold overprint of the St. Andrews club seal to the left.
Reverse—blue and multicolour. A view of the original club house at St. Andrews.

SC845	Signatory: F. Goodwin (Group Chief Executive)		
	Prefix R&A dated 14.5.2004	—	£20

Commemorates the 500th Anniversary of the Royal College of Surgeons Edinburgh, 1505– 2005

Obverse–similar to regular issue. Mainly blue; portrait of Lord Ilay to the right. Gold overprint "500 Years The Royal College of Surgeons Edinburgh–1505–2005" to the left
Reverse–as regular issue; blue on a multocoloured underprint. Illustration of Culzean Castle

	EF	UNC
SC846 *Signatory: F.Goodwin* (Group Chief Executive) Prefix RCS dated 1.7.2005.	—	£16

Issued July 2005 to commemorate the golfer Jack Nicklaus.

Obverse – similar to regular issue. Mainly blue; portrait of Lord Ilay to the right. Bear emblem over NICKLAUS to the left
Reverse – pictures of Jack Nicklaus with details of St. Andrews golf course

SC846   *Signatory: F.Goodwin* (Group Chief Executive)
Prefix JWN dated 14.7.2005. —   £16

TEN POUNDS

Size 153mm x 85mm approximately

Obverse—brown on a multicoloured underprint. Bank's coat of Arms to the right
Reverse—brown, illustration of Glamis Castle

		EF	*UNC*
SC851a	*Signatory: C. R. Winter* (Managing Director)		
	Prefix A/49 dated 3.5.1982 to prefix A/88 dated 3.1.1985...............	£75	£120
SC851b	*Signatory: R. M. Maiden* (Managing Director)		
	Prefix A/89 to prefix A/98 (possibly higher) dated 17.12.1986......	£95	£150
	Replacement note—prefix Z/1..		Rare

Obverse—brown on a multicoloured underprint. Portrait of Lord Ilay to the right
Reverse—brown on a multicoloured underprint. Illustration of Glamis Castle

	EF	UNC
SC852 *Signatory: R. M. Maiden* (Managing Director)		
Prefix A/1 dated 25.3.1987 to prefix B/31 dated 24.1.1990..............	£35	£60
Replacement note—prefix Z/1	£75	£120

Size 142mm x 75mm approximately

Similar to previous issue but reduced size

Obverse—brown on a multicoloured underprint. Portrait of Lord Ilay to the right
Reverse—brown on a multicoloured underprint. Illustration of Glamis Castle

	EF	UNC
SC853a *Signatory: G. R. Mathewson* (Chief Executive)		
Prefix B/32 dated 28.1.1992 to prefix D/3 dated 23.3.1994	—	£25
Replacement note—prefix Z/1	£45	£70
SC853b *Signatory: F. Goodwin* (Group Chief Executive)		
Prefix D/4 dated 27.6.2000 to prefix D/57 dated 19.9.2006 and ongoing	—	£20
Replacement note—prefix Z/1	£35	£50

TWENTY POUNDS

Size 160mm x 90mm approximately

Obverse—purple on a multicoloured underprint. Bank's Coat of Arms to the right
Reverse—purple, illustration of Brodick Castle

	EF	UNC
SC861 *Signatory: C. R. Winter* (Managing Director)		
Prefix A/6 dated 3.5.1982 to prefix ? dated 3.1.1985.........................	£90	£140

Obverse—purple on a multicoloured underprint. Portrait of Lord Ilay to the right
Reverse—purple on a multicoloured underprint. Illustration of Brodick Castle

SC862 *Signatory: R. M. Maiden* (Managing Director)		
Prefix A/1 dated 25.3.1987 to prefix A/3 dated 24.1.1990...............	£80	£150
Replacement note—prefix Z/1..	£120	£220

Size 150mm x 80mm approximately

Similar to previous issue but reduced size

Obverse—purple on a multicoloured underprint. Portrait of Lord Ilay to the right
Reverse—purple on a multicoloured underprint. Illustration of Brodick Castle

		EF	*UNC*
SC863a	Signatory: C. M. Winter (Chief Executive)		
	Prefix A/4 to prefix A/8 dated 27.3.1991	£75	£140
	Replacement note—prefix Z/1	£85	£120
SC863b	Signatory: G. R. Mathewson (Chief Executive)		
	Prefix A/9 dated 28.1.1992 to prefix B/3 dated 29.4.1998..............	£35	£60
	Replacement note—prefix Z/1	£55	£90
SC863c	Signatory: G. R. Mathewson (Group Chief Executive)		
	Prefix B/4 to prefix B/27 dated 30.3.1999	£35	£50
	Replacement note—prefix Z/1	£55	£90
SC863d	Signatory: F. Goodwin (Group Chief Executive)		
	Prefix B/29 to prefix C/4 dated 20.12.2007 and ongoing	—	£32
	Replacement note—prefix Z/1	£35	£60

Commemorative issue for the 100th birthday of Her Majesty the Queen Mother

Obverse—similar to regular issue . Portrait of Lord Ilay to the right. Gold Crown and Commemorative
text to the left
Reverse—purple and multicolour. Portrait of the Queen Mother with Glamis Castle in the background

		EF	*UNC*
SC864	Signatory: F. Goodwin (Group Chief Executive)		
	Prefix QETQM dated 4.8.2000	£35	£60

FIFTY POUND NOTES

Size 150mm x 85mm approximately

Obverse–mainly green on a multicoloured underprint. Portrait of Lord Islay to the right
Reverse–green and multicoloured. Illustration of Inverness Castle

		EF	UNC
SC871	*Signatory: F. Goodwin* (Group Chief Executive)		
	Prefix A/1 dated 14.9.2005 and ongoing	—	£90
	Prefix Z/1 – replacement note..	£100	£160

Obverse–mainly green on a multicoloured underprint. Portrait of Lord Islay to the right
Reverse–mainly green. Illustrations of the new RBS headquarters at Gogarburn

SC872	*Signatory: F. Goodwin* (Group Chief Executive)		
	Prefix RBS dated 14.9.2005..	£100	£180

ONE HUNDRED POUNDS

Size 160mm x 90mm approximately

Obverse—red on a multicoloured underprint. Bank's coat of Arms to the right
Reverse—red. Illustration of Balmoral Castle

		EF	UNC
SC881	*Signatory: C. R. Winter* (Managing Director) Prefix A/1 dated 3.5.1982 and 3.1.1985	£450	£1000

Obverse — red on a multicoloured underprint. Portrait of Lord Ilay to the right
Reverse — red on a multicoloured underprint. Illustration of Balmoral Castle

		EF	UNC
SC882a	*Signatory: R. M. Maiden* (Managing Director)		
	Prefix A/1 dated 25.3.1987 and 24.1.1990	£300	£550
	Prefix Z/1 Replacement Note		Rare

Size reduction; design remains the same
Size 150mm x 85mm approximately

		EF	UNC
SC883a	*Signatory: G. R. Mathewson* (Chief Executive)		
	Prefix A/1 dated 28.1.1992 to prefix A/2 dated 30.9.1998	—	£280
	Prefix Z/1 Replacement Note	£350	£550
SC883b	*Signatory: G. R. Mathewson* (Group Chief Executive)		
	Prefix A/2 dated 30.3.1999	—	£200
	Prefix Z/1 Replacement Note	£220	£350
SC883c	*Signatory: F. Goodwin* (Group Chief Executive)		
	Prefix A/2 dated 27.6.2000	—	£160
	Prefix Z/1 Replacement Note	£200	£300

THE UNION BANK
OF SCOTLAND LIMITED

The title of The Union Bank of Scotland was adopted by the former Glasgow Union Banknig Company in 1843. In 1905 the contract for printing the Bank's notes was secured by Waterlow & Sons Limited; earlier notes had been printed by Perkins Bacon. The banknotes of the Union Bank of Scotland changed relatively little over the years with the most significant design change coming in 1949 just six years before the Bank was absorbed by the Bank of Scotland.

ONE POUND

"A" size square notes (150mm x 130mm approximately)

Obverse—Blue with a large red "ONE" overlaid in red at the centre. The Bank's Coat of Arms is at the top of the note with twin equestrian statues in the lower corners.
Reverse—Large blue panel with the figure '1' circled by "The Union Bank of Scotland Limited".

		F	VF
SC901a	*Signatories: J. R. Wood* (Accountant) *and handsigned p. Cashier* .... Prefix A dated 6.4.1905 to prefix A dated 1.5.1907.		Rare
SC901b	*Signatories: G. H. Moritz* (Accountant) *and handsigned p. Cashier* Prefix B dated 2.1.1908 and 28.9.1909		Rare
SC901c	*Signatories: John Alexander* (Accountant) *and handsigned p. Cashier* Prefix B dated 12.2.1910 to prefix D dated 20.8.1913.	£400	£800
SC901d	*Signatories: J. F. McCrindle* (Accountant) *and handsigned p. Cashier* Prefix D dated 3.8.1914 to prefix H dated 10.12.1920	£280	£550

Obverse—Blue with a large red "ONE" overlaid in red at the centre and with additional red and yellow sunburst overlay. The Bank's Coat of Arms is at the top of the note with twin equestrian statues in the lower corners.
Reverse—Large blue panel with the figure "1" circled by "The Union Bank of Scotland Limited".

	F	VF
SC902 *Signatories: N. L. Hird* (General Manager) *and J. F. McCrindle* (Cashier)		
Prefix A dated 1.10.1921 and prefix B dated 2.10.1923.	£450	£800

"B" size notes (150mm x 85mm approximately)

Obverse—Blue with a large red "ONE" overlaid in red at the centre and red and yellow sunburst overlay. The Bank's Coat of Arms is at the top with twin equestrian statues in the lower corners.
Reverse—Blue panel with the figure "1" circled by "The Union Bank of Scotland Limited".

	VF	EF
SC903a *Signatories: N. L. Hird* (General Manager) *and J. F. McCrindle* (Cashier)		
Prefix A dated 2.6.1924 to prefix C dated 3.10.1927	£100	£190
SC903b *Signatories: N. L. Hird* (General Manager) *and J. F. McCrindle* (Chief Accountant)		
Prefix D dated 2.1.1929 to prefix F dated 5.12.1931	£70	£140
SC903c *Signatories: N. L. Hird* (General Manager) *and J. D. Wink* (Chief Accountant)		
Prefix G dated 1.6.1933 to prefix I dated 31.3.1936	£50	£100
SC903d *Signatories: N. L. Hird* (General Manager) *and M. J. Wilson* (Cashier)		
Prefix K dated 12.2.1937 to prefix V dated 28.9.1945	£40	£75
SC903e *Signatories: J. A. Morrison* (General Manager) *and M. J. Wilson* (Cashier)		
Prefix V dated 20.3.1946 to prefix X dated 1.6.1948	£40	£75

Obverse—blue with a large red "ONE" at the centre and with a red and yellow sunburst overlay. Redesigned Coat of Arms to the left and sailing ship emblem to the right.
Reverse—mainly blue with an illustration of an industrial scene on the river Clyde.

		VF	EF
SC904a	*Signatory: J. A. Morrison (General Manager)*		
	Prefix A dated 1.3.1949 to prefix G dated 1.9.1953.............................	£40	£70
SC904b	*Signatory: Sir William Watson (General Manager)*		
	Prefix H dated 1.6.1954	£80	£180

FIVE POUNDS

Size 196mm x 130mm approximately

Obverse—Blue with a large red "FIVE" overlaid in red at the centre. The Bank's Coat of Arms is at the top of the note with twin equestrian statues in the lower corners.
Reverse—Large blue panel with the figure "5" circled by "The Union Bank of Scotland Limited".

		F	VF
SC911	*Signatories: handsigned p. Accountant and handsigned p. Cashier*		
	Prefix A dated 25.2.1905 to prefix C dated 18.8.1920.........................	£550	£1100

Obverse—Blue with large red 'FIVE' at the centre and red and yellow sunburst overlay.
The Bank's Coat of Arms is at the top of the note with twin equestrian statues in the lower corners.
Reverse—Large blue panel with the figure "5" circled by "The Union Bank of Scotland Limited".

		F	VF
SC912a	*Signatories: N. L. Hird* (General Manager) *and handsigned p. Cashier* Prefix A dated 5.4.1921 and 4.5.1923	£400	£750
SC912b	*Signatories: N. L. Hird* (General Manager) *and J. F. McCrindle* (Cashier) Prefix A dated 4.8.1923 to prefix B dated 15.1.1927...........................	£380	£680
SC912c	*Signatories: N. L. Hird* (General Manager) *and J. F. McCrindle* (Chief Accountant) Prefix B dated 6.7.1928 to 4.5.1932...	£300	£550
SC912d	*Signatories: N. L. Hird* (General Manager) *and J. D. Wink* (Chief Accountant) Prefix C dated 2.2.1933 to 18.5.1936	£250	£460

		VF	EF
SC912e	*Signatories: N. L. Hird* (General Manager) *and M. J. Wilson* (Cashier) Prefix C dated 18.8.1937 to prefix G dated 31.8.1944.......................	£240	£450
SC912f	*Signatories: J. A. Morrison* (General Manager) *and M. J. Wilson* (Cashier) Prefix G dated 12.9.1946 to prefix H dated 3.5.1949	£240	£500

Size 182mm x 100mm approximately

Obverse—blue with a large red "FIVE" at the centre and with a red and yellow sunburst overlay. Redesigned Coat of Arms to the left and sailing ship emblem to the right.
Reverse—mainly blue with an illustration of an industrial scene on the river Clyde.

		VF	EF
SC913a	*Signatory: J. A. Morrison (General Manager)*		
	Prefix A dated 17.7.1950 to prefix C dated 1.10.1953	£90	£180
SC913b	*Signatory: Sir William Watson (General Manager)*		
	Prefix D dated 2.4.1954...	£250	£500

TEN POUNDS

Size 196mm x 130mm approximately

Obverse—Blue with a large red "TEN" overlaid in red at the centre. The Bank's Coat of Arms is at the top of the note with twin equestrian statues in the lower corners.
Reverse—Large blue panel with the figure "10" circled by "The Union Bank of Scotland Limited".

		F	VF
SC921	*Signatories: handsigned p. Accountant and handsigned p. Cashier*		
	Prefix A dated 4.4.1905 to prefix A dated 6.8.1920.		Rare

Obverse—Blue with large red "TEN" at the centre and red and yellow sunburst overlay. The Bank's Coat of Arms is at the top of the note with twin equestrian statues in the lower corners.
Reverse—Large blue panel with the figure "10" circled by "The Union Bank of Scotland Limited".

SC922a	*Signatories: N. L. Hird (General Manager) and J. F. McCrindle (Cashier)*		
	Prefix A dated 3.8.1923..		Rare
SC922b	*Signatories: N. L. Hird (General Manager) and J. F. McCrindle (Chief Accountant)*		
	Prefix A dated 4.7.1928..		Rare
SC922c	*Signatories: N. L. Hird (General Manager) and J. D. Wink (Chief Accountant)*		
	Prefix A dated 8.12.1933 and 8.7.1935		from £600

TWENTY POUNDS

Size 196mm x 130mm approximately

Obverse—Blue with a large red "TWENTY" overlaid in red at the centre. The Bank's Coat of Arms is at the top of the note with twin equestrian statues in the lower corners.
Reverse—Large blue panel with the figure "20" circled by "The Union Bank of Scotland Limited".

		F	VF
SC931	*Signatories: handsigned p. Accountant and handsigned p. Cashier* Prefix A dated 31.3.1905 to prefix A dated 4.6.1920............................		Rare

Obverse—Blue with large red 'TWENTY' at the centre and red and yellow sunburst overlay. The Bank's Coat of Arms is at the top of the note with twin equestrian statues in the lower corners.
Reverse—Large blue panel with the figure "20" circled by "The Union Bank of Scotland Limited".

SC932a	*Signatories: handsigned p. General Manager and p. Cashier* Prefix A dated 2.8.1923 to prefix A dated 14.8.1935	£380	£650
SC932b	*Signatories: handsigned p. General Manager and p. Chief Accountant* Prefix A dated 31.5.1937 to prefix B dated 2.1.1942...........................	£280	£450
SC932c	*Signatories: N. L. Hird (General Manager) and M. J. Wilson (Cashier)* Prefix B dated 30.4.1942 to prefixB dated 10.7.1944.	£200	£400

		VF	EF
SC932d	*Signatories: J. A. Morrison (General Manager) and M. J. Wilson (Cashier)* Prefix B dated 2.12.1946 and 1.9.1947	£380	£600

Size 182mm x 100mm approximately

Obverse—Blue with a large red "TWENTY" at the centre and with a red and yellow sunburst overlay. Redesigned Coat of Arms to the left and sailing ship emblem to the right.
Reverse—Mainly blue with an illustration of an industrial scene on the river Clyde.

		F	VF
SC933	*Signatory: J. A. Morrison* (General Manager)		
	Prefix A dated 1.9.1950 to prefix A dated 1.5.1953............................	£260	£420

ONE HUNDRED POUNDS

Size 196mm x 130mm approximately

Obverse—Blue with a large red "£100" overlaid in red at the centre, flanked by twin equestrian statues. The Bank's Coat of Arms is at the top of the note.
Reverse—Large blue panel with the figure "100" circled by "The Union Bank of Scotland Limited".

SC941	*Signatories: handsigned by the Accountant and Cashier*	
	Prefix A dated 7.4.1905 to prefix A dated 2.4.1919..............................	Rare

Obverse—Blue with a large red "£100" overlaid in red at the centre, flanked by twin equestrian statues. Red and yellow sunburst overlay. The Bank's Coat of Arms is at the top of the note.
Reverse—Large blue panel with the figure "100" circled by "The Union Bank of Scotland Limited".

SC942a	*Signatories: handsigned p. General Manager and p. Cashier*	
	Prefix A dated 1.8.1923 to prefix A dated 20.5.1936............................	Rare

SC942b	*Signatories: handsigned p. General Manager and p. Chief Accountant*	
	Prefix A dated 1.3.1939 to prefix A dated 2.1.1942..............................	Rare

SC942c	*Signatories: J. A. Morrison* (General Manager) *and M. J. Wilson* (Cashier)	VF	EF
	Prefix A dated 18.2.1947	£1300	£2500

Size 185mm x 105mm approximately

Obverse—Blue with a large red "ONE HUNDRED" at the centre and with a red and yellow sunburst overlay. Redesigned Coat of Arms to the left and sailing ship emblem to the right.
Reverse—Mainly blue with an illustration of an industrial scene on the river Clyde.

	VF	EF
SC943a *Signatory: J. A. Morrison* (General Manager) Prefix A dated 9.10.1950 and 10.3.1952..	£1200	£2400
SC943b *Signatory: Sir William Watson* (General Manager) Prefix A dated 1.10.1954. Only 100 printed		Rare

BOOKS
for the banknote collector

On the following pages is a list of books of interest to the banknote collector. They are listed under their area of main interest and by author alphabetically. Many of the titles are out of print but can often be acquired from your favourite numismatic bookseller.

General

IAN ANGUS, *Paper Money*, London, 1974.

COURTNEY L. COLLING Guide & checklist of World Notgeld 1914–1947, 2000.

JOE CRIBB, *Money: From Cowrie Shells to Credit Cards*, London 1986.

GEORGE S. CUHAJ (ED), *Standard Catalog of World Paper Money*, 3 vols., Krause Publications, Iola, 2008 (commonly referred to as the "Pick catalogues" from the name of the original editor)..

LESLIE DUNKLING and ADRIAN ROOM, *The Guinness Book of Money*, Enfield, 1990.

W. KRANISTER, The *Moneymakers International*, Cambridge, 1989.

MONETARY RESEARCH INSTITUTE *Bankers Guide to Foreign currency*, Housten TX, 2001.

COLIN NARBETH, ROBIN HENDY AND CHRISTOPHER STOCKER, *Collecting Paper Money and Bonds*, London, 1979.

COLIN NARBETH, *Encyclopedia of Paper Money*, London, 1967.

JOHN ORNA-ORNSTEIN, *The Story of Money*, London, 1997.

ALBERT PICK, *Briefmarkengeld*, Brunswick, 1970.
Papiergeld, Brunswick, 1967.
Papiergeldkatalog Europa seit 1900, Munich, 1973.
Paper Money Catalogue of the Americas, Munich, 1973.

FRED REINFELD, *The Story of Paper Money*.

JOHN E. SANDROCK, *World Paper Money Collection*, New York, various editions.

FRED SCHWANN, *Collecting Paper Money*, New York, 1996.

NEIL SHAFER, *The Wonderful World of Paper Money*, 1972.
Let's Collect Paper Money, 1976.

GEORGE J. STEN, *Banknotes of the World*, 2 vols, Menlo Park, 1967.
Encyclopedia of World Paper Money, New York, 1965.

Military Invasion and Occupation Notes

JAMES MACKAY, *Banknotes at War*, London, 1977.

CARLTON F. SCHWAN, *Military Payment Certificates World War II Allied Military Currency*, Ohio, 1974.

CARLTON F. SCHWAN AND JOSEPH E. BOLING, *World War II Military Currency*, Ohio, 1978.

JAMES RUTLANDER, *Allied Military Currency*, New York, 1968.

NEIL SHAFER, *Philippine Emergency and Guerrilla Currency of World War II*, Racine, 1974.

ARLIE SLABAUGH, *Japanese Invasion Money*, Chicago, 1977.

GASTONE SOLLNER, *Moneta d'Occupazione e di Liberazione della IIa Guerra Mondiale*, Mantua, 1965.

ZVI STAHL, *Jewish Ghettos' and Concentration Camps' Money (1933-45)*, Israel, 1990.

RAYMOND TOY, *World War II Allied Military Currency*, San Diego, 1969.

RAYMOND TOY AND BOB MEYER, *World War II Axis Military Currency*, Tucson, 1967.

BENJAMIN WHITE, *The Currency of the Great War*, London, 1921.

JOHN F. YARWOOD, *A Guide to British Military Tokens*, Horsham, Australia, 1998.

Algeria

PAUL DUGENDRE, *Catalogue des Billets de la Banque de l'Algerie et de la Tunisie*, Paris, 1953.

Angola

LUIS M.R. DE SOUSA, *O Papel-Moeda em Angola*, Luanda, 1969.

Argentina

JOSE MARIA MUNARI, *Papel Moneda Argentina 1935-1967*, Buenos Aires, 1967.

Australia

GREG MCDONALD, *Australian Coins and Banknotes*, Umina Beach, 1985.

ALAN NICHOLSON, *Australian Banknote Catalogue*, Melbourne, 1979.

DION H. SKINNER, *Rennick's Australian Coins and Banknotes Guide*, Adelaide, 1980.

P. STEELE, *Collect Australian Coins and Banknotes*, Dubbo NSW, 1988.

G. W. TOMLINSON, *Australian Bank Notes 1817–1963*, Melbourne, 1963.

MICHAEL VORT-RONALD, *Collect Australian Banknotes*, Dubbo NSW, 1998.

Austria

ALBERT PICK AND R. RICHTER, *Oesterreich Banknoten und Staatspapiergeld ab 1759*, Berlin, 1972.

Baltic States

A. PLATBARZDIS, *Coins and Notes of Estonia, Latvia, Lithuania*, Stockholm, 1968.

M. TITUS, *Paper Currencies of Estonia*, Menlo Park, 1971.

Belgium

J. DE MEY, *Le Papier-Monnaie Belge d'Outremer, 1896-1963*, Brussels, 1976.
Le Papier-Monnaie Belge, 1814–1976, Brussels, 1976.

IBNS, *Paper Money of the 20th Century: Belgium and Colonies*, St. Louis, 1975.
FRANCOIS MORIN, *Catalogue des Billets de Banque Belge 1900 a 1974*, Brussels, 1974.
Cataloge des Billets de Banque de Congo etc, Boom, 1974.

Bolivia

LUIS A. ASBUN-KARMY, *Monedas de Bolivia*, La Paz, 1977.

Brazil

BANCO DO BRASIL, *Cedulas Brasileiras*, Rio de Janeiro, 1965.
ALVARO GONCALVES, *Catalogo de Cedulas e Moedas Brasileiras*, Sao Paulo, 1969.
DALE A. SEPPA, *The Paper Money of Brazil*, Chicago, 1976.
VIOLO LISSA, *Catalogo do Papel-Moeda do Brasil*, Brasilia, 1981.
DOS SANTOS TRINGUEIROS, *Dinhero do Brasil*, Rio de Janeiro, 1966.
A. TODISCO, *Catalogue of Brazilian Banknotes*, IBNS, 1961.

British West Africa

RICHARD J. FORD, *British West African Currency Board Bank Notes*, Walton-on-the-Naze, 1970.

Burma

M. ROBINSON AND L.A. SHAW, *The Coins and Banknotes of Burma*, Manchester, 1980.

Canada

BANK OF CANADA, *The Story of Canada's Currency*, Ottawa, 1981.
The National Currency Collection and the Bank of Canada Currency Museum, n.d.
J.E. CHARLTON, *Standard Catalogue of Canadian Paper Money*, Toronto, 1980.
HANS ZOELL, *Simplified Catalog of Canadian-Newfoundland Coins and Paper Money*, 1961.

Chile

JOSE M. GALETOVIC AND HECTOR BENAVIDES, *El Billete Chileno*, Santiago, 1973.

China

W.H. LU, *Paper Money Catalogue of the People's Republic of China and Macau*, Kuala Lumpur, 1998.
KING-ON MAO, *History of Chinese Paper Currency*, Hong Kong, 1968-77.
History of Paper Currency of the People's Republic of China, Hong Kong, 1972.
WARD D. SMITH AND BRIAN MATRAVERS, *Chinese Banknotes*, Menlo Park, USA, 1970.
HSU YIH TZON, *The Illustrated Encyclopedia of the Chinese Banknotes*, Taipei, 1981.

Colombia

YASHA BERESINER AND EDOUARDO DARGENT, *Catalogue of the Paper Money of Colombia and Peru*, London 1973.
ERNESTO CALLEJOS, *Catalogo de Billetes Emitidos...de Colombia*, Medellin, 1978.

Cuba

NEIL SHAFER, *Cuban Paper Money 1857-1968*, St. Louis, 1970.

Cyprus

MAJOR F. PRIDMORE, *Modern Coins and Notes of Cyprus*, London, 1974.

Denmark

AXEL RUBOW, *Nationalbankens Historie 1878-1908*, Copenhagen, 1920.
FROVIN SIEG, *Seddelkatalog 1874-1976*, Ulbjerg, 1977.

El Salvador

ALCEDO F. ALMANZAR AND BRIAN R. STICKNEY, *The Coins and Paper Money of El Salvador*, San Antonio, 1973.
ENRIQUE FRANKE, *The Banknotes of the Republic of El Salvador*, San Salvador, 1974.

England

W. MARSTON ACRES, *The Bank of England from Within*, Oxford, 1931.
DAVID BEVAN, *A Guide to Collecting English Banknotes*, New Malden, 1970.
BRYAN BURKE, *Nazi Counterfeiting of British Currency in World War II*, San Bernardino, 198.7
G. CHANDLER, *Four Centuries of Banking*, 2 vols, 1964–68.
SIR JOHN CLAPHAM, *The Bank of England: A History*, Cambridge, 1944.
W. CRICK AND J. WADSWORTH, *A Hundred Years of Joint-Stock Banking*, London, 1958.
VINCENT DUGGLEBY, *English Paper Money*, London, 2002.
PHILIP GEDDES, *Inside the Bank of England*, London, 1987.
G. L. GRANT, *Standard Catalogue of Provincial Banks and Banknotes*, London, 1977.
T. GREGORY, *The Westminster Bank Through a Century*, London, 1936.
VIRGINIA HEWITT AND J. M. KEYWORTH, *As Good as Gold*, London, 1987.
C. R. JOSSET, *Money in Britain*, Newton Abbott, 1971.
JAMES MACBURNIE, *The Story of the Yorkshire and Lancashire Bank*, Manchester, 1922.
A.D. MACKENZIE, *The Bank of England Note*, Cambridge, 1953.
P. W. MATTHEWS AND A. W. TUKE, *The History of Barclays Bank*, London, 1926.
DAVID M. MILLER, *Bank of England and Treasury Notes 1694-1970*, Newcastle, 1970.
COLIN NARBETH, *Collect British Banknotes*, London, 1970.
R. OUTING, *The Provincial Banks and Banknotes of England and Wales*, Honiton, 2010.
R. S. SAYERS, *The Bank of England, 1891-1944*, Cambridge, 1976.
H. WITHERS, *National Provincial Bank, 1833-1933*, London, 1933.

Egypt

MAGDY HANAFY, *The Egyptian Currency Note*, Cairo, 2006

Finland

ERKKI BORG, *Suomessa Kaytetet Raha*t, Helsinki, 1976
FINLANDS BANK, *Inhemska Sedeltyper in Finland, 1809-1951*, Helsinki, 1952.

HANNU PAATELA, *Research Collection of Bank Notes Used in Finland 1662-1978*, Helsinki, 1978.
KURT PETTERSON, *Suomen Rahojen Hinnasta 1811-1979*, Helsinki., 1979.
TUKKO TOLVIO, *The Coins and Banknotes of Finland.*

France

JEAN LAFAURIE AND RAYMOND HABREKORN, *Catalogue des Emissions Officielles Francaises de Papier-Monnaie 1797-1952*, Auxerre, 1953-4.

M. MUSZYNSKI, *Les Billets de la Banque de France*, Villiers sur Marne, 1975 .

J. PIROT, *Catalogue of Tokens of Municipalities and Cities* (France and ex-colonies, 1914-18), Paris, 2006

ARGUS THIMONIER, *Monnaies et Billets Francxe depuis 1774*, Paris, 1960.

Germany

KURT JAEGER AND ULLRICH HAEVECKER, *Die Deutschen Banknoten seit 1871*, Cologne, 1979.

ARNOLD KELLER. *Das Papiergeld des Ersten Weltkrieges*, Berlin, 1957.
Das Papiergeld des Zweiten Weltkrieges, Berlin, 1953.
Das Papiergeld der Deutschen Kolonien, Munster, 1967.

KAI LINDMAN, serienscheine, Sassenburg, 2000.

MANFRED MULLER AND ANTON GEIGER, *Das papiergeld der Deutschen Eisenbahnen und der Reichspost*, Frankenthal, 2000

ALBERT PICK AND J. RIXEN, *Papiergeld Spezialkatalog Deutschland 1874-1980*, Berlin, 1982.

Gibraltar

D.C. DEVENISH, *Currency Notes of Gibraltar*, London, 1969.

Greece

PAUL G. PYLARINOS, *Greek Paper Money*, Athens, 1976.

A. TARASSOULEAS, *Paper Money of Greece*, Athens, 1982.

Greenland

PETER FLENSBORG, *Gronlandske Pengesedler, 1803-1967*, Copenhagen, 1970.

Guatemala

ODIS H. CLARK, *Paper Money of Guatemala, 1834-1946*, San Antonio, 1971.

DWIGHT MUSSER, *The Paper Money of Guatemala*, USA, 1959.

Hawaii

MAURICE M. GOULD AND KENNETH BRESSETT, *Hawaiian Coins, Tokens and Paper Money*, Racine, 1961.

GORDON MEDCALF AND ROBERT FONG, *Hawaiian Money and Medals*, Kailua, 1967.
Paper Money of the Kingdom of Hawaii 1859-1905, Honolulu, 1966.
AND RONALD RUSSELL, *Hawaiian Money Standard Catalog*, Honolulu., 1978.

Hungary

RICHARD A. BANYAI, *The Legal and Monetary Aspects of the Hungarian Hyper-inflation*, Tucson, 1971.

MIHALY KUPA AND BELA AMBRUS, *Magyarorszag Papirpenzei*, Budapest, 1964.
Paper Money of Hungary 1803-1918, Budapest, 1963.

Iceland

FINNUR KOLBEINSSON, *Islenzkar Myntir*, Reykjavik, 1978.

India

KISHORE JHUNJHUNWALA, *Indian Paper Money Since 1950*, Mumbai, 1998.

Indonesia

DONALD L. FOLTZ, *Paper Money of the Republic of Indonesia*, Indianapolis, 1970.

Ireland

G. BARROW, *The Emergence of the Irish Banking System*, Dublin, 1975.

MÁRTAN MAC DEVITT, *Irish Banknotes, Irish Government Paper Money from 1928*, Dublin, 1999.
Irish Banknotes, Irish Paper Money 1783-2001, Dublin, 2004.

DEREK YOUNG, *Guide to the Currency of Ireland, Legal tender Notes 1928-1972*, Dublin, 1972.
Guide to the Currency of Ireland, Consolidated Bank Notes, 1929-1941, Dublin, 1977.

Isle of Man

ISLE OF MAN BANK, *100 Years of Banking*, Douglas, 1965.

ERNEST QUARMBY, *Banknotes & Banking in the Isle of Man 1788-1970*, London, 1971.

PILCHER RALFE, *Sixty Years of Banking, 1865-1925*, Douglas, 1926.

Israel

SYLVIA HAFFNER, *The History of Modern Israel's Money from 1917-1967*, San Diego, 1968.

A.H. KAHAN, *Israel's Money and Medals*, New York, 1976.

Italy

CESARE BOBBA, *Carta Moneta Italiane, Asti*, 1974.
Catalogo della Carta-Moneta d'Occupazione, Asti, 1975.

MARIO DE FANTI, *Carta-Moneta Italiana, 1866-1961*, Casciano, 1966 .

LUIGI DE ROSA, *Il Banco di Napoli Istituto di Emissione*, Naples, 1976.

LIBERO MANCINI, *Catalogo Italiano della Cartamoneta 1746-1966*, Bologna, 1966.

ADOLFO MINI, *La Carta Moneta italiana 1746-1960*, Palermo, 1967.

GASTONE SOLLNER, *Catalogo della Carta-Moneta Italiana dal 1866 ad Oggi*, Milan, 1964.

Jamaica

JEROME REMICK, *Jamaican Banknotes*, St. Louis, 1968.

Japan

BANKOKU KAHEI KENKYUKAI, *Government and Bank of Japan Issues and Military Issues*, Tokyo, 1970.

IBNS, *Paper Money of the 20th Century: Japan*, St. Louis, 1981.

Y. OHASHI, *Nippon Shihei Taikei Zukan*, Tokyo, 1957.

Katanga

PETER SYMES, *The Bank Notes of Katanga*, Kirkcaldy, 1998.

Korea

BANK OF KOREA, *The History of Korean Money*, Seoul, 1969.

KIM IN SIK, *Illustrated Catalog of Korean Currency*, Seoul, 1978.

Luxembourg

FERN WICTOR, *Monnaies et Essais-Monnaies du Grand-Duche de Luxembourg 1796-1965*, Luxembourg, 1965.

Malaysia

IBNS, *Paper Money of the 20th Century*: Malaysia, Dallas, 1973.

K. C. BOON, *Standard Price Guide of Malaysian Banknotes and Coins 1939-2002*, Kuala Lumpur, 2003.

C.C. LOW, *Malaya Banknote Catalog*, Racine, 1967.

WILLIAM SHAW AND ALI KASSIM HAJI, *Paper Currency of Malaysia, etc*, Kuala Lumpur, 1971.

SARON SINGH, KASSIM HAJI, C.C. LOW AND TONY

LYE FONG, *Standard Catalogue of Coins and Banknotes of Malaysia, etc*, Kuala Lumpur, 1976.
STEPHEN TAN, *Standard Catalogue of Malaysia, Singapore, Brunei Coins and Paper Money*, 1998.

Maldive Islands

TIM J. BROWDER, *Maldive Islands Money*, Santa Monica, 1969.

Malta

EMMANUEL SAID, *Malta Coin, Banknote and Medal Catalogue*, Valletta, 1982.

Mexico

DOUGLAS AND DUANE, *The Complete Encyclopedia of Mexican Paper Money*, Iola, 1982.
CARLOS GAYTAN, *Billetes de Mexico*, Mexico City, 1965.
Paper Curency of Mexico, California, 1975.

Monaco

RAYMOND DE VOS, *History of the Monies, Medals and Tokens of Monaco*, New York, 1977.

Mongolia

E.D. GRIBANOV, *The Currency of the Mongolian People's Republic*, St. Louis, 1965.

Morocco

M. MUSZYNSKI AND H. SCHWEIKERT, *Le Papier-Monnaie du Maroc*, Paris, 1974.

Mozambique

BANCO NACIONAL ULTRAMARINO, *Papel-Moeda Para Mocambique, 1877-1973*, Lisbon, 1978.
COLIN R. OWEN, *The Banknotes of Mozambique*, Benoni, 1976.

Netherlands

J. MEVIUS AND F.G. LELIVELT, *De Nederlandse Bankbiljetten van 1814 tot Heden*, Amsterdam, 1981.

New Zealand

HOWARD MITCHELL, *Catalogue of New Zealand Banknotes*, Auckland, 2006.
ALISTAIR F. ROBB, *Catalogue of the Trading Bank Notes of New Zealand*, Wellington, 2006.

Nicaragua

BRIAN STICKNEY AND ALCEDO ALMANZAR, *The Coins and Paper Money of Nicaragua*, USA, 1974.

Norway

KARL SAETHRE AND HANS GUNNAR ELDORSEN, *Norske Pengeselder*, Loddefjord, Norway, 2003.

Papua New Guinea

DR WILLIAM J.D. MIRA, *From Cowrie to Kina*, Sydney, 1986.

Paraguay
DALE A. SEPPA, *Paraguayan Paper Money*, Chicago, 1974.

Peru

EDUARDO DARGENT, *El Billete en el Peru*, Lima, 1979.

Philippines

NEIL SHAFER, *A Guide Book of Philippines Paper Money*, Racine, 1964.

Poland

TADEUSZ JABLONSKI, *Polski Pieniadz Papierowny, 1794-1948*, Warsaw, 1964.
MARIAN KOWLSKI, *Katalog Banknotow Polskich 1916-1972*, Warsaw, 1973.

Portugal

FRANCISCO MALAFAYA, *Catalogo de Notafilia Portugal*, Porto, 1977.

Romania

V. COMAN, *Katalog der Rumanischen Banknoten*, Munster, 1967.
COL. R. IOAN DOGARU, *Catalogul Monedelor si Bancnotelar Romanesti*, Bucharest, 1978.
OCTAVIAN LUCHIAN, *Monede si Bancnote Romanesti*, Bucharest, 1977.

Russia

C. DENIS, *Catalogue des Monnaies Russes*, Paris, 1927.
N. KARDAKOFF, *Katalog der Geldscheine von Russland und der Baltischen Staaten*, Berlin, 1953.
LEONID Z. KATS and VALERY P. MALYSHEV, *Encyclopedia of Russian Paper Money 1769-1995*, St Petersburg, 1998.
DMITRI KHARITONOV, *Jewish Paper Money in Russia*, Prague, 2004.
PENTII LAURILA, *Soviet Paper Money and Bonds Used as Currency 1895-1990*, Tornio, Finland, 1990.
N. NAVOLOCHKIN, *Soviet Numismatics*, Moscow, 1970.

Scotland

JAMES L. ANDERSON, *The Story of the Commercial Bank of Scotland*, Edinburgh, 1910.
BANKING MEMORABILIA, *Registers of the National Bank of Scotland*, Carlisle, 2004.
C. W. BOASE, A Century of Banking in Dundee, Edinburgh, 1867.
JOHN BUCHANAN, *Glasgow Banking in Olden Times*, Glasgow, 1884.
ALEX CAMERON, *The Bank of Scotland 1695-1995, A Very Singular Institution*, Edinburgh, 1995.
S.G. CHECKLAND, *Scottish Banking: A History 1695-1973*, Glasgow, 1975.
DENNET *Scottish banknote catalogue*, Norwich, 2001
JAMES DOUGLAS, *Scottish Banknotes*, London, 1975.
20th Century Scottish Banknotes, Vols. 1 & 2, Carlisle, 1984. Revised 2002.
SIR WILLIAM FORBES, *Memoirs of a Banking-House*, Edinburgh, 1859.
WILLIAM GRAHAM, *The One Pound Note in Scotland*, Edinburgh, 1911. *The Bank Note Circulation of Scotland*, Edinburgh, 1926.
TREVOR JONES, *20th Century Scottish Banknotes: Clydesdale Bank*, Carlisle, 1998.
ALEXANDER KEITH, *The North of Scotland Bank 1836-1936*, Aberdeen, 1936.
ANDREW W. KERR, *A History of Banking in Scotland*, London, 1884.
CHARLES A. MALCOLM, *The History of the British Linen Bank*, Edinburgh, 1950.
C. MUNN, *The Scottish Provincial Banking Companies, 1747-1864*, Edinburgh, 1981.
NEIL MUNRO, *The History of the Royal Bank of Scotland 1727-1927*, Edinburgh, 1928.
ROBERT PRINGLE, *20th Century Scottish Banknotes: Royal Bank*, Carlisle, 1986.
ROBERT S. RAIT, *The History of the Union Bank of Scotland*, Glasgow, 1930.
J.M. REID, *The History of the Clydesdale Bank*, Glasgow, 1938.

South Africa

W. BERGMAN, *A History of the Regular and Emergency Paper Money Issues of South Africa*, Cape Town, 1971.

CAPT. HERBERT GREENER, *Mafeking, The Diary of a Siege*, Honiton, 2009.

HAROLD P. LEVIUS, *Catalogue of South African Paper Money since 1900*, Johannesburg, 1972.

South East Asia

COLIN BRUCE, *Standard Guide to South Asian Coins and Paper Money Since 1556*, Iola, 1982.

HOWARD A. DANIEL, *The Catalogue and Guidebook of Southeast Asian Coins and Currency*, Ohio, 1978.

Spain

IBNS, *Paper Money of the 20th Century: Spanish Civil War*, St. Louis, 1978.

FLORIAN R. VELEZ-FRIAS AND JORGE A. VILA, *Catalogo del papel Moeda Espanol*, Madrid, 1975.

JOSE A. VICENTE, *Catalogo de Billetes Espanoles 1783-1977*, Madrid, 1977.

Catalogo Basico Monedas y Billetes 1869-1977, Madrid, 1978.

Sri Lanka

H.W. CODRINGTON, *Ceylon Coins and Currency, 1924*, reprinted London 1999.

Surinam

THEO VAN ELMPT, *Surinam Paper Currency, 1760-1957*, London, 1998.

Sweden

SVEN FLODBERG, *Katalog over Sveriges Sedlar, 1858-1971*, Lund, 1972.

A. PLATBARZDIS, *Sveriges Sedlar 1661-1961*, Lund, 1963.

Sveriges Sedlar Enskilda Bankernas Sedlar 1831-1902, Lund, 1965.

LENNART WALLEN AND BJARNE AHLSTROM, *Sveriges Sedlar*, Stockholm, 1978.

Switzerland

URS GRAF, *Das Papiergeld der Schwiz, 1881-1068*, Munser, 1970 .

Syria

ADNAN JAROUEH, *The Encyclopedia of Syrian Paper Money*, 2006

Thailand

BANK OF THAILAND, *Banknotes of Thailand*, Bangkok, 1972.

SILAS LITTLE, *Banknotes of Thailand*, Falls Church, USA, 1973.

Turkey

DR MINE EROL, *Osmanli Imparatorlugunda Kagit Para*, Ankara, 1970.

CUNEYT OLCER, *50 Yilin Turk Kagit Paralari*, Istanbul, 1973.

USA

FREDERICK BART, *Comprehensive Catalog of United States Paper Money Errors*.

ELVIRA and VLADIMIR CLAIN-STEFANELLI, *American Banking*, Washington, 1975.

GROVER CRISWELL, *Confederate States of America Paper Money*, Florida, 1976.

W. P. DONLON, *United States Large Size Paper Money*, Utica, 1970.

RICHARD DOTY, *America's Money, America's Story*, Iola, 1998.

ROBERT FRIEDBERG, *Paper Money of the United States*, New York, various editions.

GENE HESSLER, *Comprehensive Catalog of US Paper Money US Essay, Proof and Specimen Notes*, 1979. the Engraver's Line

RON HORSTMAN, *Collecting National Bank Notes*.

CHESTER L. KRAUSE AND ROBERT F. LEMKE, *United States Paper Money*, Iola, 1999.

ERIC P. NEWMAN, *The Early Paper Money of America*, Iola, 1998.

ARLIE R. SLABAUGH *Confederate States Paper Money*, Iola, 2000.

Ukraine

DMITRI KHARITONOV, *Ukrainian Paper Money*, 2005

Uruguay

DALE A. SEPPA, *Uruguayan Paper Moneh*, Chicago, 1974.

Wales

IVOR WYNNE JONES, *Money Galore—the Story of the Welsh Pound*, Landmark, 2004.

Yemen

PETER SYMES, MURRAY HANEWICH AND KEITH STREET, *The Bank Notes of the Yemen*, Chester, 1998.

Yugoslavia

VOJISLAV MIHAILOVIC AND DRAGSOLAV GLOGONJAC, *Katalog Novca Srbije I Crne Gore 1868-1918*, Belgrade, 1973.

DIMITRI SPAJIC, *Paper Money of the Yugoslavian States*, USA, 1969.

Cheques and Postal Orders

STEPHEN CRIBB, *The Standard Catalogue of Postal Orders*, Ruislip, 1984.

JAMES DOUGLAS, *Collect British Cheques*, London, n.d. (c. 1981)

A Collector's Guide to Cheques and Bills of Exchange, Carlisle, n.d.

HOWARD LUNN, *Promotional Postal Orders*, Nottingham,. N.d. [1990].

ROGER OUTING, *The Cheques of Barclays Bank*, Huddersfield, 2004.

DAVID SHAW, *A Collector's Guide to British Cheques*, Shrewsbury, 1986.

MUSEUMS & LIBRARIES
on your doorstep

Listed below are the Museums and Libraries in the UK which have coin collections and many also have banknotes or items of notaphilic interest on display or available to the general public. However, before setting off on a long journey it is advisable to contact the museum you wish to visit to check that any notes they have are available for viewing.

A

Anthropological Museum, University of Aberdeen, Broad Street, **Aberdeen**, AB9 1AS (01224 272014).

Curtis Museum (1855), High Street, **Alton**, Hants (01420 2802).

Ashburton Museum, 1 West Street, **Ashburton**, Devon.

Ashwell Village Museum (1930), Swan Street, **Ashwell**, Baldock, Herts.

Buckinghamshire County Museum (1862), Church Street, **Aylesbury**, Bucks (01296 88849).

B

Public Library and Museum (1948), Marlborough Road, **Banbury**, Oxon (01295 259855).

Museum of North Devon (1931), The Square, **Barnstaple**, EX32 8LN (01271 46747).

Roman Baths Museum, Pump Room, **Bath**, Avon (01225 461111 ext 2785).

Bagshaw Museum and Art Gallery (1911), Wilton Park, **Batley**, West Yorkshire (01924 472514).

Bedford Museum (1961), Castle Lane, **Bedford** (01234 353323).

Ulster Museum (1928), Botanic Gardens, **Belfast** BT9 5AB (01232 381251).

Berwick Borough Museum (1867), The Clock Block, Berwick Barracks, Ravensdowne, **Berwick**. TD15 1DQ (01289 330044).

Public Library, Art Gallery and Museum (1910), Champney Road, **Beverley**, Humberside (01482 882255).

City Museum and Art Gallery (1861), Chamberlain Square, **Birmingham** B3 3DH (0121 235 2834).

Blackburn Museum, Museum Street, **Blackburn**, Lancs (01254 667130).

Museum Collection, Town Hall, **Bognor Regis**, West Sussex.

Museum and Art Gallery,(1893), Civic Centre, **Bolton**, Lancashire (01204 22311 ext 2191).

Art Gallery and Museum, Central Library, Oriel Road, **Bootle**, Lancs.

Roman Town and Museum (1949) Main Street, **Boroughbridge**, N. Yorks. YO2 3PH (01423 322768).

The Museum (1929), The Guildhall, **Boston**, Lincs (01205 365954).

Natural Science Society Museum (1903), 39 Christchurch Road, **Bournemouth**, Dorset (01202 553525).

Bolling Hall Museum (1915), Bolling Hall Road, **Bradford**, West Yorkshire BD4 7LP (01274 723057).

Cartwright Hall Museum and Art Gallery (1904), Lister Park, **Bradford**, West Yorkshire BD9 4NS (01274 493313).

Museum and Art Gallery (1932), South Street, **Bridport**, Dorset (01308 22116).

The City Museum (1820), Queen's Road, **Bristol** BS8 1RL (0117 9 27256).

District Library and Museum (1891), Terrace Road, **Buxton**, Derbyshire SK17 6DU (01298 24658).

D

Fitzwilliam Museum (1816), Department of Coins and Medals, Trumpington Street, **Cambridge** (01223 332900).

National Museum & Galleries of Wales, Cathays Park, **Cardiff** (029 20397951).

Guildhall Museum (1979), Greenmarket, **Carlisle**, Cumbria (01228 819925).

Tullie House (1877), Castle Street, **Carlisle**, Cumbria (01228 34781).

Chelmsford and Essex Museum (1835), Oaklands Park, Moulsham Street, **Chelmsford**, Essex, CM2 9AQ (01245 605700).

Town Gate Museum (1949), **Chepstow**, Gwent.

Grosvenor Museum (1886), Grosvenor Street, **Chester** (01244 21616).

Public Library (1879), Corporation Street, **Chesterfield**, Derbyshire (01246 2047).

503

Red House Museum (1919), Quay Road, **Christchurch,** Dorset (01202 482860).

Colchester and Essex Museum (1860), The Castle, **Colchester,** Essex (01206 712931/2).

D

Public Library, Museum and Art Gallery (1921), Crown Street, **Darlington,** Co Durham (01325 463795).

Borough Museum (1908), Central Park, **Dartford,** Kent (01322 343555).

Dartmouth Museum (1953), The Butterknowle, **Dartmouth,** Devon (01803 832923).

Museum and Art Gallery (1878), The Strand, **Derby** (01332 255586).

Museum and Art Gallery (1909), Chequer Road, **Doncaster,** South Yorkshire (01302 734293).

Dorset County Museum(1846), **Dorchester,** Dorset (01305 262735).

Central Museum (1884), Central Library, St James's Road, **Dudley,** West Midlands (01384 453576).

Burgh Museum (1835), The Observatory, Corberry Hill, **Dumfries** (01387 53374).

Dundee Art Galleries and Museums (1873). Albert Square, **Dundee** DD1 1DA (01382 23141).

The Cathedral Treasury (995 AD), The College, **Durham** (0191-384 4854).

Durham Heritage Centre, St Mary le Bow, North Bailey, **Durham** (0191-384 2214).

E

Royal Museum of Scotland (1781), Queen Street, **Edinburgh** EH1 (0131 225 7534).

Royal Albert Memorial Museum (1868), Queen St, **Exeter** EX4 3RX (01392 265858).

G

Hunterian Museum (1807), Glasgow University, University Avenue, **Glasgow** G12 8QQ (041 339 8855).

Art Gallery and Museum (1888), Kelvingrove, **Glasgow** G3 (0141 357 3929).

Museum of Transport (1974), Kelvin Hall, Bunhouse Road, **Glasgow** G3 (0141 357 3929).

City Museum and Art Gallery (1859), Brunswick Road, **Gloucester** (01452 524131).

Guernsey Museum and Art Gallery, St Peter Port, **Guernsey** (01481 726518).

Guildford Museum (1898), Castle Arch, **Guildford,** Surrey GU1 3SX (01483 444750).

H

Gray Museum and Art Gallery, Clarence Road, **Hartlepool,** Cleveland (01429 268916).

Public Museum and Art Gallery (1890), John's Place, Cambridge Road, **Hastings,** East Sussex (01424 721952).

City Museum (1874), Broad Street, **Hereford** (01432 268121 ext 207).

Hertford Museum (1902), 18 Bull Plain, **Hertford** (01992 582686).

Honiton and Allhallows Public Museum (1946), High Street, **Honiton,** Devon (01404 44966).

Museum and Art Gallery (1891), 19 New Church Road, **Hove,** East Sussex (01273 779410).

Tolson Memorial Museum (1920), Ravensknowle Park, **Huddersfield,** West Yorkshire (01484 541455).

Hull and East Riding Museum (1928), 36 High Street, **Hull** (01482 593902). *Celtic, Roman and medieval coins and artifacts from local finds. Some later coins including tradesmen's tokens.*

I

The Manx Museum, Douglas, **Isle of Man** (01624 675522).

J

Jersey Museum, Weighbridge, St Helier, **Jersey** (01534 30511).

K

Dick Institute Museum and Art Gallery (1893), Elmbank Avenue, **Kilmarnock,** Ayrshire (01563 26401).

L

City Museum (1923), Old Town Hall, Market Square, **Lancaster** (01524 64637).

City Museum (1820), Municipal Buildings, The Headrow, **Leeds,** West Yorkshire (01532 478279).

Leicester Museum and Art Gallery (1849), New Walk, **Leicester** (01533 554100).

Pennington Hall Museum and Art Gallery, **Leigh,** Lancashire.

Museum and Art Gallery (1914), Broadway, **Letchworth,** Herts (01462 65647). *Ancient British coins minted at Camulodunum, Roman, me*

City Library, Art Gallery and Museum (1859), Bird Street, **Lichfield,** Staffs (01543 2177).

Liverpool Museum(1851), William Brown Street, **Liverpool** L3 8EN (0151 207 0001).

Bank of England Museum, Threadneedle Street, **London** EC2 (020-7601 5545).

British Museum(1752), HSBC Coin Gallery, Great Russell Street, **London** WC1 (020-7636 1555).

British Numismatic Society (1903), Warburg Institute, Woburn Square, **London** WC1.

Cuming Museum (1906), Walworth Road, **London** SE17 (020-7703 3324/5529).

Gunnersbury Park Museum (1927), Acton, **London** W3.

Horniman Museum and Library (1890), **London** Road, Forest Hill, London SE23 (020-7699 2339).

Imperial War Museum, Lambeth Road, **London** SE1 6HZ (020-7416 5000).

Sir John Soane's Museum (1833), 13 Lincoln's Inn Fields, **London** WC2 (020-7405 2107).

National Maritime Museum, Romney Road, Greenwich, **London** SE10 (020-8858 4422).

Victoria and Albert Museum (1852), South Kensington, **London** SW7 (020-7938 8441).

Ludlow Museum (1833). The Assembly Rooms. Castle Square, **Ludlow** (01584 873857).

Luton Museum and Art Gallery (1927), Wardown Park, **Luton,** Beds (01582 36941).

M

Museum and Art Gallery (1858), **Maidstone**, Kent (01622 754497).

The Manchester Museum (1868), The University, **Manchester** M13 (0161-275 2634).

Margate Museum (1923), The Old Town Hall, Market Place, **Margate**, Kent (01843 225511 ext 2520).

Montrose Museum and Art Gallery (1836). Panmure Place, **Montrose**, Angus DD10 8HE (01674 73232).

N

Newark-on-Trent Museum (1912), Appleton Gate, **Newark**, Notts (01636 702358).

Newbury District Museum, The Wharf, **Newbury**, Berkshire (01635 30511).

O

Heberden Coin Room, Ashmolean Museum (1683), **Oxford** (01865 278000).

P

Peterborough Museum (1881), Priestgate, **Peterborough**, Cambs (01733 340 3329).

City Museum and Art Gallery (1897), Drake Circus, **Plymouth**, Devon (01752 264878).

Waterfront Museum, 4 High Street, **Poole**, Dorset (01202 683138). *(view by appointment).*

City Museum (1972), Museum Road, Old **Portsmouth** PO1 (023 80827261).

Harris Museum and Art Gallery (1893), Market Square, **Preston**, Lancashire (01772 58248).

R

Reading Museum and Art Gallery, (1883) Blagrave Street, **Reading**, Berks (01734 399809).

Rochdale Museum (1905), Sparrow Hill, **Rochdale**, Lancs (01706 41085).

Municipal Museum and Art Gallery (1893), Clifton Park, **Rotherham** (01709382121).

S

Saffron Walden Museum (1832) (1939), Museum Street, **Saffron** Walden, Essex (01799 522494).

Salisbury and South Wiltshire Museum (1861), The Cathedral Close, **Salisbury,** Wilts (01722 332151).

Scarborough Museum (1829), The Rotunda, Vernon Road, **Scarborough**, North Yorkshire (01723 374839).

Shaftesbury and Dorset Local History Museum (1946), 1 Gold Hill, **Shaftesbury**, Dorset (01747 52157).

City Museum (1875), Weston Park, **Sheffield** (0114 2 768588).

Rowley's House Museum, Barker Street, **Shrewsbury**, Salop (01743 361196).

Museum of Archaeology (1951), God's House Tower, Town Quay, **Southampton**, Hants (023 8022 0007).

Botanic Gardens Museum, Churchtown, **Southport,** Lancs (01704 87547).

Southwold Museum (1933), St Bartholomew's Green, **Southwold**, Suffolk (01502 722375).

Stamford Museum (1961), Broad Street, **Stamford**, Lincs (01780 66317).

Municipal Museum (1860), Vernon Park, Turncroft Lane, **Stockport**, Cheshire (0161 474 4460)

Stroud Museum (1899), Lansdown, **Stroud**, Glos (01453 376394).

Museum and Art Gallery (1846), Borough Road, **Sunderland,** Tyne & Wear (0191 514 1235).

Swansea Museum (1835), Victoria Road, **Swansea**, W. Glamorgan, SA1 1SN (0792 653765).

T

Tamworth Castle and Museum (1899), The Holloway, **Tamworth**, Staffs (01827 63563).

Somerset County Museum, Taunton Castle, **Taunton**, Somerset (01823 255510/320200). C

Thurrock Local History Museum (1956), Civic Square, **Tilbury**, Essex (01375 390000 ext 2414).

Royal Cornwall Museum (1818), River Street, **Truro**, Cornwall (01872 72205).

W

Wakefield Museum (1919), Wood Street, **Wakefield,** West Yorkshire (01924 295351).

Epping Forest District Museum, 39/41 Sun Street, **Waltham Abbey**, Essex EN 9.

Warrington Museum and Art Gallery (1848). Bold Street, **Warrington**, Cheshire, WA1 1JG (01925 30550).

Worcester City Museum (1833), Foregate Street, **Worcester** (01905 25371).

Wells Museum (18903), 8 Cathedral Green, **Wells,** Somerset (01749 3477).

Municipal Museum and Art Gallery (1878), Station Road, **Wigan**, Lancashire.

City Museum (1851), The Square, **Winchester**, Hants (01962 848269).

Wisbech and Fenland Museum (1835), Museum Square, **Wisbech,** Cambridgeshire (01945 583817).

Y

The Museum of South Somerset (1928), Hendford, **Yeovil,** Somerset (01935 24774).

Castle Museum (1938), **York** (01904 653611).

The Yorkshire Museum (1823), **York** (01904 629745).

MUST CHECK! Opening times etc before setting off on a long journey.

CLUB DIRECTORY

Most numismatic societies encompass banknotes in their agenda and many have regular speakers on the subject. Details given here are the names of the Numismatic Clubs or Societies, their dates of foundation, venue, days and times of meetings. Meetings are usually monthly unless otherwise stated. Finally, the telephone number of the club secretary is given; the names and addresses of club secretaries are withheld for security reasons, but full details may be obtained by writing to the Secretary of the British Association of Numismatic Societies, Philip Mernick, c/o Bush Boake Allen Ltd, Blackhorse Lane, London E17 5QP.

Banbury & District Numismatic Society (1967). Banbury British Rail Working Mens Club. 2nd Mon (exc Jul & Aug), 19.45. (01295 275128).

Banknote Society of Scotland (2006). St. Mary's Cathedral, Edinburgh. Thrice yearly. (01382 533839, email: bnss2006@ntlworld.com).

Bath & Bristol Numismatic Society (1950). Fry's Club, Keynsham, Bristol. 2nd Thu, 19.30. (0117 968 7259).

Bedfordshire Numismatic Society (1966). RAF Association Club, 93 Ashburnham Road, Bedford MK40 1EA. 2nd Thur, Dave, Allen, Secretary, (01234 870645).

Bexley Coin Club (1968). St Martin's Church Hall, Erith Road, Barnehurst, Bexleyheath, Kent. 1st Mon (exc Jan & Aug), 20.00. (0208 303 0510).

Birmingham Numismatic Society (1964). Friend's Meeting House, Linden Lane, Bourneville,Birmingham. 1st Wed, 19.45. (0121 308 1616).

Matthew Boulton Society (1994). PO Box 395, Birmingham B31 2TB (0121 781 6558 fax 0121 781 6574).

Bradford & District Numismatic Society (1967). East Bowling Unity Club, Leicester Street, Bradford, West Yorkshire. 3rd Mon, 19.00. (01532 677151).

Brighton & Hove Coin Club (1971). Methodist Church Hall, St Patrick's Road, Hove, East Sussex. Last Wed (exc Dec), 20.00. (01273 419303).

British Banking History Society. 14 Garsdale Road, Newsome, Huddersfield, HD4 6QZ (01484 310104). michael@wizzo.org.uk

British Cheque Collectors' Society (1980). John Purser, 71 Mile Lane, Cheylesmore, Coventry, West Midlands CV3 5GB.

British Numismatic Society (1903). Warburg Institute, Woburn Square, London WC1H 0AB. Monthly (exc Jul, Aug & Dec), 18.00. (020 7323 8585)

Cambridgeshire Numismatic Society (1946). Friends' Meeting House, 12 Jesus Lane (entrance in Park Street), Cambridge, CB5 8BA. 3rd Mon, Sept–June, 19.30. (01480 210992).

Chester & North Wales Coin & Banknote Society (1996). Liver Hotel, 110 Brook Street, Chester. 1st Tue, 20.00. (0151 478 4293)

Cheltenham Numismatic Society, The Reddings & District Community Association, North Road, The Reddings, Cheltenham. 3rd Mon, 19.45 (01242 673263)

Coin Correspondence Club (1988). Postal only. A.H. Chubb, 49 White Hart Lane, Barnes, London SW13 0PP. (0181-878 0472).

Crawley Coin Club (1969). Furnace Green Community Centre, Ashburnham Road, Furnace Green, Crawley, West Sussex. 1st Tue, 20.00. (01293 548671).

Crewe & District Coin & Medal Club (1968). Memorial Hall, Church Lane, Wistaston, Crewe, 2nd Tue (exc Jan & July), 19.30. (01270 569836).

Darlington & District Numismatic Society (1968). Darlington Arts Centre, Vane Terrace, Darlington, Co Durhm. 3rd Wed, 19.30. (01609 772976).

Derbyshire Numismatic Society (1964). The Friends' Meeting House, St Helens Street, Derby. 3rd Mon (exc August), 19.45. (01283 223893).

Devon & Exeter Numismatic Society (1965). The Courtenay Room, Sthe St. James Centre, Stadium Way, Exeter, Devon. 3rd Tue, 19.30. (01395 568830).

Edinburgh Numismatic Society (1996). Department of History and Applied Arts, Royal Museum of Scotland, Chambers Street, Edinburgh EH1 1JF. 3rd Mon, 19.30. (0131 225 7534).

Enfield & District Numismatic Society (1969). Millfield House Arts Centre, Silver Street, Edmonton, London N18 1PJ. 3rd Mon, 20.00. (0181-340 0767).

Essex Numismatic Society (1966). Chelmsford Museum, Moulsham Street, Chelmsford, Essex. 4th Fri (exc Dec), 20.00. (01277 656627). www.essexcoins.org.uk

Glasgow & West of Scotland Numismatic Society (1947). Woodside Halls, 26 Glenfarg Street, Glasgow, G3. 2nd Thu, Oct-May, 19.30. (0141 942 4776).

Harrow & North West Middlesex Numismatic Society (1968). 2nd and 4th Mon, 20.00. Call 020 8952 8765 for venue.

Havering Numismatic Society (1967). Fairkytes Arts Centre, Billet Lane, Hornchurch, Essex. 1st Tue, 19.30. (07910 124549).

Hayes & District Coin Club. The United Reformed Church Hall, Swakeleys Road, Ickenham, Middlesex. 3rd Thu, 19.45. (0181-422 9178).

Horncastle & District Coin Club (1963). Bull Hotel, Bull Ring, Horncastle, Lincs. 2nd Thu (exc Aug), 19.30. (01754 2706).

Huddersfield Numismatic Society (1947). Huddersfield Library, Princess Alexandra Walk, Huddersfield, West Yorkshire. 1st Mon (exc Jul & Aug), 19.30. (01484 866814).

Hull & District Numismatic Society (1967). The Young People's Institute, George Street, Hull. Monthly (exc Aug & Dec), 19.30. (01482 441933).

International Bank Note Society (1961). IBNS Secretary Mr D. Hunt, PO Box 412, Halifax, N. Yorks HX3 5YD (email: uk-secretary@ibns.biz, www.theibns.org).
International Bank Note Society, London Branch Room 301, Sylvia Young Theatre School, 1 Nutford Place, London, W1H 5YZ (www.ibnslondon.org.uk).
International Bank Note Society, East Midlands Chapter (1995). Highfields Community Fire Station, Beeston. Bi-monthly. (0115 928 9720).
Scottish Banknote Club (1995). West End Hotel, Palmerston Place, Edinburgh. Last Sat (exc Dec), 14.30 (0141 642 0132).
International Bank Note Society, North West Chapter (1974). Burnley. Last Sat (exc Dec), 14.30. (G. Clifford 0161 282 8063)
Ipswich Numismatic Society (1966). Ipswich Citizens Advice Bureau, 19 Tower Street, Ipswich, Suffolk. 3rd Wed, 19.30. (01473 728653).
Kent Towns Numismatic Society (1913). Adult Education Centre, 9 Sittingbourne Road (Maidstone) and King's School Preparatory School, King Edward Road (Rochester). 1st Fri of month, 19.30 alternately at Maidstone and Rochester. (01622 843881).
Kingston Numismatic Society (1966). Surbiton Library, Ewell Road, Surbiton, Surrey. 3rd Thu (exc Jan), 19.30. (020-8397 6944).
Lancashire & Cheshire Numismatic Society (1933). Manchester Central Library, St Peter's Square, Manchester M2 5PD. Monthly, Sep-June, Wed (18.30) or Sat (14.30). (0161 485 2415).
Lincolnshire Numismatic Society (1932). Grimsby Bridge Club, Bargate, Grimsby, South Humberside. 4th Wed (exc Aug), 19.30.
London Numismatic Club (1947). Warburg Institute, Woburn Square, London. Monthly, 18.30. (01223 332918).
Loughborough Coin & Search Society (1964). Wallace Humphry Room, Shelthorpe Community Centre, Loughborough, Leics. 1st Thu, 19.30. (01509 261352).
Merseyside Numismatic Society (1947). The Lecture Theatre, Liverpool Museum, William Brown Street, Liverpool L3 8EN. Monthly (exc July & Aug), 19.00. (0151-929 2143).
Mid Lanark Coin Circle (1969). Hospitality Room, The Civic Centre, Motherwell, Lanarkshire. 4th Thu, Sep–Apr (exc Dec), 19.30. (0141-552 2083).
Monmouthshire Numismatic Society. W. R. Lysaght Institute, Corporation Road, Newport. 2nd Wed, 19.30. (029 20 561564)
Morecambe & Lancaster Numismatic Society. Monthly, 19.30. (01524 411036).
Newbury Coin & Medal Club (1971). Monthly, 20.00. (01635 41233).
Northampton Coin & Medal Society (1969). Old Scouts RFC, Rushmere Road, Northampton. 3rd Mon, 20.00.
Norwich Coin & Medal Society (1967). The White Horse, Trowse. 3rd Mon, 19.30. (01603 419430).
Numismatic Society of Ireland. Ely House, 8 Ely Place, Dublin 2. Email: derekkerins@msn.com.
Numismatic Society of Nottinghamshire (1948). The Cecil Roberts Room, Central Library, Angel Row, Nottingham NG1 6HP. 2nd Tue (Sep-Apr), 19.30. (0115 9257674).
Nuneaton & District Coin Club (1968). United Reformed Church Room, Coton Road, , Nuneaton, Warwickshire. 2nd Tue, 19.30. (01203 371556).
Orders & Medals Research Society (1942). National Army Museum, Royal Hospital Road, Chelsea, London SW3. Monthly, 14.30. (020-8680 2701).

Ormskirk & West Lancashire Numismatic Society (1970). Eagle & Child, Ormskirk. Lancs. 1st Thu, 20.15. (01704 531266).
Peterborough & Districts NS (1967). Belsize Community Centre, Celta Road, Woodston, Peterborough, Cambs. Last Tue (exc July & Aug), 19.30. (01753 567763).
Plymouth Numismatic Society (1970). Mutley Conservative Club, Mutley Plain, Plymouth, Devon. 4th Wed (exc Dec), 19.30. (01752 480394).
Postal Order Society, Mal Tedds, 24 Whitworth Road, Chippenham, SN15 3QS. (01249 659599).
Preston & District Numismatic Society (1965). Eldon Hotel, Eldon Street, Preston, Lancs. 1st and 3rd Tue, 20.00. (012572 66869).
Reading Coin Club (1964). Abbey Baptist Church, Abbey Square, Reading. 1st Tue, 20.00. (01753 516390).
Redbridge Numismatic Society (1968). Gants Hill Library, Cranbrook Road, Ilford, Essex. 4th Wed, 19.30. (020-8554 5486).
Rochford Hundred Numismatic Society. Civic Suite, Rayleigh Town Hall, Rayleigh, Essex. 2nd Thu, 20.00. (01702 230950).
Romsey Numismatic Society (1969). Romsey WM Conservative Club, Market Place, Romsey, Hants SO5 8NA. 4th Fri (exc Dec), 19.30. (01703 253921).
Rotherham & District Coin Club (1982). Rotherham Art Centre, Rotherham, South Yorkshire. 1st Wed, 19.00. (01709 528179).
Royal Mint Coin Club, PO Box 500, Cardiff CF1 1HA (01443 222111).
Royal Numismatic Society (1836). Society of Antiquaries, Piccadilly, London W1. Monthly (Oct-June), 17.30. Joe Cribb, Coins and Medals, British Museum, London WC1B 3DG (020-7323 8585).
Rye Coin Club (1955). Rye Further Education Centre, Lion Street, Rye, East Sussex. 2nd Thu (Oct-Dec, Feb-May), 19.30. (01424 422974).
St Albans & Hertfordshire Numismatic Society (1948). St Michael's Parish Centre, Museum Entrance, Verulamium Park, St Albans, Herts AL3 4SL. 2nd Tue (exc Aug), 19.30. (01727 862060).
South East Hants Numismatic Society. Havant Conservative Club, East Street, Havant. 2nd Fri. (02392 389419).
South Manchester Numismatic Society (1967). Nursery Inn, Green Lane, Heaton Mersey, Stockport. Fortnightly Mon, 20.00. (0161-4763184).
S. Wales & Monmouthshire Numismatic Society (1958). The W. R. Lysaght Institute, Corporation Road, Newport. 2nd Wed, 19.30. (029 20561564).
Torbay & District Coin Club (1967). British Rail Social Club, Brunel Road, Newton Abbott, Devon TQ12 4PB. 1st Tue, 1945. (01803 326497).
Tyneside Numismatic Society (1954). RAFA Club, Eric Nelson House, 16 Berwick Road, Gateshead, Tyne & Wear. 2nd Wed, 19.30. (0161 825824).
Wessex NS (1948). The Edward Wright Room, Beaufort Community Centre, Beaufort Road, Southbourne, Bournemouth, Dorset. 2nd Thurs (exc Aug), 19.45. (020 7731 1702).
Wiltshire Numismatic Society (1965). The Raven Inn, Poulshot, Nr Devizes, Wiltshire. 3rd Mon, Mar-Dec, 20.00. (01225 703143).
Worthing & District Numismatic Society (1967). St. Paul's Centre, Chapel Road, Worthing, West Sussex. 3rd Thu, 19.30. (01634 260114).
Yorkshire Numismatic Society (1909). Swarthmore Education Centre, Woodhouse Square, Leeds. 1st Sat (exc Jan, Aug & Dec) (0113 3910848).

DIRECTORY OF AUCTIONEERS

Listed here are the major UK auction houses which handle coins, medals, banknotes and other items of numismatic interest. Many of them hold regular public auctions, whilst others handle numismatic material infrequently.

Baldwin's Auctions Ltd

11 Adelphi Terrace, London WC2N 6BJ (020-7930 6879 fax 020-7930 9450). Website: www. baldwin.sh.

Banking Memorabilia

PO Box 14, Carlisle CA3 8DZ (0169 7476465). Email: memorabilia74@btinternet.com.

Bonhams incorporating Glendining's

Montpelier Street, Knightsbridge, London SW7 1HH. (020 7393 3914). www.bonhams. com.

A. F. Brock & Company

269 London Road, Hazel Grove, Stockport, Cheshire SK7 4PL (0161 456 5050/5112). Website: www.afbrock.co.uk.

Corbitts

5 Moseley Sreet, Newcastle upon Tyne NE1 1YE (0191-232 7268 fax 0191-261 4130).

Croydon Coin Auctions

PO Box 201, Croydon, Surrey CR9 7AQ (020-8656 4583. www.croydoncoinauctions.co.uk.

Dix Noonan Webb

16 Bolton Street, Piccadilly, London W1J 8BQ (020 7016 1700 fax 020 7016 1799). Website www.dnw.co.uk.

Downies

11 & 12 Block Arcade, 98–100 Elizabeth Street, Melbourne, Vic, 3000, Australia. www. downies.com.

Dundee Philatelic Auctions

15 King Street, Dundee DD1 1JD. (01382 224946). Email: www. dundeephilatelicauctions@btconnect.com.

Edinburgh Coin Shop

11 West Crosscauseway, Edinburgh EH8 9JW (0131 668 2928 fax 0131 668 2926).

B. Frank & Son

3 South Avenue, Ryton, Tyne & Wear NE40 3LD (0191 413 8749 fax 0191 413 2957). bfrankandson@aol.com.

Heritage Auction Galleries

3500 Maple Avenue, Dallas, Texas 75219 (001 214 582 3500) www.HA.com.

Kleeford Coin Auctions

42B Shop Lane, Nether Heage, Belpher, Derbyshire DE56 2AR (tel 01773 856900).

Lakeland Coin Auctions

Agricultural Hotel, Penrith, Cumbria (venue). (01946 832693, www.lakelandcoinauctions. co.uk).

Lockdale Coins

37 Upper Orwell Street, Ipswich IP4 1BR. (01473 218588). www.lockdales.co.uk.

London Coins Auction

4–6 Upper Street South, New Ash Green, Kent DA3 8JJ. (01474 871464) www.londoncoins. com.

Morton and Eden

45 Maddox Street, London, W1S 2PE. (020 7493 5344 fax: 020 7495 6325). www. mortonandeden.com.

Neales

192–194 Mansfield Road, Nottingham NG1 3HU (0115 9624141 fax 0115 9856890).

Noble Numismatics Pty Ltd

169 Macquarie Street, Sydney 2000, Australia. (+61 2 9233 6009). E-mail: info@noble.net.au.

Spink & Son Ltd

69 Southampton Row, Bloomsbury, London WC1B 4ET. (020 7563 4000 fax 20 7563 4066). www.spink.com.

Stacks, Bowers and Ponterio

18061 Fitch, Irvine, California 92614 (+1 949 253 0916) www.bowersandmerena.com.

Tennants

The Auction Centre, Leyburn, North Yorkshire, DL8 5SG. (01969 623780) www. tennants.co.uk.

Warwick & Warwick

Chalon House, Scarbank, Millers Road, Warwick CV34 5DB (01926 499031 fax 01926 491906). www.warwickandwarwick.com.

The dealers listed below have comprehensive stocks of papermoney, unless otherwise stated. Specialities, where known, are noted. Many of those listed are postal dealers only, so to avoid disappointment always make contact by telephone or mail in the first instance, particularly before travelling any distance.

Abbreviations:

ADA—Antiquities Dealers Association

ANA—American Numismatic Association

BADA—British Antique Dealers Association

BNTA—British Numismatic Trade Association

IAPN—International Association of Professional Numismatists

IBNS—International Bank Note Society

P—Postal only

L—Publishes regular lists

F—Fairs

A. Ackroyd (IBNS)

62 Albert Road, Parkstone, Poole, Dorset BH12 2DB (tel/fax 01202 739039). *P. L. Banknotes, cheques etc.*

Arghans

Unit 9, Callington Business Park, Tinners Way, Moss Side, Callington PL17 7SH (01579 382405). *African banknotes.*

Keith Austin/KABC (IBNS)

10A-12-2 Pearl View Condo, Jalan Bunga Pudak, 11200 Talyung Bunga, Penang, Mayaysia. (0060 84890 7830). Email: kaustin@kabc.freeserve.co.uk. *L. Banknotes.*

Banking Memorabilia (IBNS)

PO Box 14, Carlisle, Cumbria (0169 747 6465). 09.00–18.00 (not Sun). *Cheques, banknotes, related ephemera. auctions.*

Bath Stamp and Coin Shop (BNTA)

Pulteney Bridge, Bath, Avon BA2 4AY (01225 463073). Mon-Sat 09.30–17.30. *British, world coins and banknotes.*

R. P. & P. J. Beckett

Maesyderw, Capel Dewi, Llandyssul, Dyfed SA44 4PJ. E-mail: orders@rppjbeckett.com Fax 01559 395631 *P. World crowns, coin sets and banknotes.*

Berkshire Coin Centre

35 Castle Street, Reading, Berkshire RG1 7SB (01734 575593). 10.00–16.00 weekdays, half-day Sat. *British and world coins and banknotes.*

Barry Boswell (IBNS)

24 Townsend Lane, Upper Boddington, Daventry, Northants NN11 6DR (01327 261877). *P. L. British and world banknotes.* E-mail: Barry.Boswell@btinternet. com.

A. F. Brock & Company

269 London Road, Hazel Grove, Stockport, Cheshire SK7 4PL (0161 456 5050/5112). Mon-Sat 09.30–17.30. www.afbrock.co.uk.

E. J. & C. A. Brooks (BNTA, IBNS)

44 Kiln Road, Thundersley, Essex SS7 1TB (01268 753835). Any time up to 23.00. *L. British banknotes.*

Cambridge Stamp Centre Ltd

9 Sussex Street, Cambridge CB4 4HU (01223 63980). Mon-Sat 09.00–17.30. *British coins and banknotes.*

Coin & Collectors Centre

PO Box 22, Pontefract, West Yorkshire WR8 1YT (01977 704112). *P. British coins and banknotes.*

Coincraft (ANA, IBNS)

44/45 Great Russell Street, London WC1B 3LU (020 7636 1188 and 020 7637 8785 fax 020 7323 2860). Mon-Fri 09.30–17.00, Sat 10.00–14.30. *L (newspaper format). Coins and banknotes.* www.coincraft.com.

Coinote Services Ltd

74 Elwick Road, Hartlepool TS26 NYL (01429 273044). *P. L. Coins and banknotes 1615 todate. Accessories and books.*

The Collector

242 High Street, Orpington, Kent BR6 0LZ (01689 890045). Mon-Sat 09.30–17.00 (closed Tue). *Coins, medals, banknotes, badges, militaria, cigarette cards and general collectables.*

Collectors' Forum

237 South Street, Romford, Essex RM1 2BE (01708 723357). Mon-Sat 09.30-18.00 Thu 09.30-14.00. *British coins, medals and banknotes.*

Corbitts (BNTA)

5 Mosley Street, Newcastle Upon Tyne NE1 1YE (0191 232 7268 fax: 0191 261 4130). *Dealers and auctioneers of all coins, medals and banknotes.*

Cornucopia Collectors

15 King Street, Dundee, DD1 2JD (01382 224946). E-mail: cornucopiacollectors@btinternet.com. *World coins, medals, banknotes and accessories.*

G. D. Courtenay

58 New Peachey Lane, Uxbridge, Middlesex UB8 3SX. *P. L. Coins, medals, tokens and banknotes.*

Clive Dennett (BNTA, IBNS)

66 St Benedicts Street, Norwich, Norfolk NR2 4AR (01603 624315). Mon-Fri 09.00–17.30, Sat 09.00–16.00 (closed Thu). *L. World paper money.*

Dorset Coin Co Ltd (BNTA)

193 Ashley Road, Parkstone, Poole, Dorset BH14 9DL (01202 739606, fax 01202 739230). *P. L. Separate coin and banknote lists.*

Duncannon Partnership

4 Beaufort Road, Reigate, RH2 9DJ (01737 244222 fax: 01737 224743) *Suppliers of albums, coin products and accessories for coins and papermoney.*

Edinburgh Coin Shop (ANA) (BNTA)

11 West Crosscauseway, Edinburgh EH8 9JW (0131 668 2928 fax 0131 668 2926). Mon-Sat 10.00–17.30. *L. World coins, medals and banknotes. Postal auctions.*

Educational Coin Company

Box 892, Highland, New York, 12528, USA (845 691 6100). *World banknotes.*

Ely Stamp & Coin Shop

27 Fore Hill, Ely, Cambs CB7 1AA (01353 663919). Mon, Wed-Sat 09.30–17.30. *World coins, medals and banknotes.*

Jos Eijsermans (Eijsermans Events, Maastricht Fair)

PO Box 1145, D–47547, Bedburg-Hau, Germany (+49 2821 71166–69 Fax: 2821 71166–71) email: Eijsermans-Events@planet.nl. *Organisers of Papermoney, fair–Maastricht.*

Evesham Stamp & Coin Centre

Magpie Antiques, Paris House, 61 High Street, Evesham, Worcs WR11 4DA (01386 41631). Mon-Sat 09.00–17.30. *British coins and banknotes.*

Richard N. Flashman

54 Ebbsfleet Walk, Gravesend, Kent, DA11 9EW. *L. P. British banknotes.*

Format of Birmingham Ltd (ANA, BNTA, IAPN, IBNS)

Second Floor, Burlington Court, Lower Temple Street Birmingham B2 4JD (0121 643 2058). Mon-Fri 09.30-7.00. *L. Coins, tokens and medals.*

B. Frank & Son (ANA, IBNS)

3 South Avenue, Ryton, Tyne & Wear NE40 3LD (0191 413 8749). *P. L. Banknotes and cheques, coins of the world.* Organiser of the North of England Coin & Banknote fair. www.b-frank-and-son.co.uk.

John Gaunt

21 Harvey Road, Bedford MK41 9LF (01234 217685). By appointment. *Numismatic books.*

Kate Gibson (IBNS)

P.O. Box 819 Camberly, GU16 6ZU. www.katespapermoney.com. *L World banknotes.*

Glance Back Books

17 Upper Street, Chepstow, Gwent NP6 5EX (01291 626562). 10.30–17.30. *World coins, medals, banknotes.*

B. Goulborn

Rhyl Coin Shop, PO Box 122 Rhyl LL18 3XR (01745 338112 or 01745 344856). *P. L. British coins and banknotes.*

Ian Gradon (IBNS)

PO Box 359, Durham, DH7 6WZ. (0191 3719 700). www.worldnotes.co.uk. *P. L. World bank notes.*

Granta Stamp & Coin Shop

28 Magdalene Street, Cambridge CB3 0AF (01223 315044) Mon-Sat 10.30-18.30. *English coins and banknotes.*

Grantham Coins (BNTA)

PO Box 60, Grantham, Lincs (01476 870565). *P. L. English coins and banknotes.*

A. D. Hamilton & Co (ANA, BNTA)

7 St Vincent Place, Glasgow G1 5JA (0141 221 5423, fax 0141 248 6019). Mon-Sat 09.00-17.30. *British and World coins and banknotes.* Website: www.adhamiltons.co.uk.

John Harvey (IBNS)

PO Box 118, Bury St. Edmunds, IP33 2NE (01284 761894). *British Isles, Scotland, Channel Islands.*

R. G. Holmes

11 Cross Park, Ilfracombe, Devon EX34 8BJ (01271 864474). *P. L. Coins, modern world crowns and foreign banknotes.*

HTSM Coins

26 Dosk Avenue, Glasgow G13 4LQ. *P. L. British and foreign coins and banknotes.*

Peter Ireland Ltd (BNTA, IBNS)

31 Clifton Street, Blackpool, Lancs FY1 1JQ (01253 21588 fax 0253 300232). Mon-Sat 09.00-17.30.*British and world coins, medals and tokens (some banknotes).*

Richard W. Jeffery

Trebehor, Porthcurno, Penzance, Cornwall TR19 6LS (01736 871263). *P. British and world coins and banknotes.*

KB Coins (BNTA)

50 Lingfield Road, Martins Wood, Stevenage, Herts SG1 5SL (01438 312661). 09.00–18.00 by appointment only. *L. Mainly British coins and banknotes.*

Lindner Publications Ltd

3a Hayle Industrial Park, Hayle, Cornwall TR27 4DX. Mon–Fri 09.00–13.00. *L. Manufacturers of albums, cabinets and accessories.* Website: www.prinz.co.uk.

Lockdale Coins

37 Upper Orwell Street, Ipswich IP4 1BR, (01473 218588). *L.* (Shop open 9.30–4.30 Mon–Sat). *World coins, medals, banknotes and accessories.* Website: www.lockdales.com.

London Coins

4–6 Upper Street South, New Ash Green, Kent DA3 8JJ. (01474 871464) www.londoncoins. co.uk. *British and world coins.*

M A Shops

Online coin mall. Tel: +49 2871 2393 415. Email: info@ma-shops.com. www.ma-shops.com. *Coins, medals, and banknotes.*

Clive Maxwell-Yates

21 Nicolas Road, Chorlton Manchester, M21 1LG (0161 881 7015). *P. L. World banknotes.*

Michael Coins

6 Hillgate Street, London W8 7SR (020 7727 1518). Mon-Fri 10.00-17.00. *World coins and banknotes.*

Graeme & Linda Monk (ANA, BNTA)

PO Box 201, Croydon, Surrey, CR9 7AQ (020 8656 4583 fax 020 8656 4583). *P. Fair organisers.*

Peter Morris

1 Station Concourse, Bromley North Station, Bromley, BR1 1NN or PO Box 223, Bromley, BR1 4EQ (020 8313 3410 Fax: 020 8466 8502). Mon-Fri 10.00–18.00, Sat 0900-14.00 or by appointment. *L. British and world coins and banknotes, numismatic books.* Website: www.petermorris.co.uk.

Colin Narbeth & Son Ltd (ANA, IBNS)

20 Cecil Court, Leicester Square, London WC2N 4HE (020 7379 6975). Mon-Sat 10.30-17.00. *World banknotes.* Website: www.colin-narbeth.com.

New Forest Leaves

Bisterne Close, Burley, Ringwood, Hants BH24 4BA (014253 3315). *Publishers of numismatic books.*

Michael O'Grady (IBNS)

PO Box 307, Pinner, Middlesex HA5 4XT (020 8428 4002). *P. British and world paper money.* E-mail: mike@ogrady.clara.co.uk

Roger Outing

P.O Box 123, Huddersfield HD8 9WY (01484 860415). *British & World Banknotes, Cheques & banking memorabilia.* www.banknotes4u.co.uk.

Penrith Coin & Stamp Centre

37 King Street, Penrith, Cumbria CA11 7AY (01768 64185). Mon-Sat 09.00–17.30. *World coins and notes.*

Pentland Coins (IBNS)

Pentland House, 92 High Street, Wick, Caithness KW14 L5. *P. British, world coins and world banknotes.*

Pettinaro Bros.

G. C. Pettinaro, Viale Tibaldi, 24, Milan 20136, Italy (00 39 02 83 95 451) email: giovanni.pettinaro@gmail.com. *World banknotes.*

John Pettit Pty Ltd

GPO Box 4593, Sydney 2001, Australia. (00612 9235 0888) www.johnpettit.com. *P. L. Rare banknote specialist*

Phil Phipps (IBNS)

PO Box 139, Tiverton, Devon EX16 0AU (07850 864554). *P. L. World banknotes.* E-mail: p.p.phipps@tesco.net.

David Pratchett

UCCE, PO Box 57648, Mill Hill, NW7 0FE. (07831662594). Website: www.coinsonline.co.uk. *Specialist in world coins and banknotes.*

Quentin Freres

18 Rue Saint Gilles, 75003 Paris, France (33 1 42 713794, fax 33 1 42 713754). email: quentin@worldnet.fr. *Specialists in world banknotes.*

George Rankin Coin Co Ltd (ANA, BNTA)

325 Bethnal Green Road, London E2 6AH (020 7729 1280 fax 020 7729 5023). Mon-Sat 10.00-18.00 (half-day Thu). *World coins and banknotes.*

Mark T. Ray (Collectors World)

188 Wollaton Road, Wollaton Road, Wollaton, Nottingham NG8 1HJ (0115 9280347) *P. British coins and banknotes.*

Scottish Banknotes

Sconser, Isle of Skye, IV48 8TD (01478 650450) Email: johnaunc@aol.com. *Scottish Banknotes*

Scot Mint

5 Main Street, Ayr, Scotland, KA8 8BU. (01292 268244 Fax: 01292 268626). e-mail: rob@scotmint.com *Banknotes Coins,*

Safe Albums (UK) Ltd

Freepost (RG 1792), Wokingham, Berks RG11 1BR (01734 328976 fax 01734 328612). *P. Banknote albums, coin holders,*

Simmons Gallery (ANA, BNTA, IBNS)

P.O Box 104, Leystone, London E11 IND (0207 8989 8097 fax 020 7831 2090). Website: simmonsgallery.co.uk. *L. Coins, tokens and medals.*

E. Smith (ANA, IBNS)

PO Box 348, Lincoln LN6 0TX (01522 684681 fax 01522 689528). *P. Organiser of the Leeds coin fair. World banknotes*

Spink & Son Ltd (ANA, BNTA, IAPN, IBNS)

69 Southampton Row, Bloomsbury, London WC1B 4ET (020 7563 2820). Mon-Sat 09.30–17.30. *World coins, medals and decorations, banknotes and numismatic books— new and secondhand.* Website: www.spink.com.

Stamp & Collectors Centre

404 York Town Road, College Town, Camberley, Surrey GU15 4PR (01276 32587 fax 01276 32505). Mon, Tue, Thu, Sat 09.00–17.00, Wed, Fri 09.00–1900. *World coins, medals and banknotes.*

Mel Steinberg & Son

P.O Box 752, San Anselmo, CA94979 (415 897 1654) E-mail: melsteinberg@mindspring.com. *World Banknotes*

St Edmunds Coins and Banknotes

PO Box 118, Bury St Edmunds, Suffolk, IP33 2NE (01284 761894). *Coins and banknotes.*

Sterling Coins & Medals

2 Somerset Road, Boscombe, Bournemouth, Dorset BH7 6JH (01202 423881). Mon-Sat 09.30–16.30 (closed Wed). *World coins and banknotes.*

UK Banknotes—Stephen Kendrick (IBNS)

PO Box 178, Liverpool L37 6WT 01704 381188).Website: www.ukbanknotes.co.uk, *British and world banknotes.. Provincial banknotes*

Vera Trinder Ltd

38 Bedford Street, Strand, London WC2E 9EU (020 7836 2365/6). Mon-Fri 08.30-17.30. *L. Catalogues and books, albums, envelopes, cases and accessories.*

Vista World Banknotes

5 Greenfields Way, Burley-in-Wharfdale, Ilkley, W.Yorks, LS29 7RB. *World Notes list.* E-mail: vistabanknotes@ barclays.net.

Pam West, British Notes (IBNS, ANA, PCDA)

PO Box 257, Sutton, Surrey SM3 9WW (020 8641 3224). *P. L. English banknotes, British banknotes accessories.* www. britishnotes.co.uk.

West Essex Coin Investments (BNTA, IBNS)

Croft Cottage, Station Road, Alderholt, Fordingbridge, Hants SP6 3AZ (01425 656 459). *P. L. British and World coins and paper money.*

R & J White (IBNS)

PO Box 5936, Basildon SS13 1WZ (07788 405159). www. banknotes4sale.com *P. L. Banknotes and world ephemera.*

Trevor Wilkin

PO Box 182, Cammeray, NSW, Australia (0061 2 9438 5040. trevorsnotes@bigpond.com. *P. L. World banknotes. Specialist in polymer notes.*

wrb-banknotes

P.O Box 52, Downham Market, PE38 0WX. Email: rdennettnotes@aol.com

Barry Wright

54 Dooley Drive, Bootle, Merseyside. L3O 8RT. *P. L. World banknotes.*

D. Yapp

PO Box 4718, Shrewsbury, Shrewsbury Mail Centre, SY1 9EA (01743 232557). *World and British notes.* www. david-yapp.com.

Ye Olde Banknote Shoppe

www.oldbanknotehop.co.uk, email jim@ oldbanknoteshop.co.uk.

UK and world banknotes and coins.

BANKS, MINTS & NUMISMATIC
bureaux of the world

Many national banks and mints operate numismatic bureaux and sales agencies from which coins, notes and other numismatic products may be obtained direct. The conditions under which purchases may be made vary considerably. In many cases at the present time bureaux will accept orders from overseas customers quoting their credit card number and its expiry date; but in others payment can only be made by certified bank cheque, or international money order, or by girobank. Cash is seldom, if ever, acceptable. It is best to write in the first instance to enquire about methods of payment.

A

National Mint, Baghe Arg, Kabul, Afghanistan

Bank Mille Afghan, Kabul, Afghanistan

Banque d'Algerie, Sucursale d'Alger, 8 Boulevard Carnot, Alger, Algeria

Banco de Angola, Luanda, Daroal, Angola

Casa de Moneda de la Nacion, Avenida Antartica, Buenos Aires, BA, Argentina

Royal Australian Mint, Department of the Treasury, Canberra, ACT, Australia

GoldCorp Australia, Perth Mint Buildings, GPO Box M924, Perth, Western Australia 6001

Oesterreichsiches Hauptmunzamt, Am Heumarkt 1, A-1031 Wien, Postfach 225, Austria

Oesterreichische Nationalbank, A-1090 Wien, Otto Wagner-platz 3, Austria

B

Treasury Department, PO Box 557, Nassau, Bahamas (*coins*)

Ministry of Finance, PO Box 300, Nassau, Bahamas (*banknotes*)

Bank of Bahrain, PO Box 106, Manama, Bahrain

Eastern Bank, PO Box 29, Manama, Bahrain

Monnaie Royale de Belgique, Avenue de Pacheco 32, B-1000 Bruxelles, Belgium

Banque Nationale de Belgique SA, Caisse Centrale, Bruxelles, Belgium

Banque de Bruxelles SA, 2 Rue de la Regence, Bruxelles 1, Belgium

Casa de la Moneda, Potosi, Bolivia

Banco Central de Bolivia, La Paz, Bolivia

Casa da Moeda, Praca da Republica 173, Rio de Janeiro, Brazil

Hemus FTO, 7 Vasil Levski Street, Sofia C-1, Bulgaria

Banque de la Republique, Bujumbura, Burundi

C

Banque Centrale, Douala, Boite Postale 5.445, Cameroun

Royal Canadian Mint, 320 Sussex Drive, Ottawa 2, Ontario, Canada K1A 0G8

Casa de Moneda, Quinta Normal, Santiago, Chile

Casa de Moneda, Calle 11 no 4-93, Bogota, Colombia

Numismatic Section, The Treasury, Avarua, Rarotonga, Cook Islands

Banco Centrale de Costa Rica, Departamento de Contabilidad, San Jose, Costa Rica, CA

Central Bank of Cyprus, PO Box 1087, Nicosia, Cyprus

Artia, Ve Smekach 30, PO Box 790, Praha 1, Czech Republic

D

Den Kongelige Mønt, Amager Boulevard 115, København S, Denmark

Danmarks Nationalbank, Holmens Kanal 17, 1060 København K, Denmark

Banco Central de Santo Domingo, Santo Domingo, Dominican Republic

E

Banco Central, Quito, Ecuador

Mint House, Abbassia, Cairo, Egyptian Arab Republic

Exchange Control Department, National Bank of Egypt, Cairo, Egyptian Arab Republic

Banco Central de la Republica, Santa Isabel, Equatorial Guinea

Commercial Bank of Ethiopia, Foreign Branch, PO Box 255, Addis Ababa, Ethiopia

F

Currency Board, Victoria Parade, Suva, Fiji

Suomen Rahapaja, Katajanokanlaituri 3, Helsinki 16, Finland

Suomen Pankki, PO Box 10160, Helsinki 10, Finland

Hotel de Monnaie, 11 Quai de Conti, 75-Paris 6e, France

G

Banque Centrale Libreville, Boite Postale 112, Gabon

Verkaufstelle fur Sammlermunzen, D-638 Bad Homburg vdH, Bahnhofstrasse 16–18, Germany

Staatliche Munze Karlsruhe, Stephanienstrasse 28a, 75 Karlsruhe, Germany

Staatliche Munze Cannstatt, Taubenheimerstrasse 77, 7 Stuttgart-Bad, Germany

Bayerisches Hauptmunzamt, Hofgraben 4, 8 Munich, Germany

Hamburgische Munze, Norderstrasse 66, 2 Hamburg 1, Germany

Bank of Ghana, PO Box 2674, Accra, Ghana

Pobjoy Mint, Mint House, 92 Oldfields Road, Sutton, Surrey SM1 2NW

Royal Mint, Llantrisant, Mid Glamorgan, Wales, CF7 8YT

Royal Mint Coin Club, PO Box 500, Cardiff, CF1 1HA

Bank of Greece, Treasury Department, Cash, Delivery & Despatch Division, PO Box 105, Athens, Greece

Casa Nacional de Moneda, 6a Calle 4-28, Zona 1, Ciudad Guatemala, Republica de Guatemala CA

States Treasury, St Peter Port, Guernsey, Channel Islands

Bank of Guyana, PO Box 658, Georgetown, Guyana

H

Banque Nationale de la Republique d'Haiti, Rue Americaine et Rue Fereu, Port-au-Prince, Haiti

Banco Central de Honduras, Tegucigalpa DC, Honduras CA

State Mint, Ulloi utca 102, Budapest VIII, Hungary

Artex, PO Box 167, Budapest 62, Hungary

Magyar Nemzeti Bank, Board of Exchange, Budapest 54, Hungary

I

Sedlabanki Islands, Reykjavik, Iceland

Indian Government Mint, Bombay 1, India

Arthie Vasa, Keabajoran Baru, Djakarta, Indonesia

Perum Peruri, Djakarta, Indonesia

National Mint, Tehran, Iran

Bank Markazi Iran, Tehran, IranCentral Bank of Iraq, PO Box 64, Baghdad, Iraq

Central Bank of Ireland, Dublin 2, Republic of Ireland

The Treasury, Government Buildings, Prospect Hill, Douglas, Isle of Man

Israel Stamp and Coin Gallery, 4 Maze Street, Tel Aviv, Israel

Istituto Poligraphico e Zecca dello Stato, Via Principe Umberto, Roma, Italy

J

Decimal Currency Board, PO Box 8000, Kingston, Jamaica

Mint Bureau, 1 Shinkawasakicho, Kita-ku, Osaka 530, Japan

Numismatic Section, Treasury Department, St Helier, Jersey

Central Bank of Jordan, Amman, Jordan

Banque Nationale du Liban, Rue Masraf Loubnan, Beirut, Lebanon

K

Kremnica Mint, štátny podnik, Štefánikovo nám, 25/24. 96715 Kremnica, Slovak Republic

Central Bank, PO Box 526, Kuwait

L

Bank of Latvia, K. Valdemara iela 2A, LV-1050, Riga, Latvia

Phone (+371) 6702 2300; Fax (+371) 6702 2420

Bank of Lithuania, Cash Department, Gedimino av. 6, 2001 Vilius, Lithuania

Caisse Generale de l'Etat, 5 Rue Goethe, Luxembourg-Ville, Grande Duche de Luxembourg

M

Institut d'Emission Malgache, Boite Postale 205, Tananarive, Madagascar

Central Bank of Malta, Valletta 1, Malta

Casa de Moneda, Calle del Apartado no 13, Mexico 1, DF, Mexico

Le Tresorier General des Finances, Monte Carlo, Principaute de Monaco

Banque de l'Etat du Maroc, Rabat, Morocco

Banco Nacional Ultramarino, Maputo, Republica de Mocambique

British Bank of the Middle East, Muscat

N

Royal Mint, Dharahara, Katmandu, Nepal

Nepal Rastra Bank, Katmandu, Nepal

Rijks Munt, Leidseweg 90, Utrecht, Netherlands

Hollandsche Bank-Unie NV, Willemstad, Breedestraat 1, Curacao, Netherlands Antilles

Central Bank of Curacao, Willemstad, Curacao, Netherlands Antilles

The Treasury, Private Bag, Lambton Quay, Wellington, New Zealand

Banco de Nicaragua, Departamento de Emison, La Tresoria, Apartada 2252, Managua, Nicaragua

Nigerian Security Printing and Minting Corporation, Ahmadu Bello Road, Victoria Island, Lagos, Nigeria

Central Bank of Nigeria, Tinubu Square LB, Lagos, Nigeria

Norges Bank, Oslo, Norway

Den Kongelige Mynt, Hyttegaten, Konigsberg, Norway

P

Pakistan State Mint, Baghban Pura, Lahore 9, Pakistan

National Development Bank, Asuncion, Paraguay

Casa Nacional de Moneda, Calle Junin 791, Lima, Peru

Central Bank of the Philippines, Manila, Philippines

Bank Handlowy w Warszawie, Ul. Romuald Traugutta 7, Warsaw, Poland

Desa Foreign Trade Department, Al. Jerozolimskie 2, Warszawa, Poland

Casa da Moeda, Avenida Dr Antonio Jose de Almeida, Lisbon 1, Portugal

R

Cartimex, 14-18 Aristide Briand St, PO Box 134-135, Bucharest, Roumania

Bank of Foreign Trade, Commercial Department, Moscow K 16, Neglinnaja 12, Russian Federation

Banque Nationale du Rwanda, Boite Postale 351, Kigali, Republique Rwandaise

S

Numismatic Section, Box 194, GPO, Apia, Samoa

Azienda Autonoma di Stato Filatelica-Numismatica, Casalla Postale 1, 47031 Repubblica di San Marino

Banque Internationale pour le Commerce, 2 Avenue Roume, Dakar, Senegal

Bank of Yugoslavia, PO Box 1010, Belgrade, Serbia

The Treasury, PO Box 59, Victoria, Seychelles

Bank of Sierra Leone, PO Box 30, Freetown, Sierra Leone

The Singapore Mint, 249 Jalan Boon Lay, Jurong, Singapore

South African Mint, PO Box 464, Pretoria, South Africa

Government Printing Agency, 93 Bukchang Dong, Chungku, Seoul, Republic of South Korea

Fabrica Nacional de Moneda y Timbre, Jorge Juan 106, Madrid 9, Spain

Bank of Sri Lanka, PO Box 241, Colombo, Sri Lanka

Hong Kong and Shanghai Banking Corporation, PO Box 73, Colombo 1, Sri Lanka

Sudan Mint, PO Box 43, Khartoum, Sudan

Bank of Sudan, PO Box 313, Khartoum, Sudan

Bank of Paramaribo, Paramaribo, Suriname

Kungelige Mynt och Justeringsverket, Box 22055, Stockholm 22, Sweden

Eidgenossische Staatskasse, Bundesgasse 14, CH-3003, Berne, Switzerland

Central Bank of Syria, Damascus, Syrian Arab Republic

T

Central Mint of China, 44 Chiu Chuan Street, Taipei, Taiwan, ROC

Royal Thai Mint, 4 Chao Fah Road, Bangkok, Thailand

Numismatic Section, The Treasury, Nuku'alofa, Tonga

Central Bank of Trinidad and Tobago, PO Box 1250, Port of Spain, Trinidad

Banque Centrale de Tunisie, Tunis, Tunisia

State Mint, Maliye Bakanligi Darphane Mudurlugu, Istanbul, Turkey

U

Bank of Uganda, PO Box 7120, Kampala, Uganda

Numismatic Service, US Assay Office, 350 Duboce Avenue, San Francisco, CA, 94102, USA

Office of the Director of the Mint, Treasury Department, Washington, DC, 20220, USA

Philadelphia Mint, 16th and Spring Garden Streets, Philadelphia, PA, 19130, USA

Franklin Mint, Franklin Center, Pennsylvania, 19063, USA

Banco Central del Uruguay, Cerrito 351, Montevideo, RO del Uruguay

V

Ufficio Numismatico, Governatorato dello Stato della Citta de Vaticano, Italy

Banco Central de Venezuela, Caracas, Venezuela

Y

Yemen Bank, Sana'a, Yemen.

Z

Bank of Zambia, PO Box 80, Lusaka, Zambia

Chief Cashier, Reserve Bank, PO Box 1283, Harare, Zimbabwe

BANKNOTES AND THE LAW

Counterfeit Currency

A counterfeit is a forgery or imitation of a coin or banknote produced with the intention of defrauding the revenue of the State or deceiving members of the public. By the Coinage Offences Act (1861) it was a felony to counterfeit gold or silver coins. Lesser offences included the gilding of farthings and sixpences to pass them off as half-sovereigns, the possession of moulds, machines or tools clandestinely removed from the Royal Mint, the impairment or diminution of gold or silver coins by filing or clipping (or even the possession of such filings and clippings).

The Coinage Act of 1870 made provision for the counterfeiting of base-metal coins, or the stamping of letters or words on coins of any kind, or the forging of colonial coinage. The most celebrated prosecution under this Act occurred in 1930 when Martin Coles Harman was convicted and fined £5 for issuing bronze coins resembling the British penny and halfpenny for the island of Lundy of which he was then the proprietor. Interestingly, no attempt was made to prosecute the Birmingham Mint which actually struck the coins (prudently omitting the H mintmark).

The making of medals or coins resembling current coin became a misdemeanour under the Counterfeit Medal Act of 1883. This Act is invoked from time to time against manufacturers or distributors of medallic pieces or coin jewellery. Such pieces, often struck in 9 carat gold, are deemed to infringe the Act if, for example, they have a figure even vaguely resembling St George and the Dragon on one side. The use of the royal effigy, however, without due authorisation, is regarded as a misdemeanour punishable by an unlimited fine and the confiscation of tools, dies and instruments. At the present time it is a serious offence to make a counterfeit of a currency note or coin with the intention of passing it off or tendering it as genuine. This offence carries a maximum penalty of ten years' imprisonment or an unlimited fine, or both. Making a counterfeit of a currency note or coin without lawful authority incurs a penalty up to two years' imprisonment or an unlimited fine, or both.

Passing or tendering as genuine anything which is known or believed to be a counterfeit of a currency note or coin renders the criminal on conviction to a term of ten years' imprisonment or an unlimited fine, or both. The mere possession of any forged note or coin is itself a criminal offence. Possessing countertfeits without authority or permission so to do, and doing so knowingly, renders the possessor liable to two years' imprisonment or an unlimited fine, or both. The Act also stipulates that the reproduction of a current banknote—of the Bank of England or of the Scottish and Northern Irish banks is a serious offence. This clause covers even such apparently innocent acts as making a photocopy (whether in black and white or full colour) of a current banknote, the photography of such a note or the illustration of such a note in any book, magazine or newspaper. Strict regulations are laid down concerning the legitimate illustration of notes, whether current or not, in books and periodicals; such illustrations must be either greatly reduced or enlarged *and* must bear a prominent defacement, such as SPECIMEN or CANCELLED. It is also a serious offence to utilise a reproduction of a current British banknote in any medium. Theoretically this includes such things as tea-towels, T-shirts, mugs, plates and other souvenirs in glass or ceramics, but in practice the law seems to turn a blind eye to such practices. Imitations and parodies of notes and coins are also regarded as infringements of the law, but in these instances prosecution of the offender seldom proceeds; a warning is generally regarded as sufficient, provided that the offending article or articles are withdrawn and suppressed.

The advent of high-definition colour photo-copying in recent years has brought the offence of reproduction into prominence once more. The regulations have been tightened considerably and there have been several cases of successful prosecution. In each case, however, the intent deliberately to deceive the public by passing a colour photocopy as a genuine note was proved. Technically the offence takes places as soon as the photocopy is made, for whatever purpose, but as a rule only those cases in which an element of fraudulent deception subsequently arose were pursued with the full rigour of the law. The law is quite clear, however, and it is a criminal offence to make a colour photocopy or photograph of any current British note unless permission to do so has been obtained from the Treasury. The maximum penalty on conviction is an unlimited fine.

The note-issuing banks have, of course, taken steps in recent years to incorporate further security devices into their notes, notably the use of latent images and underprints in colours which are difficult, if not impossible to photocopy accurately. At the same time, the adoption of metal strips and more complex watermark devices has theoretically made the task of the forger much more difficult. If, by some unlucky chance, someone passes a dud note on to you, you must make no attempt to pass it in turn. To do so renders you liable to prosecution for uttering a forgery. Forged notes must be handed over to the police as soon as possible. If you receive a forged note in payment for goods or services you are entitled to claim its face value from the person who gave it to you. Even if the person giving you the note did not realise that it was counterfeit, it is assumed in law that he or she represented to you that the note was worth its face value at the time the note was passed. If the tenderer knew that the note was forged, he can be prosecuted; but at the end of the day he is still liable to you for the fraud and can be sued in the civil courts for the recovery of the sum involved. If, on the other hand, you received the money as a gift, you have no legal claim against the person who gave it to you. If you pay someone with a counterfeit note or coin unknowingly, you have committed no offence, but you must pay again. The degree of culpability is often difficult to prove or disprove, but it is unlikely that a prosecution would be initiated on the basis of a single note.

Legal Tender

The dictionary defines this as currency which a creditor is bound by law to accept as payment of a money debt. Debts and purchases must be paid for in cash of legal tender unless the creditor or seller is willing to accept payment in another form, such as a postal order, money order, cheque or, nowadays, credit card. Bank of England notes of any denomination are legal tender in England and Wales. Formerly Bank of England pound notes (but no other) were legal tender in Scotland. Technically, since the demise of the pound note, no Bank of England notes are legal tender in Scotland, although in practice they circulate freely north of the Border. Even more surprisingly, Scottish banknotes are not legal tender anywhere, not even in Scotland! The subtle difference is reflected in the actual wording of the promise on English and Scottish banknotes. Thus English notes are inscribed "*I promise to pay the bearer on demand the sum of . . .*" without stipulating any specific place, the promise being made by the Chief Cashier. Scottish notes, on the other hand, have the promise in the third person. It is the bank itself which makes the promise "*to pay the bearer on demand . . . pounds sterling at their head office here in Edinburgh, by order of the Board*". In practice, however, Scottish banknotes are accepted without question, not only throughout Scotland but also in parts of England, and are generally accepted in London, although there is no obligation on the part of a creditor so to do.

Apart from gold coins, the base-metal pound coin is legal tender for payment of any amounts. So, too, presumably, are the various two-pound and five-pound base-metal coins of recent years, even though they have been struck as commemoratives and not intended for general circulation in the ordinary sense. Smaller denominations are only legal tender up to a maximum value in each case. In the case of 50p coins, 25p crowns and 20p coins, they may be used alone, or in combination with each other, in payment of amounts up to £10. 10p and 5p coins, alone or in combination, may be used for sums up to £5. Bronze 1p and 2p coins, however, can only be used for payment of amounts up to 20p. In practice, of course, you can probably get away with making payment in larger quantities (within reason!) although strictly speaking there is no obligation on the part of your creditor to accept them.

Value Added Tax

This is a matter which primarily concerns dealers, but it also applies to those who dabble in notes on a part-time basis, and has implications for collectors at all levels. Briefly, anyone conducting a business, or in self-employment, who has a turnover in excess of £70,000 per annum, must register with HM Customs and Excise for the collection and payment of Value Added Tax. Anyone whose turnover is less than £70,000 is exempt from the obligation to register, but is at liberty to register if he or she feels that this would be advantageous. It is nice to think that there is an element of choice in this, although one would be hard pressed to think why anyone would voluntarily register for VAT unless they absolutely had to! Assuming that you are a dealer with a turnover above the magic limit, then you are committing a serious offence if you fail to register. Registration then lays you open to the full machinery of the system. You have to charge VAT on all goods and services, issuing VAT invoices and receipts and keeping detailed accounts which are liable to snap inspection at any time. You have to make quarterly returns to Customs and Excise of the amount of tax you have collected. From this you are allowed to deduct the VAT which you yourself have paid out in the course of your business, and you then have to remit the difference to the VAT collector. Of course, should the amount you have paid exceed the tax you have collected, you receive a repayment in due course. This arises in businesses which handle zero-rated goods and services, but coins and medals do not come within that category.

From January 1, 1995 the special margin scheme of accounting for VAT currently available for certain second-hand goods, such as cars, was extended to almost all second-hand goods. The scheme allows businesses buying and selling eligible goods to account for VAT only on the difference between the buying and selling prices of these items.

A special system of accounting has been introduced which enables some dealers to account for VAT without the need to keep a detailed record of every transaction. Certain works of art, antiques and collector's items, including "secondhand" notes, defined in Notice 712 *Second-hand goods*, were exempt from VAT at import. From January 1, 1996 these items became subject to VAT at import at an effective rate of 2.5 per cent.

Importing Banknotes by Mail

Elsewhere in this volume will be found the names and addresses of mints, banks and numismatic bureaux around the world from whom it may be possible to obtain currency direct. It is a wise precaution to write to these bodies in the first instance for details of their sales and distribution. In some cases they appoint a dealer in Britain as an agent and this is a method of purchase that removes a great deal of the hassle and red tape. Nowadays, however, many mints and banks are quite happy to use the credit card system to make it easy to part you from your money. The problem arises, however, when the notes are despatched. As a rule, banks and mints stipulate quite clearly that they will not accept orders prepaid in cash, and it is an offence to send coins or banknotes out of the country as payment, except through banks authorised for this purpose. Cheques drawn on British banks should not be used. Indeed, this may be actively discouraged by the imposition of heavy clearance and handling charges at the other end. The converse is also true, although Americans seem to think that dollar cheques drawn on some obscure mid-West bank will be eagerly accepted here, and are consequently aggrieved when it is tactfully pointed out to them that this creates enormous problems—to say nothing of the swingeing bank charges incurred in converting such cheques to sterling. Other than credit cards, the Girobank system is probably the best method of remitting currency from one country to another; full details may be obtained from any post office. Details on the preferred method of sending remittances, or transferring cash to another country, as well as the transmission of coins by post to different countries, will be found in the *Royal Mail International Service Guide*.

The receipt of postal packets containing banknotes from abroad makes you liable for Value Added Tax on their importation. As a rule, the despatching mint or bank will have affixed a Customs declaration to the packet, listing the contents, their weight and value, and it is on that basis that VAT will be calculated. The position regarding the import and export of coins by post is more complicated, and applies also to goods sent on approval. In such cases you must consult your Customs and Excise office who will advise you on the correct procedure and what your liabilities will be to tax in either case. This also applies to dealers taking stock out of the country to a show and then re-importing the unsold stock afterwards, or importing material purchased at the show.

Buying and Selling

When goods are sold, the seller and the buyer enter into a contract which confers rights and imposes obligations on both parties. The contract need not be in writing. There is no law governing the quality of goods sold by a private individual. If you purchase a coin from a fellow-collector as a result of an informal meeting at the local numismatic society it is incumbent on you to ensure that what you buy is what you think you are buying. If you purchase something from a dealer or shopkeeper, however, you are entitled under the Sale of Goods Act to goods of "merchantable quality" which means that they must be reasonably fit for their purpose. Items sold under a specific description, on the other hand, must correspond exactly with that description. If they do not, the seller *even a private individual* can be sued under the Sale of Goods Act. This is an important distinction because there is an erroneous notion that the Act does not apply to transactions between private individuals. If A sells a coin to B, purporting it to be a rare date, and B subsequently

discovers that the date has been deliberately altered, then B can sue A. Even if A claims that he made the sale in good faith, believing the coin to be a genuine rare date, he will still be liable for restitution (giving B his money back) and may also face a claim for damages. The Sale of Goods Act thus overturns the traditional adage *caveat emptor* which, in its full formula, translates as "let the buyer beware for he ought not to be ignorant of the nature of the property which he is buying from another party". Traditionally this was the maxim applicable at auctions. Once the auctioneer's gavel had dropped, the successful bidder had, in effect, made a contract with the vendor and was bound to pay for the lot, even if he subsequently discovered that what he had purchased was not what he had imagined. The view was that it was up to the purchaser to ensure beforehand that what he purchased was genuine and answered the description in the sale catalogue.

Because of vexatious disputes arising from questions of authenticity, and with the Sale of Goods Act breathing down their necks, many auctioneers now have a safety net, in the form of extensions. These enable successful bidders to delay payment for two or three weeks while they seek expertisation of doubtful material. In other words, the law allows a cooling-off period, but only for the legitimate purpose of verifying the authenticity of items over which there may be some doubt. This is only operative in cases where a coin or medal is sold as genuine, and described and estimated in value accordingly. In many doubtful cases, however, an auctioneer will cover himself by adding the crucial words "as is" to the description of a lot. Then, indeed, it is a case of *caveat emptor*. The auctioneer has done everything humanly possible to draw attention to the controversial nature of the item, and it must then rest on the judgment of the purchaser.

On the subject of auctions there are legal aspects which are not always apparent, as well as subtle differences in law and practice between England and Scotland. These tend to arise in cases where coins and medals come up for sale at provincial general mixed auctions, rather than in the sales conducted by numismatic auctioneers. Goods up for auction may be subject to an upset price which is made public as the price at which the bidding will start. A reserve price, on the other hand, is known only to the auctioneer, and if it is not reached, the goods will not be sold. Upset prices are common in Scotland, reserve prices in England. If no upset price is specified and the goods are not subject to a reserve price then the highest bid secures them, even though it may not be as high as the vendor hoped for. If a seller notifies other bidders that he is bidding for his own goods, or that he has employed an agent to bid for him, the bidding is legal. If he does not give notice and bids himself, or gets someone to bid for him, thus forcing up the price, the sale is fraudulent, and the buyer can purchase the goods for the amount of the last bid he made before fraudulent bidding started.

One frequently hears dark, but usually apocryphal, tales of "the ring" in action to depress the bidding and secure items below the price commensurate with their actual value. This is a fraudulent practice and in law is regarded as a criminal conspiracy. In practice, however, it would be very difficult for a group of dealers or other individuals to keep the bidding down merely by sitting on their hands. This practice could only operate successfully in sales which were largely, if not entirely, frequented by dealers. But coin sales, like other specialist collector-orientated auctions, are characterised by a high proportion of private bidders in attendance. Any conspiracy by a ring would merely allow some private bidder to step in and secure the lot at a bargain price. Rings are illegal, but in practice prosecutions are very rare as it is extremely difficult to obtain proof of their operations. What is more likely to happen is that dealers have been known to act in concert to force up the bidding to frighten off some unwelcome interloper. Here again, such tales are legion, but astonishingly lacking in specific details. The golden rule in attending auctions is to know what you are going after, and to have a pretty precise idea of how much you are prepared to pay. Do not be stampeded in the heat of the moment into going way beyond your limit.

Taxation of Profits on Disposal

The Inland Revenue define an asset as "any form of property (other than sterling) wherever situated". A disposal includes a sale, exchange or gift of an asset, or the receipt of a capital sum in respect of them. In layman's terms you dispose of an asset when you sell it, give it away, exchange it or lose it. A transfer of assets between husband and wife doesn't count (unless they are legally separated), nor does the transfer of an asset you leave when you die. If a disposal results in a profit you could be liable to tax. Any profit made on the sale of certain assets, including banknotes, coins and other collectables, constitutes a capital gain and is subject to Capital Gains Tax (CGT) which is now charged at 18% or 28% rates according to the individual. However the government allows you to make a total capital gain in the current tax year of £10,100 before tax becomes chargeable. If this is the case, and the total proceeds from disposal do not exceed £10,100, then a simple declaration to this effect is all you need to make in the relevant section of your annual tax return.

Computing the actual capital gain is a complicated matter. Some assets are not liable to CGT: these include personal possessions worth up to £6,000 each, such as jewellery, paintings or antiques and thus banknotes worth less than this figure, would also be exempt. However, if a collector was to dispose of a collection and the tiotal realised more than £6,000 even though the individual notes did not reach this figurte, CGT would be applied.

How do you establish what a gain is? The Inland Revenue tend to regard this publication, Krause or other relevant catalogues as their yardstick. The difference between the nominal or catalogue value and what you eventually got for the note *assuming that the latter was greater,* might be regarded as the capital gain, but even then the position is complicated by inflation in the intervening years eroding the real value of the note.

At this stage things get really complicated as you have to work out the indexation allowance and other factors. It is beyond the remit of this book, and it would be irresponsible of us to pretend otherwise, to give in-depth tax advice. Therefore we would suggest in the first instance you check the HM Revenue & Customs website at www.hmrc.gov.co.uk or take expert advice from a qualified financial professional.

Advertisers
Directory

Dealer Directory

See our website at tokenpublishing.com for up-to-date dealer entries, with hyperlinks taking you directly to their websites.